Modeling Trading System Performance

Modeling Trading System Performance

Monte Carlo Simulation

Position Sizing

Risk Management

and Statistics

Howard B. Bandy

Blue Owl Press, Inc.

AmiBroker is a trademark of AmiBroker and Tomasz Janeczko.

Equity Monaco is a trademark of TickQuest.

Excel is a trademark of Microsoft.

Market System Analyzer is a trademark of Adaptrade Software.

MetaStock is a trademark of Thomson Reuters.

Stator is a trademark of Anfield Capital Pty.

TradeStation is a trademark of TradeStation Technologies.

Wealth-Lab is a trademark of Wealth-Lab.

ISBN-10: 0979183820
ISBN-13: 9780979183829
LCCN: 2011920753

Published by
Blue Owl Press, Inc.
3220 Crescent Avenue
Eugene, OR 97408

Published 2011
Second Printing with revised index March 2015
Printed in the United States
18 17 16 15   10 9 8 7 6 5 4 3 2

DISCLAIMER

This book is an educational document. This is a textbook, not a trading manual. You are expected to bring your own trading system, use your own data, make your own analysis, make your own decisions, and enjoy your own rewards. Nothing in this book is intended as, nor should it be construed to be, investment advice.

The views expressed herein are the personal views of Dr. Howard B. Bandy. Neither the author nor the publisher, Blue Owl Press, Inc., have any commercial interest in any of the products mentioned. All of the products described were purchased by the author at regular retail prices.

Investing and trading is risky and can result in loss of principal. Neither this book in its entirety, nor any portion thereof, nor any follow-on discussion or correspondence related to this book, is intended to be a recommendation to invest or trade mutual funds, stocks, commodities, options, or any other financial instrument. Neither the author nor the publisher will accept any responsibility for losses which might result from applications of the ideas expressed in the book or from techniques or trading systems described in the book.

The programs used as examples have been tested and are believed to be correct. Even so, this book may contain typographical errors and other inaccuracies. Past performance, whether hypothetical, simulated, backtested, or actual, is no guarantee of future results. Results will depend on the specific data series used. Please verify the accuracy and correctness of all programs before using them to trade.

No example, program, or spreadsheet is intended to be exactly appropriate for use in every situation. The materials presented in this book should be used as examples, to be modified by each reader for his or her specific situation. Program and spreadsheet code beyond that in listings in the book is not provided and is not available for download.

ACKNOWLEDGMENTS

Thanks to the many people who had suggestions for this book, who read early drafts of sections that were in their areas of expertise, who sent me results from their trading systems to analyze, and who encouraged me along the way.

Particular thanks to Robert Grigg. Robert is tireless in his efforts to spread the word about trading system development. Robert read every word several times, and pointed out many trivial mistakes and typographical errors. But Robert's most important contribution was stepping back from the intimate understanding of trading system development and statistical testing of trading results that he has; and to review the material from the point of view of a reader new to the subject, and to insist that every example be meaningful and all the necessary background material be included.

Contents

Preface

This book, *Modeling Trading System Performance* (MTSP), is intended to be an introduction to techniques that can be used to model the performance and risk of trading systems.

MTSP is a sequel to my earlier book, *Quantitative Trading Systems* (QTS). QTS discusses the design, testing, and validation of trading systems. Although it illustrates examples using the AmiBroker trading system development platform, the concepts it discusses are universal.

MTSP is completely platform independent. It assumes the trading system development work is complete. It makes no assumptions about the platform used to develop and test the trading system. It is equally applicable to users of AmiBroker, Excel, MetaStock, TradeStation, Wealth-Lab, or any other platform.

The models in MTSP are Microsoft Excel spreadsheets. The input is either a list of trade by trade results or a table describing the distribution of a set of results. All of the models, examples, and techniques are fully described and fully disclosed. They can be replicated using free or low cost tools.

MTSP uses analogies from gambling to illustrate the effects of uncertainty and to build easily understood simulation models using Monte Carlo simulation.

The simulation models are extended to trading and used to study several aspects of trading, particularly those needed to treat trading as a business. Topics include:

- The relationship between bar length, frequency of trading, length of holding period, profit potential, exposure to closed trade drawdown, and exposure to intra-trade drawdown.
- The relationship between account risk, trading system risk, position sizing, risk of ruin, and goal achievement.
- How to assess the health of a trading system and what to do when it shows signs of being broken.

INTENDED AUDIENCE

Individual traders and trading companies who:

- Have experience in trading system development and trading.
- Want an introduction to Monte Carlo simulation of trading systems.
- Are interested in the characteristics of trading systems, holding periods, risk, profit potential.
- Want practical tools to assess position sizing methods and their effects.
- Want to know how to tell when a trading system is broken, and what to do about that.

ASSUMPTIONS

While this book is intended to be a tutorial, the reader is expected to be reasonably familiar with:

- Computer operations
- Basic techniques used with the Windows operating system, such as the menu system, drag-and-drop, navigating through the file system
- A spreadsheet, such as Excel
- Basic trading methods and terminology

What you will find in this book

Preface – This document (Available as a free download)

Contents – (Available as a free download)

Chapter 1 – Introduction (Available as a free download)

Chapter 2 – Trading as a Business (Available as a free download)

Chapter 3 – Trading Systems (Available as a free download)

Chapter 4 – Expectancy and Roulette

Chapter 5 – Blackjack

Chapter 6 – Monte Carlo Simulation

Chapter 7 – Objective Function

Chapter 8 – Bar Length and Holding Period

Chapter 9 – Holding Period

Chapter 10 – Position Sizing

Chapter 11 – Is It Broken?

Chapter 12 – Summary

Appendix – Tools, Tables, Glossary, References

Index – (Available as a free download)

Versions used

Excel 2007

THE AUTHOR

Dr. Howard Bandy:

- Has university degrees in mathematics, physics, engineering, and computer science.
- Has specialized in artificial intelligence, applied mathematics, modeling and simulation.
- Was professor of computer science and mathematics, and a university dean.
- Designed and programmed a well-known program for stock selection and timing.
- Was a senior research analyst for a CTA trading firm.
- Is the author of *Quantitative Trading Systems, Modeling Trading System Performance,* and *Introduction to AmiBroker. Advanced AmiBroker* is in preparation. All published by Blue Owl Press, Inc.

Chapter 1

Introduction

DECISIONS AND UNCERTAINTY

Most of the decisions we make in life are choices that involve weighing opportunity against risk. Most of the calculations are extremely complex and involve estimating costs and values of things not easily quantified – where to live, whom to marry, what employment to pursue. All are specific applications of making decisions under uncertain conditions. It seems that the more important the decision, the less opportunity we have to practice and the more important it is to be correct early in the process.

How we handle our finances is certainly an important area, and one where we don't get many practice runs. For traders, the goal is maximizing trading profits while minimizing the risk of bankruptcy. In the spectrum of life's activities, this is a problem that is relatively easy to quantify and analyze. The major aspects already have easily measured units of value – dollars. And, given a little understanding of probability and statistics, along with some computer data analysis, we can outline a plan.

OVERVIEW

This book was written to help answer questions that I regularly receive from colleagues and clients. The form of the comments and questions are along the lines of:

- Developing trading systems that pass tests of statistical significance when applied to out-of-sample tests is hard.
- What can I expect when I begin trading this system?
- Am I trading the right issue with the right frequency?
- What are the characteristics of high-growth trading systems?
- How large a trading account do I need?
- What are my year-to-year returns likely to be?
- How long will it take me to reach my retirement goals?
- How likely am I to lose a significant portion of my money?
- How can I tell when the system is broken?
- Should I use aggressive position sizing?

These questions are at the heart of "trading as a business."

I see a progression of stages of maturity of technically-oriented traders and system developers.

- Keeping funds in a savings account.
- Buying and holding stocks and mutual funds on an ad hoc basis.
- Buying stocks or mutual funds on the advice of a broker or advisor.
- Looking at charts of price and volume, and trying to identify meaningful patterns.
- Using support and resistance levels and percent drawdown to manage positions.
- Learning about formula-based trading systems, moving averages, trailing stops.
- Deciding to move from discretionary to mechanical systems.
- Designing trading systems and coding them in an analysis platform's language.
- Backtesting trading systems.
- Optimizing trading systems.
- Selecting a personal objective function and choosing among alternative systems.
- Performing walk forward runs and analysis of out-of-sample results.
- Learning about statistics and validation.
- Learning about risk – market risk, holding period risk, trade risk, portfolio risk, account risk.
- Learning about utility function and personal risk tolerance.
- Setting personal account management goals.
- Performing Monte Carlo simulations.
- Applying statistical measures to trading performance.
- Determining risk levels, setting position size, analyzing likely account performance.
- Managing wealth – staying liquid – quitting when goals have been met and while ahead.

This book assumes that the reader understands trading system design, testing, and validation, has developed trading systems that appear to be profitable (have positive expectancy) when tested on out-of-sample data, and is ready to work further in modeling trading system performance.

Key topics of the book include:
- Trading as a business
- Trading versus investing
- Liquidity
- Background in probability
- Background in gambling
- Comparison between gambling and trading
- Application of probability to trading
- Background in Monte Carlo simulation
- Application of Monte Carlo simulation to trading
- Utility of money
- Measuring risk
- Risk of ruin
- Comparison of trading systems
- Variability in trading results
- Absorbing boundaries – retire or ruin
- Managing risk
- Drawdown estimation
- Account size determination
- Background in position sizing
- Comparison of position sizing methods
- Use of leverage
- Planning to retire
- Statistics for traders
- Do it yourself tools

The emphasis is on:
- Understanding what is predictable and what is not
- Understanding variability and risk
- Characteristics of trading systems
- Monte Carlo simulation
- Trading as a business
- Realistic estimates of equity growth

The book is independent of any specific trading system development platform. Most of the analysis is done in Microsoft Excel. No expensive software is required. Spreadsheet formulas are provided, links to tools used are listed, and an extensive bibliography is provided.

INTENDED READERS

This book makes extensive use of probability and statistics. Achieving meaningful results requires a relatively large amount (typically one hundred or more data points) of clearly quantified trading data – usually in the form of closed trades, or daily or weekly equity balance. And there is a little algebra.

Traders or investors whose methods are based on chart analysis or other non-quantifiable methods will probably have difficulty producing the trading data that is required for the statistical analysis described in this book. Formula-based analytical methods lend themselves much better to producing trade results that are used both to establish trading baselines and estimate future performance.

Traders who use bars shorter than one minute and who hold for less time than a few minutes fall into the category of high frequency traders. High frequency traders use high speed computers running sophisticated analytical trading algorithms, high bandwidth communications lines, with offices and computers physically located close to the trading venue. They are backed by large, well financed operations. Their bids and offers are posted for less than a second and are often cancelled and replaced many times before being filled. Their positions are held for short periods – from less than a second to several seconds. They expect to make a profit of less than one cent per $100 traded. They always pay very low commissions, and may receive payment if their trades add liquidity to the market. They account for 50 percent or more, depending on the reporting source, of trading volume in 2010. That percentage is up from single digit amounts a few years ago, and rising.

Traders or investors who use monthly bars and those whose holding period is longer than a few months, even if their methods are fully quantified, will have difficulty generating enough data to establish baselines and to validate their trading systems. Investors who base their decisions on economic or corporate fundamentals will find nothing related to their methods in this book, other than illustrations of increased risk associated with long holding periods. I have written a paper entitled "Use of fundamental data for active investing in US equities" that explains my reasons for thinking that fundamental data has no value. You can download a free copy from http://www.blueowlpress.com/activities.html

This book is intended for traders who use analytical methods to buy and sell stocks, futures, ETFs, mutual funds, and options; whose trades typically last between a few minutes and a few months; and whose analysis is based on price bars that range from one minute to one week.

The language and terminology used in analyzing trading systems is shared with that of probability, statistics, information theory, game theory, and gambling. Some in the investment industry will term what is being discussed here as speculating or gambling. And some readers may object that the treatment of trading is not clearly differentiated from gambling. Although some authors try to make a clear distinction, I do not believe it is possible. John Kelly, working with Claude Shannon on information theory and communications for Bell Laboratories in 1956, gave us the Kelly formula which relates the probability of winning to the optimal size of a bet. A few years later, Shannon introduced Kelly and Ed Thorp, resulting in Thorp's book, *Beat the Dealer*, which showed the practical application of the Kelly formula to blackjack. Later, Thorp successfully applied his techniques to the stock market. Terms such as win to loss ratio, reward to risk ratio, risk of ruin, odds, probability, and bankruptcy are common to both fields. Whether we feel trading and gambling should be closely associated or not, they are associated, and this book does not make a strong effort to separate them.

There is one very significant difference between gambling and trading. In gambling, the house almost always has a sizable advantage. Well designed trading systems give an advantage to the trader. This book discusses ways to recognize that advantage, measure the associated risk, capitalize on the advantage, and analyze trading as a business.

While this book is not intended to describe trading systems, many of the examples used are actual trades that were made with real money by real people whom I personally know. The markets are clearly not efficient. This book helps you capitalize on that.

OVERVIEW OF THE MONTE CARLO TECHNIQUE

A set of trade results or an equity curve, even when they are truly out-of-sample or actual trades, contribute one data point toward a statistical analysis. We will make several assumptions about the future, all based

on the best and least biased information we have. In order of preference, the best data would be actual trades made with actual money,
then paper trades, then trades resulting from out-of-sample and walk
forward runs. If in-sample data is used, the analysis will over-estimate
the likelihood of success and under-estimate the likelihood of failure –
perhaps by a very significant amount.

In setting up a Monte Carlo simulation, we will:

• Assume that the system continues to identify profitable trades
  in the future as well as it did over the period sampled.

• Assume that the conditions over the reported period are representative of the future – there will be periods of rising prices,
  falling prices, high volatility, low volatility, and so forth, but
  they will be similar to those covered by the period sampled.

• Assume that future trades will have the same characteristics
  in terms of trading frequency, ratio of win to loss accuracy,
  profit factor, maximum adverse excursion, maximum favorable
  excursion, and so forth.

But what we cannot assume is that the order of periods of market condition continues unchanged. That is, we cannot assume that future
trades occur in the same sequence as they did in the reported period.

Monte Carlo simulation gives a practical and statistically sound technique for estimating future trading results. It involves repeatedly
choosing trades from the list of sample trades at random and creating a simulated trading history. From that sequence, we can generate
a summary of trading results, and an equity curve with drawdown
calculation. Each simulated equity curve contributes one data point to
the analysis. In fact it is possible that one of the sequences is exactly
the original sample data in the original sequence and gives exactly the
same equity curve. This point is important and bears repeating – the
set of trade results and equity curve that results from a backtest, or even
from a single simulation run, contributes a single data point toward the
analysis of the performance of a trading system. After running many
rearrangements, the distribution of likely results can be determined.

Using data randomly and repeatedly chosen from a statistical distribution is central to the Monte Carlo simulation technique. Chapter 6
gives background on the technique and later chapters give detailed examples of its application.

DETECTING SYSTEM BREAKDOWN

A regularly heard question asks what happens if the future fails to behave as the past. The answer is that the projected distribution will no longer apply. Several sections of this book specifically address techniques that help determine when the actual performance is significantly different than the expected performance. And, in particular, to help determine when the system is broken. As long as the system performs as expected, the distribution describes what might be expected; and when the system stops performing as expected, we can detect that and then modify the trading method.

Throughout this book the projections of day-by-day or trade-by-trade equity, drawdown, and trading methodology will be based on a four year horizon, where each year has 252 trading days. If a system has 20 trades per year, there will be 80 trades in four years, and the analysis will be carried out using sequences of 80 trades. A system that trades twice a year will have eight trades in its four years. An intra-day system that averages two trades per day will have 2016 trades in its four years.

TRADING SYSTEM EXAMPLES

During a recent seminar on trading, several colleagues made presentations describing their trading systems. All had done high quality design, testing, and validation. The data they presented was from out-of-sample tests, including walk forward runs. All data is net after allowing for reasonable commissions and slippage.

Several questions arise at every one of these discussions:
1. Is this system good enough to trade?
2. What is the best way to trade this system?
3. How can I tell when the system is broken?

This book is intended to address these issues – with a little background and theory to justify the approach I recommend, and some practical tools you can use to apply it yourself.

What follows is a brief summary of each of those presentations.

THE STOCK TRADER

She has developed an indicator that gives signals that a stock is over-extended, either relatively too high in price or too low, and is likely to revert to the mean soon. She has a margin account with $100,000 in cash and is willing to use an additional $100,000 in margin funding.

The characteristics of her system are:
- Uses end-of-day data.
- Computes signal points in advance.
- Uses limit orders to enter and either limit or market-on-close orders to exit.
- Has a profit target.
- Has a maximum holding period.
- Holds one to three days.
- Has directional accuracy greater than 70 percent.
- Trades highly liquid US common stocks.
- Trades both long and short, although only the long side is shown here.
- Is 100 percent mechanical.
- Has about 220 long trades per year.

Since prices of individual stocks are highly correlated, there are periods when up to five positions are held, and other periods with no holdings.

The summary of trades that follows is based on a constant position size of $10,000 per trade. This may not be the appropriate method to trade this system, but it is appropriate when gathering information necessary to perform the analysis. Since five positions, each of $10,000, total less than her trading account, she could use this method in actual trading.

AmiBroker software was used to design, test, and validate the trading system. Figure 1.1 shows the summary of the test run that produced the sample data used in the Monte Carlo simulation. AmiBroker is also used to compute the signal points in advance for use each day.

While AmiBroker was used in this example, the analysis throughout this book is independent of the development platform used to generate the trades.

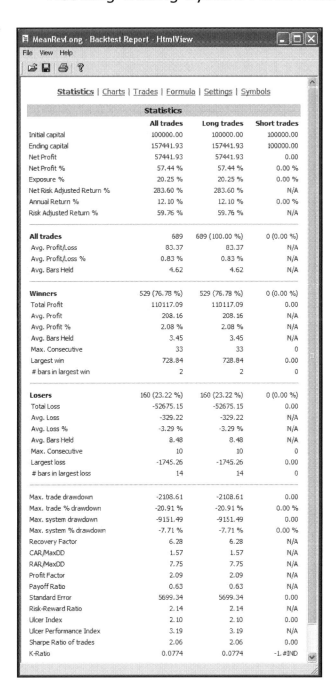

FIGURE 1.1

The 689 trades are sorted and placed in bins, each $10 wide. Figure 1.2 shows the resulting histogram. 216 of the trades exited at a profit target and had $290 profit.

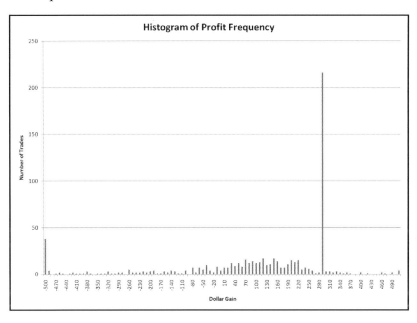

FIGURE 1.2

Figure 1.3 shows the equity curve from the backtest. Initial equity is $100,000. Each trade was made taking a $10,000 position.

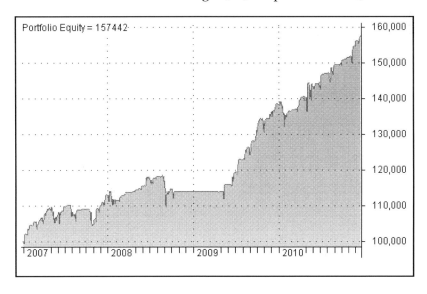

FIGURE 1.3

1. Is this system good enough to trade?

   Based on the summary and the single backtest equity curve shown above, the system looks very promising. One hundred equity curves, each covering a four year period, were generated using Monte Carlo simulation.

   Ten of them were plotted together in a "straw broom" chart which is shown in Figure 1.4. The dotted line is the average of the ten. Note how each begins with $100,000 in equity, but the paths are different as trades occur in different order. Final equity after four simulated years of trading can be read from the right-hand edge. Drawdown can be estimated as equity curves drop from recent highs.

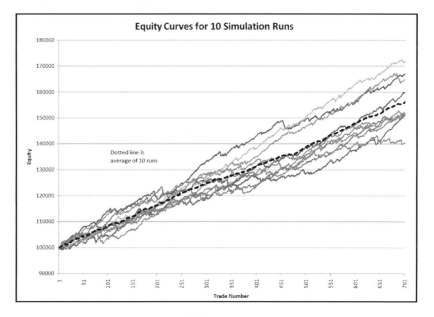

FIGURE 1.4

The 100 results have been used to create a chart showing the probable distribution of final equity. It is shown in Figure 1.5. The midpoint of the distribution is $157,654. That is about 12% compound annual rate. The system is exposed only about 20% of the time, so the effective risk adjusted rate is about 60%, assuming there are equally attractive opportunities from other trading systems while this system is in cash.

Note that about 5% of the simulation runs resulted in a final equity of $143,913 or less, and about 5% resulted in a final equity of $171,357 or greater. While any of these results at the 5% level are unlikely, they could occur and still be consistent with proper operation of this system.

Later chapters have detailed descriptions explaining how these charts are created and interpreted. You can do it yourself using Excel and tools that are free.

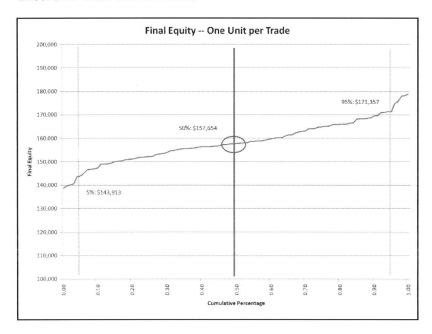

FIGURE 1.5

The same 100 results have been used to create a chart of the probable distribution of maximum drawdown. Expected drawdown, that is the drawdown measured at the 50% point of the range of simulation results, is $3,113. If future performance follows the distribution of trades, drawdown will be less than $3,113 about half the time and greater about half the time. 5% of the time—one four-year period out of 20—drawdown will exceed $4,972. See Figure 1.6.

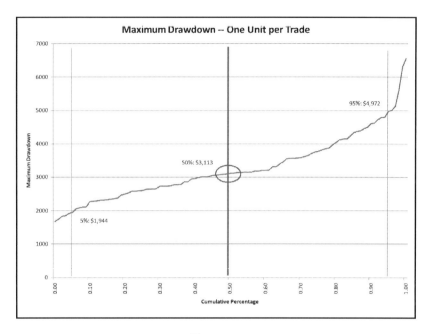

FIGURE 1.6

Everyone in attendance agreed that this system is good enough to trade.

2. What is the best way to trade this system?

Some alternatives are:

- Trade a single unit of $10,000 at each signal. The results are those shown in the figures just above.
- Trade a fraction of the account balance on each trade. With $100,000 in cash and an equal amount in margin funds, she has $200,000 available. Her holdings will vary between all cash and five positions. Based on her cash holding, she can use from 0 to 40% of her cash for each position.

These, and other options, are discussed in later chapters.

3. How can we tell when the system is broken?

To answer, compare recent performance with a benchmark. A logical candidate to be the benchmark is the sample data from the period used to set up the Monte Carlo simulation runs. Comparisons that are meaningful and easy to make are:

- Compare the mean profit (or some other meaningful metric) of recent trades with the mean profit of the benchmark.

This tests whether recent trades are different than the benchmark sample.

- Compare the mean profit of recent trades with random performance. This tests whether recent trades are better or worse than breakeven.
- Compare the accuracy of recent trades with accuracy of the benchmark.

Systems with high accuracy are easy. This trader's accuracy is 76 percent. If she has 5 or fewer wins in any 10 trade sequence, the system is probably broken. Similarly, 9 or fewer wins in 15; or 13 or fewer wins in 20. Each of these conditions is expected to occur by chance less than 5% of the time. (See Chapter 11 for charts showing these values and for formulas that can be used with any combination of length of sequence and accuracy.) Since she has about 700 trades in four years, and there are 691 10-trade sequences in that period, then she will observe 5 or fewer wins in a 10 trade sequence and think the system is broken about 34 times, or about once a month. (But expect these 34 to come in groups, rather than spaced evenly at one per month.) As is explained in greater detail in later chapters, her response should be to stop taking trades with real money, but continue to track performance. When performance returns to within the expected parameters, she should resume making real trades. If it never returns, she is safely in cash and not trading a broken system.

THE ETF TRADER

This system models and trades SPY, the Exchange Traded Fund based on the S&P 500 index. The trader has $100,000 in a margin account and is willing to use an additional $100,000 of margin funding. He has permission to trade futures and options in the account.

The characteristics are:

- Computes indicators and signals prior to the close each day.
- Trades Market On Close – MOC.
- Holds exactly one day.
- Uses no stops and no profit targets.

The system is always in the market, either long SPY or short SPY. A four year period that establishes the benchmark, each trade being made with a single unit of $10,000.

The trader felt that he could risk losing up to 40% of his initial stake, $40,000. But if he experienced a drawdown of $40,000, he would have to stop trading the system. His goal was to increase the account to $400,000, at which point he would stop trading, withdraw his money from the market, and retire.

This trader has more alternative ways to trade than the stock trader. He can:

- Model SPY, trade SPY with a position size of a single unit of $10,000 per signal.
- Model SPY, trade SPY with a position size that is a fraction of the account equity on each signal.
- Model SPY, but take trades in leveraged ETFs, such as SDS or SSO.
- Model SPY, but take trades in a futures contract, such as ES.
- Model SPY, but take trades in one or more common stocks that are closely correlated with SPY, such as AMG, LUK, or UTX.
- Model SPY, but take trades in options – options on SPY, on ES, or on common stocks.

Later chapters go into detail about these alternatives.

He demonstrated a system that was about 53% accurate in predicting whether the next close will be higher or lower than the one when the position is taken. He was interested in determining what level of accuracy produced what results.

Figure 1.7 shows the straw broom chart of ten simulation runs.

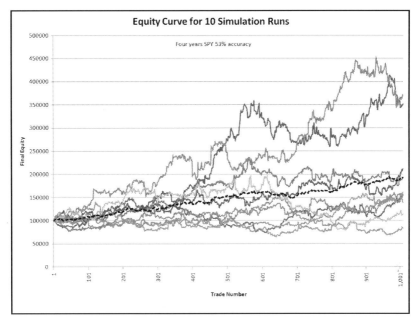

FIGURE 1.7

A single backtest could produce any one of these equity curves. Based on some of them, the system looks profitable but with high drawdowns. Based on others, the system is not profitable.

Figure 1.8 shows the distribution of the final equity. The average final equity of the 100 simulation runs is $165,818. That is about a 13% annual compound rate for the four years.

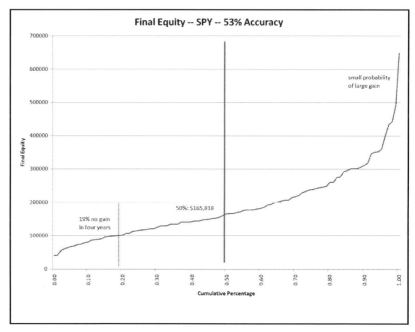

FIGURE 1.8

Figure 1.9 shows the distribution of the drawdown. Over 92% of runs had drawdowns over at least $40,000. The expected drawdown is $60,284. There is a greater than 10% probability that the drawdown will exceed $100,000. In this study, drawdown was measured in absolute dollar amounts. If the trader relaxes his requirement, say to 40% of maximum equity, the drawdown limit will be reached less often.

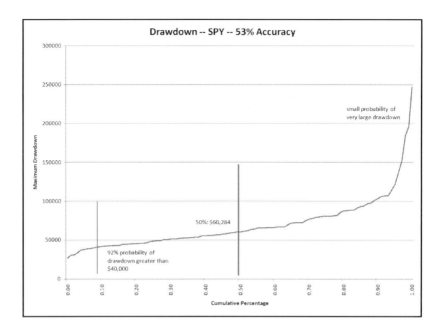

FIGURE 1.9

The class was understandably uncomfortable with these results. An accuracy level of 53% is clearly not high enough. The distribution of 100 runs shows how high the risk really is.

Later chapters explore accuracy in more detail, including more charts, guidelines, and do-it-yourself tools. We will see that higher accuracy both increases the return and decreases the risk. A system that predicts the direction of the one day change in SPY with sufficient accuracy is very desirable. The wide variety of alternatives for trading such a system further increases its value.

THE FUTURES TRADER

The woman who presented this system is interested in trading agricultural commodities, including corn, wheat, and oats. She is using trend-following methods, such as the crossover of two moving averages, to take either long or short positions. Her characteristics are:

- Uses daily data.
- Pre-computes the price at which a cross will take place.
- Monitors the markets during floor trading hours.
- Takes positions at the market price when the cross takes place.

For the simulation, each position is one contract. Using a well defined unit, and taking all positions in single unit size, is important in establishing simulation baselines.

The average profit is $117 per contract per trade. The average trade is held six days. Figure 1.10 shows the summary of trades.

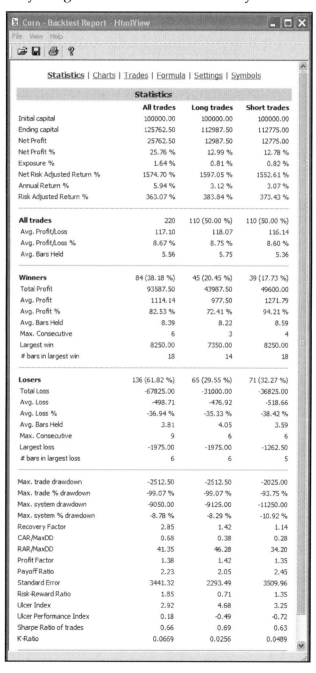

	All trades	Long trades	Short trades
Statistics			
Initial capital	100000.00	100000.00	100000.00
Ending capital	125762.50	112987.50	112775.00
Net Profit	25762.50	12987.50	12775.00
Net Profit %	25.76 %	12.99 %	12.78 %
Exposure %	1.64 %	0.81 %	0.82 %
Net Risk Adjusted Return %	1574.70 %	1597.05 %	1552.61 %
Annual Return %	5.94 %	3.12 %	3.07 %
Risk Adjusted Return %	363.07 %	383.84 %	373.43 %
All trades	220	110 (50.00 %)	110 (50.00 %)
Avg. Profit/Loss	117.10	118.07	116.14
Avg. Profit/Loss %	8.67 %	8.75 %	8.60 %
Avg. Bars Held	5.56	5.75	5.36
Winners	84 (38.18 %)	45 (20.45 %)	39 (17.73 %)
Total Profit	93587.50	43987.50	49600.00
Avg. Profit	1114.14	977.50	1271.79
Avg. Profit %	82.53 %	72.41 %	94.21 %
Avg. Bars Held	8.39	8.22	8.59
Max. Consecutive	6	3	4
Largest win	8250.00	7350.00	8250.00
# bars in largest win	18	14	18
Losers	136 (61.82 %)	65 (29.55 %)	71 (32.27 %)
Total Loss	-67825.00	-31000.00	-36825.00
Avg. Loss	-498.71	-476.92	-518.66
Avg. Loss %	-36.94 %	-35.33 %	-38.42 %
Avg. Bars Held	3.81	4.05	3.59
Max. Consecutive	9	6	6
Largest loss	-1975.00	-1975.00	-1262.50
# bars in largest loss	6	6	5
Max. trade drawdown	-2512.50	-2512.50	-2025.00
Max. trade % drawdown	-99.07 %	-99.07 %	-93.75 %
Max. system drawdown	-9050.00	-9125.00	-11250.00
Max. system % drawdown	-8.78 %	-8.29 %	-10.92 %
Recovery Factor	2.85	1.42	1.14
CAR/MaxDD	0.68	0.38	0.28
RAR/MaxDD	41.35	46.28	34.20
Profit Factor	1.38	1.42	1.35
Payoff Ratio	2.23	2.05	2.45
Standard Error	3441.32	2293.49	3509.96
Risk-Reward Ratio	1.85	0.71	1.35
Ulcer Index	2.92	4.68	3.25
Ulcer Performance Index	0.18	-0.49	-0.72
Sharpe Ratio of trades	0.66	0.69	0.63
K-Ratio	0.0669	0.0256	0.0489

FIGURE 1.10

The system did poorly for the first 18 of 48 months. While the final 30 months look good, it is important to use all of the data to establish the trade distribution for the simulation. Figure 1.11 shows the equity curve from the out-of-sample test.

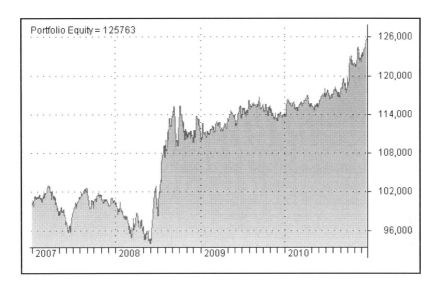

FIGURE 1.11

Figure 1.12 shows the straw broom chart.

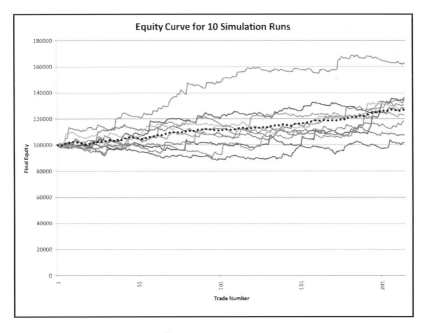

FIGURE 1.12

Figure 1.13 shows the final equity. There is a small probability of no gain over the four year period.

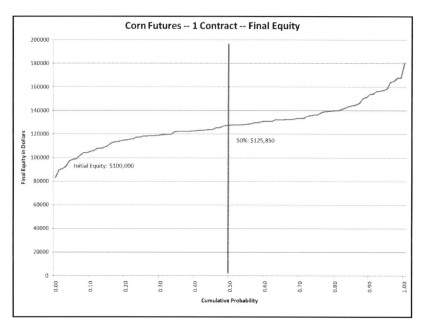

FIGURE 1.13

Figure 1.14 shows the probably distribution of drawdown. Drawdown at the 50% point in the distribution is $9,725. There is a 5% probability the drawdown will be $15,700 or greater.

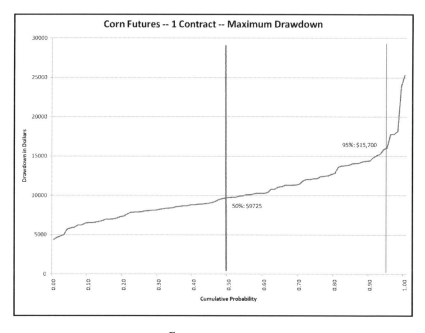

FIGURE 1.14

Most participants did not like this system as it was traded.

- The winning percentage is low – only 38%.
- Midpoint of the final equity is $125,850 – an annual compound rate of return of less than 6%.
- Midpoint of the drawdown is $9,725, with 5% probability of $15,700 drawdown.

Class members felt the ratio of expected drawdown to expected reward was too low, and risk of a large drawdown was too great.

These results are trading a single corn contract in a $100,000 account. At the time this is being written, initial margin on corn is $2,025, and maintenance margin is $1,500. Some rules of thumb suggest determining the minimum account size by adding the drawdown that is 95% probable to twice initial margin, which would be $19,750 in this case. Trading one contract for every multiple of $19,750, would allow 5 contracts for the $100,000 account. In that case, the CAR would be about 30%.

FRACTIONAL POSITION SIZING

This system lends itself well to analyzing position sizing that risks a fraction of the account balance on each trade.

A series of simulations, each 1000 runs, was run using values of f, the fraction to risk, from 0.01 to 0.40.

Risk per contract was set to be $2,000, slightly more than the largest loss of the 220 trades, which was $1,975.

To calculate the number of contracts to be taken on the next trade, multiply the current account balance by f. Divide that amount by $2,000, then round down to the next integer to obtain the position size. Fractions of 1% and 2% were too small to allow any trades. One of the output columns from the simulation was the maximum number of contracts. Using fraction 0.03, 53% of the runs used at most 1 contract, 44% used 2 contracts, and 3% used 3 contracts.

Figure 1.15 shows the terminal wealth at the 50% point of each set of runs. Terminal wealth, or terminal wealth relative, TWR, is the multiple that the final account balance is of the initial account balance. A terminal wealth of 2.0 means the account doubled in four years. The jagged line connects the points determined from the simulation runs. The smooth line is a 2nd degree polynomial best fit to the experimental data. The peak occurs at a fraction of 0.24. An independent calculation based on the geometric mean of the trades suggests it is 0.235. The value of f at the peak is the optimal f—that fraction that results in the highest terminal wealth.

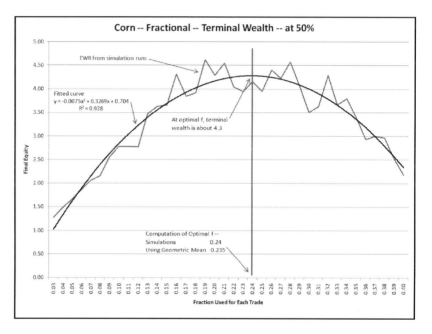

FIGURE 1.15

Figure 1.16 shows the distribution of final equity for a fixed fraction of 0.24. The terminal wealth at the 50% point is 4.16. About half the time equity after four years will be greater than 4.16 times initial equity; about half it will be less. The vertical scale is limited in order to show detail in the midrange. There is a high probability of a very high terminal wealth.

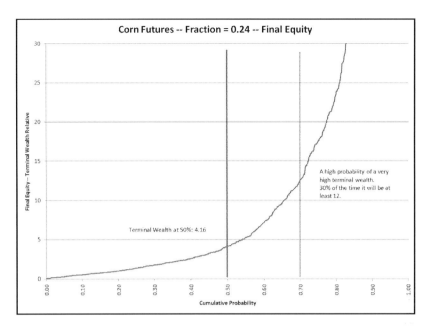

FIGURE 1.16

Figure 1.17 focuses more closely on the left side of the distribution. It shows there is about a 20% chance there will be no net gain after four years, and a 5% chance of a loss of more than 70% of the trading account.

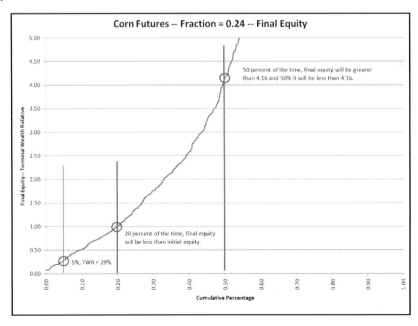

FIGURE 1.17

Figure 1.18 shows the distribution of the closed trade drawdown at a fraction of 0.24. At the 50% point, drawdown is 74% of maximum equity. 5% of the time drawdown will exceed 91%.

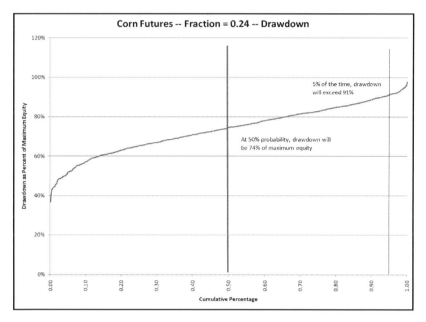

FIGURE 1.18

Figure 1.19 shows the distribution of drawdown for the range of fractions. The dotted line shows the drawdown at the 95% level; the solid line at the 50% level. Note the vertical line at 0.24 and compare the values of drawdown at 50% and 95% to figure 1.18.

The circles at points A, B, and C help identify more prudent fractions. If the trader is willing to take a 50% risk of a 40% drawdown—Point A—he can use a fraction of 0.10. Note that he risks a 5% chance of a 60% drawdown—Point B. A safer fraction is 0.06, which shows a 5% chance of drawdown no worse than 40%—Point C.

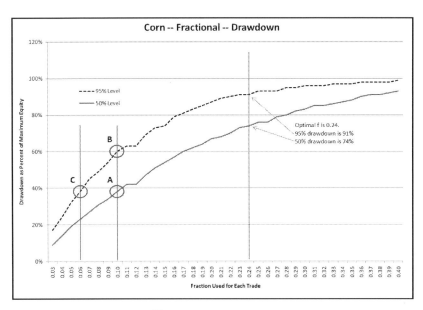

FIGURE 1.19

Figure 1.20 shows the distribution of final equity when traded at a fraction of 0.06. The midpoint of terminal wealth is 1.87. There is a 9% chance of no gain, and a 5% chance of quadrupling the account.

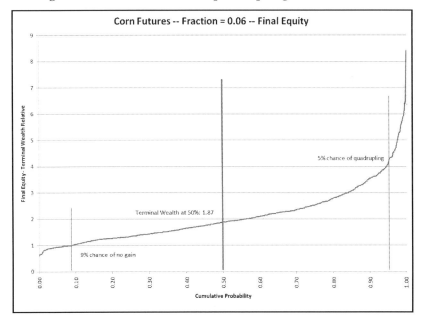

FIGURE 1.20

Figure 1.21 shows the distribution of drawdown when traded at a fraction of 0.06. The midpoint is a drawdown of 23%. There is a 5% chance the drawdown will exceed 38%

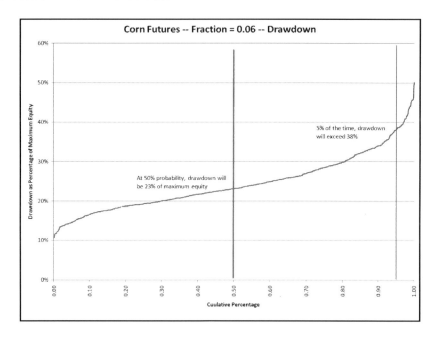

FIGURE 1.21

When traded at a fraction of 0.06, the midpoint of final equity is 1.87, which is a CAR of about 17% for the four years. With the midpoint drawdown at 23%, this system is more reasonable. One of its drawbacks is the accuracy ratio of only 38%, which makes it difficult to tell when the system begins to break down.

Later chapters expand on these studies, and explain how you can perform similar analysis on your data.

Chapter 2

Trading as a Business

A question often heard around traders is how to best make trading a business. What do you need to have your trading account grow from, say, $100,000 to several million dollars?

Because of year to year variations in rates of return and drawdown, it is risky to count on trading to generate monthly profits. Throughout this book, we will focus on growth of the trading account. If you want to model regular withdrawals, there is an example demonstrating how to do that.

THE TRADING ACCOUNT

How much money is in my trading account now?

How much of my assets am I willing to use to fund trading positions? Call that the "active" portion. The remainder will be inactive, and will not be at risk. Drawdowns will be measured relative to the active portion and the equity it generates. A trader might have a combination of cash, real estate, collectibles, and retirement funds totaling $500,000, with $100,000 of that in the trading account.

What is my monetary goal, and in how much time? The trader might have a goal of building the $100,000 into $1,000,000 in four years.

What size of loss will cause me to stop trading? Losses can be measured as a portion of initial equity or of highest equity. If the limit is 40%, and based on initial equity, the trader will continue as long as the funds in the active trading account remain above $60,000. If the limit is 40%, and based on highest equity, the trader will continue as long as funds remain above 60% of the highest equity. Equity and drawdown can be computed on either a closed trade basis or an intra-trade (or open trade) basis.

THE TRADING SYSTEM

Modeling Trading System Performance (MTSP) is a sequel to *Quantitative Trading Systems* (QTS). QTS explained the process of the design, testing, and validation of trading systems. In *MTSP*, we are not concerned with the system itself – only the trades that result from it.

You can test any list of trade results, including actual trades, out-of-sample test results, or hypothetical results, but in order for the trading account to grow the system must be profitable (have a positive mathematical expectation) in the future.

The system is the combination of the logic and the data. Characteristics that are important include:

- The issue to trade, including its liquidity.
- Being sufficiently mechanical that it can be tested and statistically validated.
- The length of the bars used to generate the trading signals, such as hourly, daily, or weekly.
- Methods of entering trades, such as at a limit price, at a stop price, or at the market at the next trading opportunity, including being able to fill actual orders at prices suggested in the simulation.
- The length of time the typical trade is held.
- Frequency of trading.
- The statistical distribution of gains per trade. Analysis of these stats will show the mean, standard deviation, percentage of trades that are winners, win to loss ratio, and fatness of the tails. Actual trade results (or hypothetical results) are used rather than theoretical distributions.
- Proper use of leverage. A futures system that always buys one contract, without regard to the size of the account or the trading history, is unleveraged. Similarly, a stock system that always buys $10,000 worth of an issue is unleveraged. Growing an account requires use of leverage and compounding.

IS THE SYSTEM WORKING OR BROKEN?

HOW DO I KNOW THE SYSTEM WORKS?

Future profits depend on the system being profitable in the future. The best estimates we can get of future performance are results of trades made using data that was not used during the development of the system – that is, out-of-sample data. It would be folly to trade a system that is untested; and equally poor judgment to trade a system known to be unprofitable in backtests. Even if the system appeared to be profitable using in-sample backtest results, that is no guarantee that it will be profitable in the future. Use of in-sample results always over estimates future profitability and under estimates future drawdown. It is not uncommon for systems that are profitable using in-sample data to be unprofitable in the future. Use in-sample results to plan your trading business at your financial peril.

How Can I Tell When the System is Broken?

Encountering a large drawdown is one of the primary reasons traders stop trading. Understanding, estimating, and limiting drawdowns, and determining whether a drawdown is within reasonable expectations of the system or a symptom that the system is broken, are among the primary goals of this book.

The price and volume data consists of a combination of signal and noise. The trading system logic has been designed to recognize the signal portion of the data in anticipation of profitable trading opportunities. Systems rely on the continued synchronization between the logic and the data. As variations occur in the data stream, the degree of synchronization shifts. When they are in sync, the system is profitable; when they are out of sync, the system is unprofitable. One of the most difficult questions traders face is how to determine whether the system is working as expected, or is temporarily out of sync, or is broken.

Determination of whether the system is working or broken relies on comparison of recent trading results to some benchmark. Comparison implies that there is some metric, such as profit per trade, available for both the recent results and the benchmark. There are two easily established benchmarks:

- Previous performance – compare recent results against actual trades previously made with the system, or against the out-of-sample results from the validation process.
- Random – compare recent results against random results.

Statistical analysis is used to evaluate the comparison. Several sections of *MTSP* explain statistical testing procedures, suggest appropriate tests, and give rules for actions.

Is It Possible to Meet the Goal?

Having a terminal wealth 10 times the initial wealth in 4 years requires an annual compounded rate of 78% per year. That is, $1.78 \wedge 4 = 10.0$.

Whether this is possible depends on several factors:

- The distribution of trade results, including the average profit per trade and variation among trades.
- The number of trades per year.
- The portion of the active account used to take each position.

If the mean trade profit is 0.5%, winning trades are about equal in size to losing trades, trades are 60% accurate, and there are 52 trades per year, then the annual percentage profit will be approximately:

> $(0.995 \wedge 21) * (1.005 \wedge 31) = 0.900 * 1.167 = 1.050$. This is well below the required 1.78.

If there are 252 trades per year, the annual percentage profit will be approximately:

> $(0.995 \wedge 101) * (1.005 \wedge 151) = 0.602 * 2.123 = 1.278$. By using correct position sizing, the goal can be successfully accomplishing if the drawdown remains within accept bounds.

MANAGING THE BUSINESS

As a trader planning to grow your account, you are running a business. Just as with any other business, you need office space, equipment, supplies, and personnel, all of which require funds – either directly expended or as lost opportunity. Calculate your monthly expenses and determine where that money will come from. Throughout this book, we will assume that the trading account has no withdrawals to meet business or living expenses.

Structure your business so that it can be run like a DVD. When there appears to be a problem, or you want to take a break, press Pause and go flat. Analyze and modify as necessary, then press Resume. You do not need to remain exposed to risks during the adjustment period.

You will need time. Time to generate signals, place trades, record and analyze results.

And you will need skills. In particular, you need to be enough of a statistician to understand the techniques used to determine the health of the system.

GAMBLING AND TRADING

We begin with some examples from gambling that illustrate some of these points, after which we will extend the examples to trading.

Chapter 3

Trading Systems

Modeling Trading System Performance is a sequel to my earlier book, *Quantitative Trading Systems (QTS)*. Those readers who are familiar with *QTS* may comfortably skip this chapter.

In *Quantitative Trading Systems*, I outline the process of design, testing, and validation of trading systems that I think is necessary in order to have reasonable confidence that a trading system can be profitable in the future.

As I set out to write *QTS*, I wanted to avoid having my book placed on the shelf in that section reserved for books that espoused nebulous and untestable ideas, often written with the intent of selling some additional product or service. I wanted every reader to be able to think about my statements and ideas, incorporate their own thoughts and alternatives, and test them using a professional-grade trading system development platform.

I chose AmiBroker to implement the concepts in *QTS*. Not because I have a partnership relationship with AmiBroker. I do not. I purchased my copy of AmiBroker at full retail price. I chose AmiBroker because it was the only platform I could find that was capable of implementing the procedures I feel are essential to successful trading systems. As an added benefit, the cost of AmiBroker is about one-tenth the cost of other popular platforms, even though none of those are capable of the necessary tasks.

Even though *QTS* uses AmiBroker, it is much broader in scope than being just an AmiBroker book.

If you have not yet read *QTS*, I encourage you to do so. The brief outline in this chapter cannot do justice to its 368 pages of text, including some 80 fully explained and coded examples.

The next few pages outline the key points about trading systems I feel are not only important, but essential. In the final analysis, the question each and every designer of a trading system must ask before he or she makes their first trade is "How confident am I that this system will work tomorrow with real money?"

QUANTITATIVE

I am a strong believer in the quantitative approach to trading. For me to consider making a trade based on some concept, I must be able to write a set of rules that describe that concept, test those rules over the historical data of the tradable issue, and become reasonably confident that the system will work on unseen data. I have no argument with people who can successfully interpret chart patterns. To the extent those patterns can be described and quantified, they are candidates for quantitative trading.

OBJECTIVE FUNCTION

I am a strong believer that the personal and professional preferences and requirements of the trader and his or her organization should form the basis for the trading systems used. In particular, I believe that the design of the system should match the person or organization right from the start. I know how difficult it is for me to change my thoughts or behavior to accept some concept or perform some act contrary to my personality.

By proper design and implementation of the objective function (or fitness function) by which trading results can be measured and compared, those trading systems that rank high are very likely to be tradable without cognitive dissonance. I recommend designing the system to match the person, rather than trying to train the person to accept a system that does not match his personality or requirements.

SYSTEM DESIGN

The premises of technical analysis are:

- The market is sufficiently inefficient that there are patterns in the data that can be recognized that precede profitable trading opportunities.
- Those patterns are persistent enough that trading systems can be designed, tested, and validated, with enough time remaining for profitable trading.

As I define and describe it, a trading system has two components:

- The logic and set of rules that defines the model.
- The data the model processes.

The data consists of two components:

- Signal that contains the profitable patterns.
- Noise, which is everything not specifically recognized as signal, even if it contains valuable information that could be detected by some other set of logic.

Entries are important. There are many valid techniques for entering trades:
- Trend following, such as breakout or moving average cross-over.
- Mean regression, including buying weakness and selling strength.
- Comparative relative strength, such as rotation among sectors.
- Patterns, such as sequences of prices.
- Seasonalities, such as times of the month or phases of the moon.
- Statistics, based on analysis of price action following some condition.
- Cycles.

Exits are important. There are several ways to exit a trade:
- Sell signal determined by the rules.
- Holding period maximum.
- Profit target.
- Trailing exit, such as parabolic.
- Maximum loss stop.

The logic defines the rules. The data defines the price series. Together they comprise a trading system.

It is not necessary to trade the series used to develop the model. In my simple-minded one-liner: "Model something easy, trade something profitable." For example, it is often easier to develop a trading system using an index-related exchange traded fund (ETF) than using an individual security. But it can be much more profitable to make the trades in the individual security, or in a related ETF.

IN-SAMPLE TESTING

The period of time, and the data associated with that time, used to refine the rules is called the in-sample period and the in-sample data.

The length of the in-sample period is "whatever length best fits the system." Using too long a period includes data that represents many periods of time and many different economic conditions. It is difficult to fit a single model to many conditions. Using too short a period reduces the opportunity for the model to identify and synchronize itself with the signal component of the data.

System development is a repeated cycle of test and modify, until the results are acceptable.

The process of optimization is testing many alternatives of logic and parameter values, searching for those that are best. Best is measured by the objective function. Optimization in itself is neither good nor bad. It is simply an organized method for performing the search.

The results of in-sample testing are always good. We do not stop fooling with the system until the results are good.

OUT-OF-SAMPLE TESTING

Due to the repeated adjustment of the logic to fit the in-sample data, there is a serious risk that the model has become over-fit to the data; that it has learned to recognize the noise component rather than the signal component.

Out-of-sample testing is used to check for over-fitting and to give an estimate of future performance of the system. Out-of-sample is testing done using data that was not used during development of the system.

Financial data is different than other data used for experiments and statistical tests. Every time a trading system makes a profitable trade, it removes some of the inefficiency that it was designed to recognize. If enough systems recognize and profitably trade based on that same inefficiency, they will remove the inefficiency, and the characteristics of data in the future will be different. Consequently, out-of-sample data must be more recent than in-sample data.

The length of the out-of-sample period is "as long as the system continues to perform profitably."

Eventually every system fails. Without periodic adjustment to changing conditions, either the model falls out of synchronization with the data or the inefficiency has been removed. In either case, the system is no longer profitable. Perhaps the parameters can be adjusted by returning to the in-sample phase. Or perhaps the system will never work again.

WALK FORWARD VALIDATION

Practice is important. Whether we are performing an athletic activity or trading, we want to be comfortable with the action and confident that it will go smoothly. One of the critical actions for a trading system designer is the transition from development to live trading. There is no doubt that tomorrow is out-of-sample.

Walk forward testing is the process of repeating a series of steps:
1. Select an in-sample period of time.
2. Perform an organized search for the set of parameters that perform best using the in-sample data. That is, re-optimize.
3. Rank the results using the objective function.
4. Select the single set of parameters associated with the best result.
5. Move the time period forward and select an out-of-sample time period that immediately follows the in-sample period.
6. Test the profitability of the system on the out-of-sample data, and record those results.

Continue to step forward, moving both the in-sample period and out-of-sample period by the length of the out-of-sample period, until the final out-of-sample period includes the most recent data. Record the values for the parameters for the most recent step.

Evaluate the concatenated out-of-sample results from all the walk forward steps. Look at the trade statistics, such as the percentage of winning trades, expected gain per trade, win to loss ratio, maximum system drawdown, and so forth. Also plot and examine the equity curve. Decide whether these results are good enough to risk trading tomorrow. If you do decide to trade the system, use the latest values of the parameters—those chosen during the final walk forward step.

Walk forward testing provides two essential functions:
1. Every walk forward step is a practice step in the transition between in-sample testing and out-of-sample trading.
2. The concatenated out-of-sample results are the best estimate of the future performance of the trading system.

MONITOR REAL-TIME RESULTS

If the performance as measured by the walk forward tests is not adequate, do not trade the system. Return to the design, test, and validation stages.

If it is adequate, the degree of confidence the designer of the system can have about the future performance is directly related to the degree of objectivity that was used during its development and the results of the walk forward tests.

Even when that confidence is very high at the time the system is put into operation, the system will go through periods of both good and poor performance.

It is essential to monitor the real-time results, and to have a basis with which to compare them.

SUMMARY

Modeling Trading System Performance assumes that the reader has worked through the system development process and has a trading system that has been trading or appears to be tradable.

When everything is going well, confidence is high, the model is in sync with the data, and profits are good. The important question is "What position size should be used for the next trade in order to maximize equity growth while minimizing risk of ruin?"

Eventually, performance fades. As it would be inappropriate to take a position of any size if the system is broken, the important question then is "Is the system working or is it broken?"

This book is intended to give the reader the techniques and tools to answer both those questions.

Chapter 4

Expectancy and Roulette

EXPECTANCY

Expectancy, or expectation, or mathematical expectation, or edge, is the amount you can expect to win given a single event.

Expectancy is the amount gained, on average, per play or trade. It can be defined in terms of percentage or in terms of the unit being wagered.

EXPECTANCY AS A PERCENTAGE

Expectancy as a percentage is computed as:

E = (percent won on winning plays) * (percent of plays that are winners) − (percent lost on losing plays) * (percent of plays that are losers).

For example, consider a trading system that:
- wins 60% of the time with an average gain per profitable trade of 0.5%
- loses 40% of the time with an average loss per losing trade of 0.4%

E = (0.5)*(0.6) − (0.4)*(0.4) = 0.14%

EXPECTANCY IN UNITS WAGERED

Expectancy in terms of units wagered is computed as:

E = (units won on winning plays) * (percent of plays that are winners) − (units lost on losing plays) * (percent of plays that are losers).

For example, consider a trading system that takes positions in units of $10,000:
- wins 60% of the time with an average gain per profitable trade of $450
- loses 40% of the time with an average loss per losing trade of $250

E = ($450)*(0.6) − ($250)*(0.4) = $170

Both definitions are useful and will be used in this book.

EXPECTANCY MUST BE POSITIVE

In order to be profitable in the long run, your expectancy must be positive.

When the process – trading system or gambling game – provides you a positive expectancy, you can expect to have a gain after many plays. The greater the number of plays, the closer your gain will be to the expectancy. However, you can turn a game with a positive expectancy into a losing game by making bets that are too large, as we will see in detail in later chapters.

When the process provides you a negative expectancy, you can expect to have a loss after many plays. The greater the number of plays, the closer your loss will be to the expectancy. No bet sizing, position sizing, or sequencing method can turn a process that has a negative expectancy into a winning system. If the expectancy of the next play is negative, the amount being wagered only affects the amount of the expected loss; it has no effect on the probability of that loss.

ROULETTE

That is not to say that you cannot go into a casino, play a game with a negative expectancy, and win – at least for a little while. A simulation using roulette as an example will illustrate.

FIGURE 4.1

Figure 4.2 shows the American and European roulette wheel layouts. The basic difference between the wheels is the number of zeros and associated green pockets. The sequence of numbers is different, but that does not affect the results of the game. The wheel is designed to place all the red and black, even and odd, high and low numbers equally. The design is standard in every casino. The croupier, sometimes called a dealer even for non-card games, rotates the wheel in one direction and rolls the ivory ball in the opposite direction. The ball eventually slows until it lands in one of the pockets in the wheel. Bets made for the number associated with that pocket win.

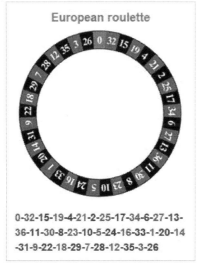
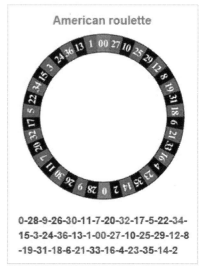

European roulette

0-32-15-19-4-21-2-25-17-34-6-27-13-36-11-30-8-23-10-5-24-16-33-1-20-14-31-9-22-18-29-7-28-12-35-3-26

American roulette

0-28-9-26-30-11-7-20-32-17-5-22-34-15-3-24-36-13-1-00-27-10-25-29-12-8-19-31-18-6-21-33-16-4-23-35-14-2

FIGURE 4.2

The payoff for a bet depends on how many numbers are included in the winning combination.

Bet Position	Payout
Single Number Bet	35 to 1
Split Bet (any 2 numbers)	17 to 1
Street Bet (any 3 numbers in a row)	11 to 1
Square Bet (any 4 numbers in a group)	8 to 1
Line Bet (any 6 numbers in a group)	5 to 1
Column / Dozen Bet (any 12 numbers in a column)	2 to 1
Red / Black / 1 to 18 / 19 to 36 / Odd / Even	1 to 1

FIGURE 4.3

Assume that you and your best friend are in Las Vegas for the evening and have a limited budget. You have $20 remaining in your entertainment account. You would like to see a live show and have a drink. Tickets to the show are $20 each and a drink is included with each ticket. There is a large screen in the lounge that will project the show; it is free, but drinks are $2 apiece. Your friend suggests you play roulette and turn your $20 into enough to see the live show. If your bankroll grows to $40, you will see the live show. If it drops to $4, you will go to the lounge, buy a drink each, and watch the big screen. Whichever happens first determines your evening plan.

You consider two possibilities.

One. Play even money bets at $1 per play until you reach either $4 or $40. If you win an even money bet, you keep your $1 bet and you are paid $1. If you lose an even money bet, you lose your $1 bet. Examples of even money bets are red versus black, or odd versus even. There are 18 red pockets, 18 black pockets, and (in the United States) 2 green pockets. If you bet red, you win whenever the ball drops into a red pocket, and you lose whenever it drops into either a black or green pocket. There are 18 ways to win and 20 ways to lose.

Two. Play single number bets (say your lucky number, 7) at $1 per play until you reach either $4 or $40. If you win a single number bet, you keep your $1 bet and you are paid $35. Said another way, the payout for winning is 35:1.

The expectancy at roulette for either even money bets or single number bets is -5.26%. As stated above, the calculation is: E = (units won on winning plays) * (percent of plays that are winners) – (units lost on losing plays) * (percent of plays that are losers)

Using $1.00 chips as the unit and computing expectancy for the even money case, E = ($1.00) * (18/38) – ($1.00) * (20/38) = 0.4737 - 0.5263 = -$0.0526 per $1 bet.

If done in percentages, E = (100%) * (18/38) – (100%) * (20/38) = -5.26%.

For the single number bet, E = ($35.00) * (1/38) – ($1.00) * (37/38) = 0.9211 – 0.9737 = -$0.0526

Since the game has a negative expectancy as seen from your perspective, you will be a net loser and wind up with the $4 outcome if you play indefinitely. Using either calculation based on probability theory or a Monte Carlo simulation, we can compute the probabilities or odds that you will get $4 or $40 in either of your plans. The $4 limit and $40 goal are called absorbing barriers. In later chapters these barriers will be discussed in more detail as warnings of impending ruin and goals for retirement.

FAIR WHEEL

As a basis for comparison, consider that you are playing even money bets and the payout is fair. That is, you found a casino where the green pockets result in a tie and you neither win nor lose, so the expectancy is 0.0. Figure 4.4 shows the equity you will have in your bankroll after 50 plays, 100 plays, and 1000 plays. Note that as the number of plays increases, it is more and more likely that the equity will wind up at one of the two absorbing barriers.

- After 50 plays, there is a 2.4% chance you will have lost $16 and have $4 left, and there is a 0.4% chance that you will have $40.
- After 100 plays, 11.2% you will have $4, and 4.8% you will have $40.
- After 1000 plays, 54.1% you will have $4, and 43.2% you will have $40.

The probability of reaching $40 is lower than that of reaching $4 because $40 is $20 away from your starting equity and $4 is only $16 away.

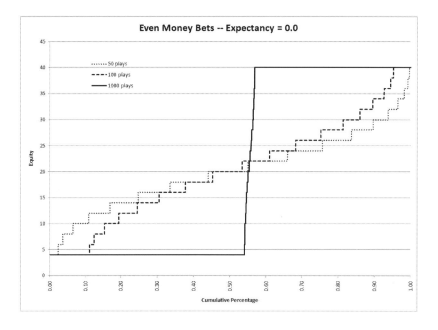

FIGURE 4.4

CASINO WHEEL

If you are playing even money bets in a normal casino in the United States, the expectancy is -0.0526. Figure 4.5 shows the equity you will have after 50, 100, and 1000 plays.

- After 50 plays, there is a 5.6% chance you will have lost $16 and have $4 left, there is a 0.1% chance that you will have $40, and the remaining 94.3% of the time your equity will be some value in between.

- After 100 plays, 24.2% you will have $4, 1.4% you will have $40, and 74.4% some value in between.

- After 1000 plays, you will almost certainly have reached one of the barriers – 89.8% you will have $4, 9.7% you will have $40, 0.3% some value in between.

The negative expectancy makes winning enough for you to reach your $40 goal very unlikely.

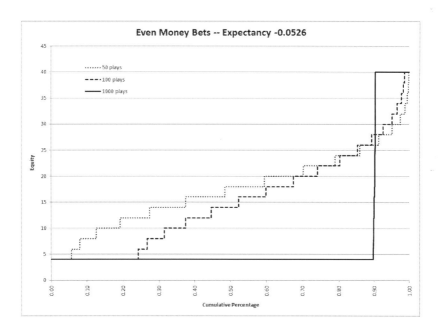

FIGURE 4.5

If you are playing single numbers, you must win once in one of the first 16 turns. If you lose all 16, you will have $4 remaining and you will go to the lounge. The probability of winning on any single play is 0.0263 – that is, 1 / 38. The probability of losing on any single play is 0.9737 – that is, 1 minus 0.0263. The probability of losing 16 times in a row is 0.9737 raised to the 16th power, which is 0.653. You can expect to will lose $16 without a single win 65.3% of the time – you go to the lounge 65.3% of the time. You will win enough to go to the live show 34.7% of the time. Figure 4.6 shows the distribution of your bankroll as determined by a Monte Carlo simulation. The figures are in close agreement, with the simulation showing a 65.0% chance of having $4 and 35.0% chance of having $40 or more.

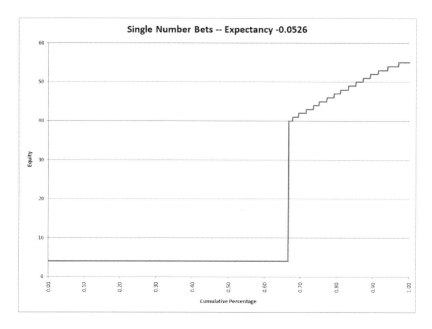

FIGURE 4.6

CONCLUSION

The conclusion is that the side – house or player, system or market – that has the positive expectancy will come out ahead in the long run. But if you absolutely must play a game where you have a negative expectancy, make high odds bets for a short number of plays – either win and quit, or be ruined and quit.

Of course, this is a contrived example. Relatively minor changes in the conditions make other options possible. If the couple had $22, they could make a single bet of $18 on an even money bet and have a 47% chance of $40 and a 53% chance of $4.

INDEPENDENCE OF EVENTS

Roulette is a game where the probability of each play is identical to all the others. In the language of probability, the individual events are independent and identically distributed – sometimes abbreviated iid.

To be independent means that the process has no memory. Keeping track of which pocket the roulette ball falls into has no value. Coin flips are independent. The serial correlation of a series of independent events is zero.

To be identically distributed means that the probability distribution is the same for all of the events. At roulette, the probability of the ball falling into a red pocket is 18 out of 38 on every play.

Compare with blackjack, the probability of receiving an ace on the next card changes as cards are dealt and removed as possible next cards for you.

DRUNKARD'S WALK

Motion of small particles such as smoke, and gambling games such as blackjack and roulette, share a fundamental mathematical property with trading systems—the random walk. Random walk is based on the mathematical model of Brownian motion, named after Robert Brown who first documented the motion in 1827. The Brownian motion of individual gains or losses in blackjack, roulette, and trading is called one-dimensional because the changes take place in only one dimension—up or down.

A colorful analog description of one-dimensional Brownian motion is the drunkard's walk. Imagine an inebriated person who steps from a pub into a narrow street. To the right, the street leads to his home; to the left is a shallow canal. He can only step to the right or the left, and he is so inebriated that he cannot remember which direction his last step was. After some number of random steps, even if he has a slight bias in one direction or the other, he will end his journey either at home or in the canal. If he is equally likely to step either right or left, then the likelihood of his reaching home depends on his position between the two end points. If he is 300 steps from home and 100 steps from the canal, then the probabilities are 0.25 and 0.75, respectively, that he arrives at each. Home is three times as far, so he is one-third as likely to reach it first.

ABSORBING BARRIERS

Since reaching either home or the canal ends his journey, these are called *absorbing barriers* or *absorbing boundaries*. Gamblers and traders have an absorbing barrier equivalent to the canal. It is the point at which the balance in their account is so low that they will not, or cannot, continue. Prudent gamblers, and traders, also have a barrier equivalent to arriving safely at home. It is when they are satisfied with their gains and quit while they are ahead. We will give the two barriers names—*ruin* and *retire*.

In any game or trading system where you have a chance, however small, of losing any given play and you have a limited bankroll, however large, there is a non-zero probability that you will eventually have a sequence of results that bankrupt you. This is true even if you have positive expectancy. Stated simply, if you play any game long enough, a run of bad luck will eventually bankrupt you.

You may decide that losing a substantial portion of your trading account is bad enough – that you do not need to lose everything before you admit defeat and quit. Whatever that level of loss is, whether expressed in dollars or percent, whether computed from your starting balance or your highest equity, you have some limit. It is the point at which you are ruined and you must quit—your ruin barrier. The process ends at that point with that equity balance.

Since all games result in ruin if played indefinitely, you should quit while you are ahead. The level, whether in dollars or percent, that gives you enough so that you no longer need to play is also an absorbing barrier.

If your system has a negative expectancy, you will reach ruin quickly, and you have a low probability of reaching retirement.

If your system has positive expectancy, there is still some non-zero probability that you will reach ruin. Choosing a level for retirement, along with an efficient position sizing method, will maximize your chance to retire before ruin.

Chapter 5

Blackjack

A Brief Analysis of Blackjack

Rules and Background

To have a framework for discussion of several topics in this book, we will begin with an analysis of the game of blackjack—a gambling game played in casinos and social clubs around the world. An excellent website for information about blackjack is http://wizardofodds.com/blackjack.

We can learn about risk, position sizing, and variability of equity results in trading by studying expectancy, bet size, and risk of ruin in gambling. Some of the analysis will be done through algebraic formulas; other portions will be done using Monte Carlo simulation.

Blackjack is a card game where the player is playing against the house or dealer. It is played with one to eight decks of ordinary cards. Cards from two through ten are each scored according to the number of pips on that card. All face cards count ten. Ace counts either one or eleven, at the option of the player. A hand that contains an ace that is scored eleven is termed *soft*. A hand where all aces are scored one is termed *hard*. The player's goal is to have a hand that is closer in score to 21, without going over 21, than the dealer's.

One or more players sit at a table, usually opposite the dealer. At the beginning of each hand, each player places a bet on the table in front of him.

There are variations of the procedure the dealer follows, but the one described here is typical. The dealer deals one card, usually face up, to each of the players, one card to himself face down, a second card face up to each player, a second card to himself face up.

The best hand is an ace and any ten-card. The score is 21 and the hand is called *blackjack*. Any player who has blackjack, providing the dealer does not also have blackjack, wins immediately and is paid 3 to 2. Being paid 3 to 2 means, for example, a bet of $10 will win an additional $15.

In turn, each player scores his cards and decides whether to take one or more additional cards (take a hit) or to play the two cards he already has (stand). A player may stand with a hand of any score. If he takes a card that causes his hand to exceed 21, his hand has *busted* and he immediately loses his bet. As long as his hand is still under 21, he may continue to take additional cards. Under some circumstances, the player may double his bet, called *doubling*, and take exactly one more card. If the first two cards a player receives are the same, he may split them into two hands, place an additional bet for the new hand, receive a second card for each of the original pair, and play both hands. A variety of rules cover conditions under which the player may re-split if his second card again pairs the first, and also whether doubling is permitted after splitting.

After all players have completed their play, the dealer turns his face-down card so that both cards are face up. The dealer must either stand or take a hit according to a set of rules posted at the table. A typical set of rules for the dealer is that the dealer must: hit hands that score 16 or less; stand on hands that score 18 or more; hit a hand that scores soft 17; stand with a hand that scores hard 17.

If the dealer busts, all players whose hands have not busted win and are paid an amount equal to their bet: 1 to 1. If the dealer does not bust, the dealer loses to and pays (1 to 1) each player whose score is closer to 21, wins from each player whose score is further from 21, and ties or *pushes* each player who has the same score. No money is won or lost on pushes. In most variations of the rules, it does not matter how many cards are in any single hand.

Variations on the game include the number of decks of cards being used, what percentage of the cards available to the dealer are dealt to players before the decks are reshuffled, under what conditions players can split matching cards into two hands, under what conditions players can *double down* by doubling their bet and taking exactly one more card, what the payoff premium is for players who have blackjack.

BASIC STRATEGY

Blackjack has been well analyzed, and there are many good books and websites describing strategies the player might use. Whether the player takes a hit, stands, splits, or doubles depends only on the dealer's face-up card and the score of the player's hand. One strategy, called the *basic strategy*, is a set of rules that are easily memorized. Figure 5.1, shows the basic strategy.

BlackjackInfo.com
Blackjack Basic Strategy Chart

3 decks, S17, DAS, No Surrender, Peek									
Estimated casino edge for these rules: 0.30 %									

Your Hand	Dealer Upcard									
	2	3	4	5	6	7	8	9	10	A
5	H	H	H	H	H	H	H	H	H	H
6	H	H	H	H	H	H	H	H	H	H
7	H	H	H	H	H	H	H	H	H	H
8	H	H	H	H	H	H	H	H	H	H
9	H	D	D	D	D	H	H	H	H	H
10	D	D	D	D	D	D	D	D	D	H
11	D	D	D	D	D	D	D	D	D	H
12	H	H	S	S	S	H	H	H	H	H
13	S	S	S	S	S	H	H	H	H	H
14	S	S	S	S	S	H	H	H	H	H
15	S	S	S	S	S	H	H	H	H	H
16	S	S	S	S	S	H	H	H	H	H
17	S	S	S	S	S	S	S	S	S	S
A,2	H	H	H	D	D	H	H	H	H	H
A,3	H	H	H	D	D	H	H	H	H	H
A,4	H	H	D	D	D	H	H	H	H	H
A,5	H	H	D	D	D	H	H	H	H	H
A,6	H	D	D	D	D	H	H	H	H	H
A,7	S	DS	DS	DS	DS	S	S	H	H	H
A,8	S	S	S	S	S	S	S	S	S	S
A,9	S	S	S	S	S	S	S	S	S	S
2,2	P	P	P	P	P	P	H	H	H	H
3,3	P	P	P	P	P	P	H	H	H	H
4,4	H	H	H	P	P	H	H	H	H	H
5,5	D	D	D	D	D	D	D	D	H	H
6,6	P	P	P	P	P	H	H	H	H	H
7,7	P	P	P	P	P	P	H	H	H	H
8,8	P	P	P	P	P	P	P	P	P	P
9,9	P	P	P	P	P	S	P	P	S	S
T,T	S	S	S	S	S	S	S	S	S	S
A,A	P	P	P	P	P	P	P	P	P	P
Dlr	2	3	4	5	6	7	8	9	10	A

Key:						
H	= Hit	S	= Stand	P	= Split	
D	= Double (Hit if not allowed)					
DS	= Double (Stand if not allowed)					

FIGURE 5.1

Figure 5.2, courtesy of wizardofodds.com, shows the distribution of payoff amounts resulting from play of 1.7 billion hands, each played using flat betting (the same bet size at the start of each hand) and the basic strategy. The mean is -0.0029, or about -0.3%. The standard deviation is 1.14% – about 4 times the mean. (Typical trading systems also have small means and standard deviations several times as large.)

Net Win in Blackjack			
Net win	Total	Probability	Return
8	1079	0.00000063	0.00000506
7	10440	0.00000612	0.00004287
6	64099	0.00003761	0.00022563
5	247638	0.00014528	0.00072642
4	1307719	0.00076721	0.00306885
3	4437365	0.00260331	0.00780994
2	99686181	0.05848386	0.11696773
1.5	77147473	0.04526086	0.06789129
1	540233094	0.31694382	0.31694382
0	144520347	0.08478716	0
-0.5	76163623	0.04468366	-0.02234183
-1	684733650	0.40171937	-0.40171937
-2	71380000	0.0418772	-0.0837544
-3	3559202	0.00208811	-0.00626434
-4	828010	0.00048578	-0.00194311
-5	152687	0.00008958	-0.00044789
-6	30536	0.00001791	-0.00010749
-7	3972	0.00000233	-0.00001631
-8	305	0.00000018	-0.00000143
Total	1704507420	1	-0.00291455

FIGURE 5.2

If each hand played is considered independent of hands previously played and of cards seen by the player whose turn it is to play next, then the player is at a disadvantage of about 0.3% on each hand. That is, the player's expectancy is -0.3%; and for every $100 played, the player can expect to have $99.70 returned. Typically about 60 hands are played each hour. Tables have both minimum and maximum allowable bets, with $5 being a common minimum. A player who plays for an hour placing $5 bets for each hand has bet $300 in total *action* for that period. He can expect, on average, to have $299.10 remaining at the end of the hour.

Rule variations affect the advantage the house has. Figure 5.3, courtesy of the website wizardofodds.com, gives the increase in the player's return per unit bet relative to standard rules.

Rule Variations	
Rule	**Effect**
Single deck	0.48%
Early surrender against ten	0.24%
Player may double on any number of cards	0.23%
Double deck	0.19%
Player may draw to split aces	0.19%
Six-card Charlie	0.16%
Player may resplit aces	0.08%
Late surrender	0.08%
Four decks	0.06%
Five decks	0.03%
Six decks	0.02%
Split to only 3 hands	-0.01%
Player may double on 9-11 only	-0.09%
Split to only 2 hands	-0.10%
European no hole card7	-0.11%
Player may not double after splitting	-0.14%
Player may double on 10,11 only	-0.18%
Dealer hits on soft 17	-0.22%
Blackkjack pays 7-5	-0.45%
Blackjack pays 6-5	-1.39%
Blackjacks pay 1 to 1	-2.27%

FIGURE 5.3

Everyone who has played or witnessed blackjack understands that it is possible to be either a net winner or a net loser after an hour's play. The loss of $0.90 is the average, but there is considerable variation. We will examine the question of what the likely results are, and what the variation of those results is, using Monte Carlo analysis.

The advantage, or disadvantage, the player has can be expressed as an *expectancy*. Expectancy is the amount, on average, that the player can expect to win for every unit bet. When the house has an edge of 0.3%, expectancy, as seen by the player is -0.3%. The table of rule variations shows several rules that are to the advantage of the player, such as when only a single deck is used; and to the player's disadvantage, such as when blackjack pays less than 3 to 2.

CARD COUNTING

Public awareness of the possibility of making money playing blackjack began with a paper written by Baldwin, Cantey, Maisel, and McDermott and published in 1956 in a statistical journal that became the 1957 book, *Playing Blackjack to Win*. That was followed by a more widely read 1962 book, *Beat the Dealer*, by Ed Thorp. The concept recognizes that expectancy changes during blackjack play as the cards remaining in the deck change. (This is unlike roulette and other casino games where expectancy remains constant.) When a high proportion of low cards have already been played and the remaining deck is rich in tens and aces, the deck is more favorable to the player and the expectancy rises. If the player has the ability to keep track of the state of the deck, called *card counting*, he can make changes in his play strategy and change the size of his bet (increasing the bet spread) to capitalize on the advantage. Several methods of counting were developed and players were able to win consistently. For more details about blackjack, including history, strategies, and counting techniques, visit one of the many websites such as www.blackjackforumonline.com/, blackjackdoc.com, bj21.com/, or www.readybetgo.com.

While card counting is not illegal, beginning in the 1980s, casinos made several changes that make it less likely that the player will have a positive expectancy. Some of these include: increasing the number of decks; dealing only a portion of the cards before reshuffling; limiting the bet spread that a player can make; shuffling whenever a player increases his bet; and shuffling whenever a new player arrives. Recently the casinos have gone ever further. Some tables use machines that continuously shuffle. Discards are put into the machine and shuffled back into the deck as soon as they are collected, making them immediately available to be dealt in the next hand, resetting the distribution of cards at the beginning of each hand so the house always has the 0.3% advantage. Some tables have readers built in to the table that recognize every card as it is dealt and continuously compute the player's expectancy using algorithms that are both more complex and more accurate than those used by players. Whenever the expectancy is to the advantage of the player, the decks are reshuffled to remove that advantage.

Arnold Snyder's research, published as *The Snyder Profit Index*, gives guidelines for ranking the ease with which a player can get an advantage by looking at playing conditions. The conditions he evaluates are:

- The number of decks being used—one is excellent and gives the player an advantage. Two returns the advantage to the house, and more are increasingly worse for the player.
- The shuffle point—what proportion of the cards will be dealt before the deck is reshuffled. The player seldom gets a positive expectancy until 50% of a single deck or a higher proportion of multiple decks has been seen by the player.
- The rules—as in figure 5.3.
- The number of players—more players reduce the number of hands per hour and make seeing all cards more difficult.
- Your betting spread—higher spreads between your minimum bet and your maximum bet attract unwanted attention, while lower spreads reduce your expected profit when the expectancy is positive.
- Your counting method and your proficiency in its use.

In summary, to get a bankable advantage, you need favorable rules, as few decks as possible dealt as deeply as possible, the casino's tolerance of a wide betting spread, and skill using an accurate counting method. A player at a table dealing six decks who bets the minimum while waiting for the expectancy to change to his favor is unlikely to have a net positive expectancy. In spite of that, the discussion of blackjack will continue because there are many important concepts easily illustrated using blackjack.

Bankroll Analysis

Leaving the details of blackjack strategy, we will focus on analysis of the player's bankroll in two situations. First, assuming the expectancy is -0.3%, which is typical for a player using basic strategy in a multi-deck game. Second, assuming an expectancy of +0.5%, which is possible for a skilled counter playing accurately. Expectancy of -0.3% means that the casino has an advantage that will reduce your bankroll by $3 for every $1000 played. Expectancy of +0.5% means that you can expect to increase your bankroll by $5 for every $1000 played.

While the expected amount won on a given hand increases to +0.5%, the standard deviation of the amount won remains about the same at 1.14%. Interestingly, the standard deviation changes very little from basic strategy to skillful counting. Rather, the entire distribution shifts to the right by the difference in expected gain per hand.

The cumulative number of betting units won and lost playing blackjack hands behave according to laws of Brownian motion or random walk. (Trading results behave very similarly, which is why we are spending so much time examining blackjack.) When an object follows a random walk pattern, its distance from its starting point is proportional to the square root of the number of steps it has taken since it began. In the case of blackjack, each step is a hand played. In the case of a trading system, each step is a trade, or perhaps a day. As a result of playing each hand, some number of betting units are won or lost, according to the distribution shown in figure 5.2. Most often, either one unit is lost or one unit is won. If there had been a full complement of splitting and doubling, a maximum of eight units could be won or lost. On average, 0.003 units are lost. Figure 5.4 shows the curves that define the distance from the expected value that a cumulative win and loss path might take as a function of the number of hands played. Each curve begins at zero. After each step, the amount won or lost is added to the bankroll represented by that curve. Amounts won and lost are based on the basic strategy which has a mean of -0.3% and a standard deviation of 1.14%, both are in units of betting units per step. The center dotted line of the seven lines is the mean. The three dotted lines on either side are the one, two, and three standard deviation lines. In the ordinary course of play, the distance from the mean of the players remaining bankroll in terms of betting units will be within the plus and minus one standard deviation lines about 68% of the time, within the plus and minus two standard deviation lines 95% of the time, and within the plus and minus three standard deviation lines about 99.7% of the time. The horizontal axis of the chart represents 7,500 steps – about one month of play for a full-time player. (25 days per month, 5 hours per day, 60 hands per hour.) The vertical axis is the number of betting units. After 7,500 hands, each with an expected loss of 0.3%, the bankroll is expected to be down by about 22 betting units. The value of

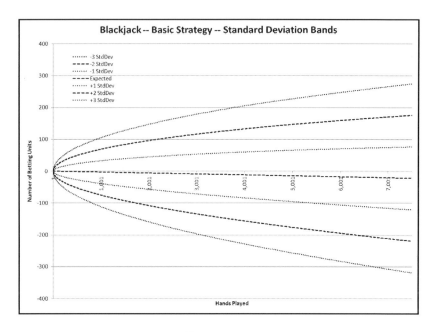

FIGURE 5.4

the mean line is about -22 at the right edge of the chart. The width of the standard bands at 7,500 steps is 1.14 times the square root of 7500, or about 99 betting units. Based on the standard deviation curves alone, the player can estimate how many occurrences in a given period of time a seriously low deviation from the mean can be expected. Sixteen percent (the lower half of the 32% that is outside the 68%) of hands can be expected to be at least one standard deviation below the mean. In 7,500 hands, that 16% is 1200 hands. Similarly, expect to be below two standard deviations about 187 hands, and below three standard deviations about 11 hands. As playing time and the number of hands increases, the player should expect increasingly deeper drawdowns in proportion to the square root of the number of hands played. By hand 7,500, expect to have experienced a monthly worst drawdown of about 317 betting units. If playing continues for a year, 90,000 hands, expect a drawdown of 1290 or more. In any given month, the player's initial bankroll must be large enough to allow losses of 317 betting units. In a year, expect a drawdown of 1290 betting units. Experienced blackjack professionals recommend that the bankroll be several hundred to 1000 times the basic bet size—a recommendation consistent with the graphs.

Figure 5.5 shows that the equity curves do follow the direction expected, but variability is considerable. This figure has the same mean and
six standard deviation bands as in the previous figure, along with 20
randomly generated runs of 7500 blackjack hands, each played using
the same basic strategy described in the distribution given above. Note
the excursions away from the mean and toward the outer bands, usually followed by return toward the mean. Even when using basic strategy, which has a negative expectancy, there are many winning months.
By the time 20 months have been completed and averaged together (the
heavy line slightly trending down), the equity curve follows the mean
closely.

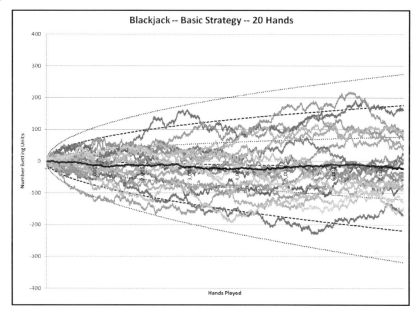

FIGURE 5.5

With counting and accurate play, the expectancy rises to 0.5%. Figure
5.6 shows the results from 20 runs of 7,500 hands each, along with the
average of those 20. The drawdowns for these runs are relative to a
slightly rising mean, but the player should still be prepared to be be-
hind over 300 betting units in any single month.

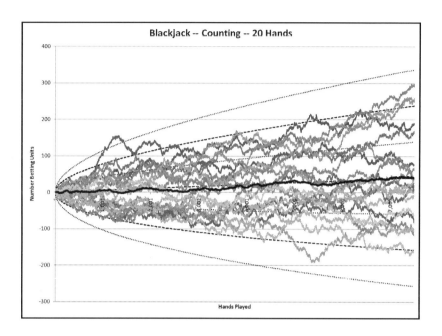

FIGURE 5.6

In summary:

- Final equity is equal to expectancy times number of bets (there is no compounding)
- Deepest loss and best gain increase without limit as the square root of the number of bets

RISK OF RUIN

The longer the player plays, the deeper the drawdown experienced will be. In any game (or trading activity) where there is a possibility of loss, the largest loss always lies in the future, and the probability of ruin approaches certainty as the time of play increases.

There is *always* a ruin absorbing barrier. Having a retire barrier gives the player or trader an opportunity to leave the game and avoid ruin.

No matter how large the initial bankroll, there is some percentage or dollar amount that is a limit to the loss that can be tolerated. That limit will be a combination of factors, including financial and psychological. For discussion, assume it is easily quantified, translated into terms of dollars, and given a value—say 40% of the initial bankroll. Since there is always some chance this limit could be reached in any given year, the player must decide how large a risk of that happening he is willing to accept. Assume it is a 5% risk. Restated, the player is willing to accept a 5% risk of a 40% drawdown in any year. Willingness to accept a 5% risk means that if the player makes a career of playing, or trading, on average he will experience a drawdown of at least 40% one year of every 20. Unfortunately, there is no way to know in advance which years will be the ruinous years. There may be none in 31 years, or there may be one in any of the first five years—those two possibilities are equally likely, and either could occur with a probability of about 20%.

The question we must answer is "What is the starting bankroll, in terms of betting units, such that the probability of a 40% drawdown is less than 5%?" Begin by determining the z-score corresponding to the left 5% tail on the normal distribution. By computation or table lookup we find that is about -1.64. To illustrate, the shaded area in the left tail of figure 5.7 contains 5% of the normal distribution. To avoid falling into the left tail most years (95% of the time), begin with a bankroll large enough so that a 40% drawdown is less than 1.64 standard deviations.

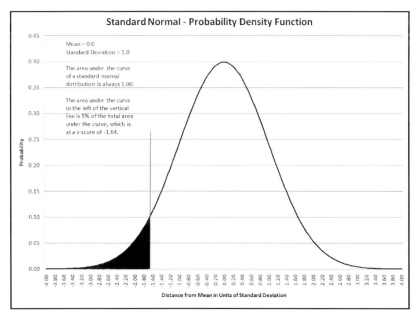

FIGURE 5.7

In general, the size of the bankroll is related to the size of the basic betting unit in the following way:

Assume the size of a single betting unit is B dollars, then adjust later as necessary.

- MaximumLoss = (mean - 1.64 standard deviation) * B
- MaximumLoss = acceptable risk * bankroll

Specifically:

- One year is 90,000 hands. Expectancy is 0.005. So the mean equity is 450 * B.
- One standard deviation is 1.14 (betting units) times the square root of 90,000 or 342 * B.
- Acceptable risk is 0.40.
- Bankroll is to be determined.

The two equations become:

- MaximumLoss = (450 * B - 1.64 * 342 * B) * B = -111 * B
- MaximumLoss = 0.40 * Bankroll

Setting the two right-hand sides equal to each other and solving, the ratio of the bankroll to the betting unit must be 277. For every dollar of bet size, the player needs a bankroll of $277. To be less well capitalized increases the probability of a drawdown greater than 40% to a level higher than 5%.

Figure 5.8 shows the distribution of the bankroll after one year of play. The units are one bet size. For example, if the bet size is $10.00, then the mean is $4,500.

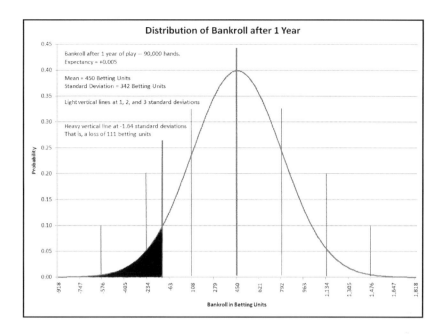

FIGURE 5.8

If the player wants to have enough reserve so that there is only a 1% risk of a 40% drawdown, replace the -1.64 with -2.33 in the equations above, and find that the ratio must be about 870. 2.33 is the number of standard deviations below the mean corresponding to a left tail with an area under the curve of 1%.

The goals of the player are to maximize the amount of gain in a given time period while minimizing the probability of bankruptcy or ruin. There is no way both goals can be achieved with certainty. Trying for more gain always increases the probability of ruin. Lowering the risk of ruin always lowers the maximum gain. Increasing exposure to the game using leverage always increases the probability of ruin. Decreasing the number of hands played always decreases maximum gain.

EARNING A LIVING PLAYING BLACKJACK

Since the expectancy for the player using only the basic strategy is negative, there is no way for him to earn a living playing blackjack. As will be discussed in more detail later, there is no betting (or position sizing) method that will convert a system with a negative expectancy into a long-term winning system.

There are (or, at least, there were) people who earn their living playing blackjack. It could be that there are a great many who try and we only hear the success stories, but let's assume there are enough real successes to convince us it is possible. How is it possible? The answer lies in changing strategy and in changing the size of the bet as conditions change. The player bets the minimum when the expectancy is negative, and increases his bet when it becomes positive. This is a position sizing technique and we will apply it to trading in later chapters.

Let's turn to the player who is counting cards and has an expectancy of +0.5%. If he wants to make a modest living of about $60,000 per year playing blackjack, what does his business plan look like?

In 12 months of 7,500 hands per month, he will play 90,000 hands per year. The number of dollars won per hand is 0.005 times the amount bet per hand. To win an average of $60,000 in 90,000 hands, the bet size must be $133.33. Assume he rounds that up to $135, so his average winnings per year will be 90,000 * 0.005 * $135 = $60,750. The total action resulting from betting $135 on each of 90,000 hands is $12,150,000. If he wants to limit his chance of a 40% drawdown to 5%, his initial bankroll must be 277 * $135 or $37,395. To limit his chance of a 40% drawdown to 1%, his initial bankroll must be $117,450. These values are consistent with the advice of experts.

Figure 5.9 shows the distribution of 1000 one-year periods of playing with an expectancy of +0.005. Note that there is about a 5% chance that there will be no gain. The average is 453, in agreement with the calculations.

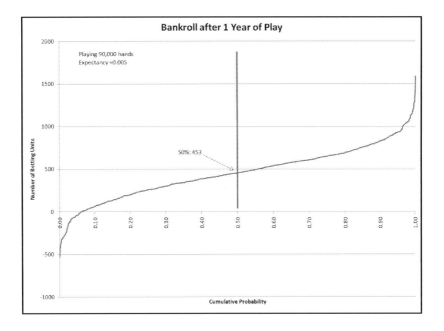

FIGURE 5.9

Figure 5.10 shows the distribution of the drawdown from maximum equity during one year of play. The drawdown at the 5% level is 292 betting units, in agreement with 277 from the calculations.

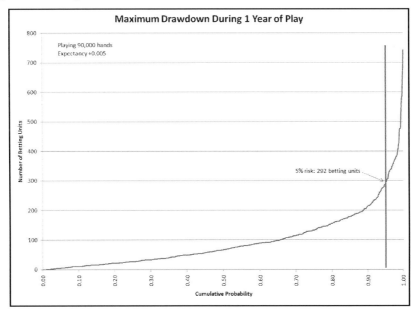

FIGURE 5.10

ENFORCING THE ABSORBING BARRIERS

Assume the player begins with a bankroll of $100,000, finds conditions where he has an expectancy of +0.005, and makes $135 bets. If the player enforces his ruin barrier and quits if the drawdown reaches 40% of his highest equity, and / or retires when his bankroll is double the original amount, both final equity and drawdown change. Tests were made with and without barriers. Figure 5.11 shows the final equity with two lines. The dotted line shows the result when neither barrier is enforced, the solid one when both are.

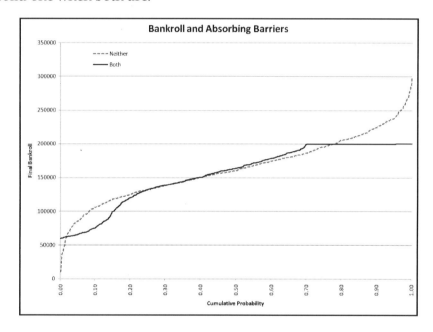

FIGURE 5.11

Figure 5.12 shows the worst drawdown with two lines. The dotted line shows the result when neither barrier is enforced, the solid one when both are.

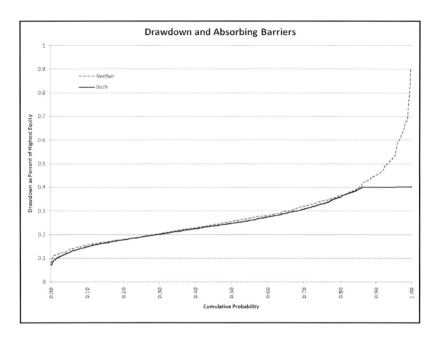

FIGURE 5.12

In these examples, enforcing the ruin barrier completely reduced the risk of a drawdown larger than 40% of highest equity. In the process, it also caused some of the higher final equity runs to be limited, and it removed those few cases where the final equity would have been near zero.

Placement of absorbing barriers involves choices made by the player or trader. There are no general rules regarding setting the levels for barriers. We will return to discussions of them in later chapters.

TRADING IS SIMILAR TO BLACKJACK

If you were learning to play blackjack with the expectation of making a living at the game, you might use a computer program to sharpen your skills before going to the casinos.

In blackjack, flat betting starts each hand with a bet that is the same size regardless of conditions. In trading, it is useful when analyzing the potential of a system to take each position with the same number of dollars or the same number of contracts

In blackjack, counters vary their play and their bet size as conditions and bankroll change. In trading, position size can be changed as playing conditions or equity change.

TRADING IS DIFFERENT THAN BLACKJACK

Blackjack expectancy and variance are stationary (or nearly so).

In blackjack, the amount bet is the amount lost when a hand is lost. The risk on a hand is the size of the bet. In most trading circumstances, a losing trade does not lose the entire amount, so risk is not necessarily the size of the position.

Before we turn the analysis to trading systems to see if they fare better as businesses, the next section describes how to set up Monte Carlo simulations such as those used in this chapter.

Chapter 6

Monte Carlo Simulation

Background

Simulation, a type of modeling, is a technique for representing a process or physical construction using an abstract model in order to study and understand it. If we were studying highway bridges, we could use physical models that test the strength of the materials and the rigidity of the structure. If we were studying the behavior of bodies in motion, we could use closed form mathematical equations—mathematical models. For many classes of problems, such as where there are no physical models, where working with physical models is too dangerous, where there are no closed form mathematical equations, where the mathematics is very complex, and where there are many possible solutions, then computer modeling using numerical simulation is a practical solution.

History of Monte Carlo simulation

In the 1940s two earthshaking events took place: the Manhattan Project to develop the first atomic bomb and the building of the first electronic computer. ENIAC, as the computer was known, was directed by John Mauchly and Prespert Eckert. John von Neumann was a consultant to the nuclear weapons project. Working with Stanley Frankel and Nicholas Metropolis at Los Alamos, they developed a mathematical model of a thermonuclear reaction, and ran it on the ENIAC. In 1946 Stanislaw Ulam joined the project and suggested the computation include some statistical sampling. Stan's project needed a name. Nick suggested Monte Carlo, in part because Stan's uncle frequently borrowed money to "go to Monte Carlo," and because the name fit the project.

The spirit of Monte Carlo simulation is described in a letter written by von Neumann.

> *Consider a spherical core of fissionable material surrounded by a shell of tamper material. Assume some initial distribution of neutrons in space and velocity. The idea is to follow the development of a large number of individual neutron chains as a consequence of scattering, absorption, fission, and escape.*

> *At each stage a sequence of decisions has to be made based on statistical probabilities appropriate to the physical and geometric factors. The process is repeated until a statistically valid picture is generated.*

Traditionally, analysis of that process was done using complex differential equations, but Monte Carlo simulation became the preferred method.

By 1949, several symposia on the Monte Carlo method were held, sponsored by the Rand Corporation, U.S. National Bureau of Standards, and the Oak Ridge Laboratory. Monte Carlo simulation was here to stay.

Faster computers have facilitated its application in areas including: science, engineering, telecommunications, finance, games, econometrics, operations research, and analysis of trading systems.

THE MONTE CARLO PROCESS

Monte Carlo simulations are computational algorithmic processes that use repeated sampling.

Initialize:
1.   Define the system being studied in terms of probability density functions (pdfs).

Repeatedly (1000 or more times):
2.   Select a random sample from the pdf as input to the algorithm. This is called a realization.
3.   Perform the calculations that represent the system, and produce an output value based on the specific input.
4.   Record the individual results into an output distribution.

Analyze:
5.   Evaluate the output distribution.

Each of the simulation runs in step 2 is equally likely. Step 4 results in a large number of separate and independent results, each representing a possible path the system may follow—a possible outcome.

The result of a single simulation of a system (such as a single backtest run) is a qualified statement. For example, "The system appears to be profitable."

The result of a probabilistic Monte Carlo simulation is a quantified probability. For example, "There is an 80% probability that the system will have a compound annual rate of return of 12% or more."

Our goal is to apply Monte Carlo simulation to trading systems, where the process being studied is the sequence of closed trades or daily equity.

STATISTICAL DISTRIBUTIONS

Key components of Monte Carlo simulation are distributions of the samples or events that constitute the system under study. Two concepts are closely related – densities and distributions.

Densities, often described by the term probability density function, pdf, are illustrated by the often-used histograms that show how many occurrences of each specific instance of a variable were observed; or, for a theoretical function, the proportions of the possible values. [Strictly, probability density functions apply to continuous variables, with probability mass functions the equivalent for discrete distributions. The term probability distributions function will be used for both in this discussion.]

For example, take the sum of the pips on the upper surfaces of two tossed dice. The possible values range from 2 to 12, and the proportion of each can be computed by enumerating the possible outcomes and by using laws of probability. Since each die contributes a number between 1 and 6 with equal likelihood, the possible results for the two dice are illustrated in figure 6.1.

		Sum of two tossed dice					
		Die 1					
		1	2	3	4	5	6
	1	2	3	4	5	6	7
	2	3	4	5	6	7	8
Die 2	3	4	5	6	7	8	9
	4	5	6	7	8	9	10
	5	6	7	8	9	10	11
	6	7	8	9	10	11	12

FIGURE 6.1

Assume that the two dice are thrown 36 times, with each possible pairing occurring one time. Each combination of the two dice is equally likely, and the number of ways each sum can happen is shown in figure 5.2.

Sum	2	3	4	5	6	7	8	9	10	11	12
Number ways	1	2	3	4	5	6	5	4	3	2	1

FIGURE 6.2

Figure 6.3 shows the same data displayed as a histogram.

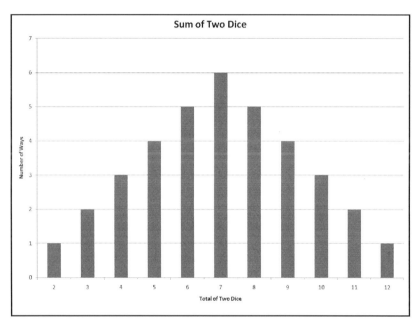

FIGURE 6.3

Figure 6.4 shows the same data again, this time as a histogram with each possible sum expressed as a fraction. Figure 6.4 is the probability density function, pdf, of the sum of two dice. This is the actual or theoretical distribution – there is no randomness involved.

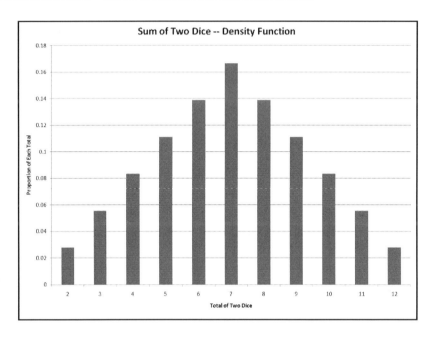

FIGURE 6.4

Closely related to the probability density function is the cumulative distribution function, CDF. Each point in the CDF is the sum of all lower points of the pdf. The scale on the vertical axis of all CDFs is 0.0 to 1.0. The CDF for the sum of two tossed dice is shown in figure 6.5.

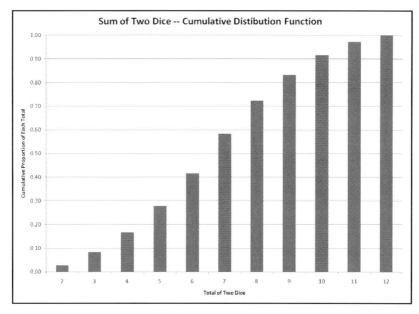

FIGURE 6.5

Since the sum of the two dice is limited to a finite number of possible values, the distribution is called a discrete distribution. If the data can take on any value, including fractions of arbitrary precision, the distribution is called a continuous distribution. Technically, density functions associated with discrete distributions are called mass density functions, mdf. Density functions associated with continuous distributions are called a probability density function, pdf. For simplicity, in this book, all density functions will be referred to as probability density functions, pdf.

A Simple Monte Carlo Simulation

The CDF in this example of the sum of two tossed dice is easily computed, but that is not always the case. If we did not know the mathematics, we could run a Monte Carlo simulation to estimate the pdf and CDF. The process would be to pick two random integers, each between 1 and 6 to represent the number of pips on the top of each die, and add them together. We would do this many times, keeping a running count of the number of times each of the possible results occurred. After 1000 simulated tosses, the results are as shown in figure 6.6.

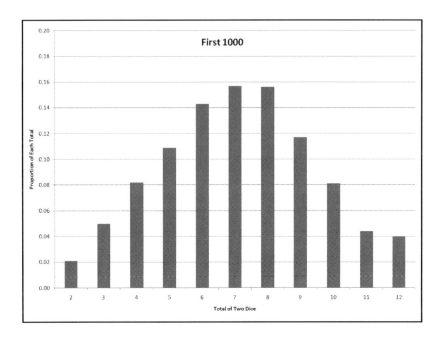

FIGURE 6.6

The histograms for the next nine runs, each of 1000, are shown in figure 6.7.

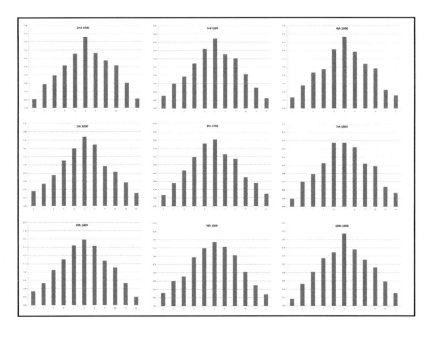

FIGURE 6.7

All of these have similar shapes, and any one of them would probably be accurate enough to convince a casual student that the distribution is triangular, as expected. By combining the ten runs, a clearer picture of the probable distribution appears. If we were to analyze the 10,000 runs, we would see that the distribution for each pip count has a mean that is equal to the pip count and that follows the Normal distribution, as predicted by the law of large numbers and the central limit theorem. See figure 6.8. The midpoint of the box is the mean of the 10 runs. The boxes contain the + / - 1 standard deviation range, and the whiskers contain the + / - 2 standard deviation range.

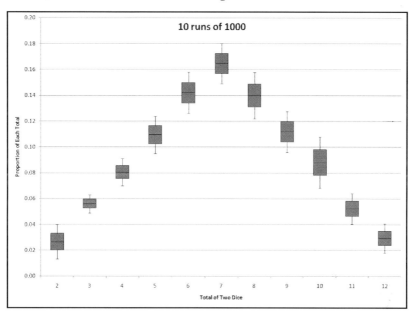

FIGURE 6.8

In general, decreasing the error estimates by a given factor requires that the number of runs increase by the square of that factor. To decrease the error by a factor of 2 requires 4 times the number of runs.

The law of large numbers tells us that when we take a large number of independent samples from a fixed probability distribution, the average of these values is close to the mean of that distribution. The central limit theorem tells us that when we take a large number of independent samples from virtually any probability distribution, then our sample average will have a probability distribution that is approximately Normal. The law of large numbers is the principle upon which Monte

Carlo simulation is built. Monte Carlo simulations rely on the law of large numbers and central limit theorem to give results that approximate theoretical results and can be tested to give statistically sound estimates of confidence in those approximations.

If desired, we can use goodness-of-fit calculations, such as chi-square, Anderson-Darling, or Kolmogorov-Smirnov, to determine whether the observed experimental data came from some given theoretical distribution and with what degree of confidence. All three goodness-of-fit measures are similar. Chi-square is easiest to calculate. Anderson-Darling is preferred for distributions where the fit in the tails is important.

For use in Monte Carlo simulations, the CDF is the most important of the two (pdf and CDF) representations. But CDFs for different distributions appear very similar, while the pdf is the most readily recognized. Goodness-of-fit tests work equally well whether they are comparing CDFs or pdfs. For informal use, a visual comparison of the two pdfs is quick and may be sufficient.

Figure 6.9 shows the agreement between the theoretical distribution of the dice and that estimated by the simulation.

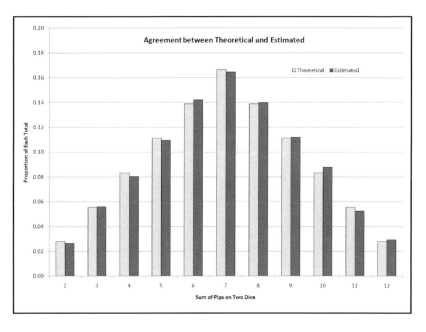

Figure 6.9

GENERATING DATA

In Monte Carlo simulations, the distributions – as represented by the CDFs – are critically important.

Figures 5.10 and 5.11 show the pdf and CDF for the familiar Standard Normal distribution, with a mean of 0.0 and a standard deviation of 1.0.

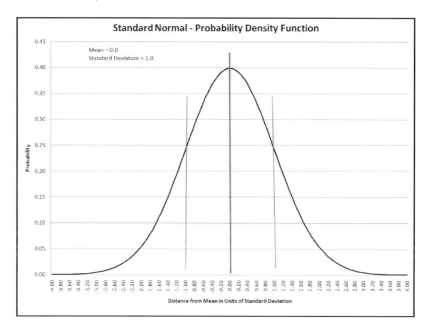

FIGURE 6.10

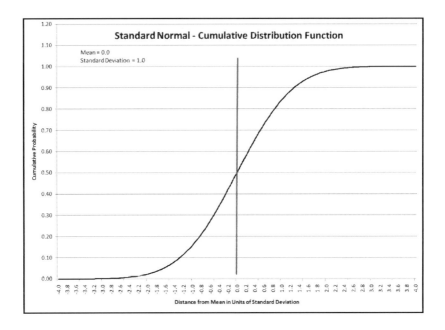

FIGURE 6.11

The technique for generating an individual random value from a CDF begins with an inversion of the CDF. Figure 6.12 shows the Inverse Standard Normal CDF.

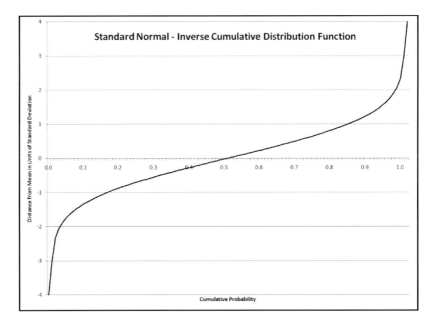

FIGURE 6.12

The reason for inverting the CDF is so that the result has the properties of a mathematical function. The independent variable runs along the horizontal axis and is defined for the range of 0.0 to 1.0. The dependent variable runs along the vertical axis and has the values associated with the functional definition. To be a properly defined function, there can be only one value of the dependent variable for a given value of the independent variable. That is, for a given location on the x-axis, a line extending vertically will intersect the line defining the function at one and only one point.

If our Monte Carlo simulation called for use of a series of values from a normal distribution, we would use the Inverse CDF of the Standard Normal distribution in combination with uniform random numbers. Uniform random numbers come from a distribution where each number has an equal chance of being chosen. To facilitate their use, they are normalized to the range 0.0000 to 0.9999, corresponding to the range of the Inverse CDF. The Standard Uniform distribution is the foundation of a large area of modeling and simulation, and will be discussed in more detail in the next section. To generate each value, called a random variable, from the Normal distribution, first generate a number from the Uniform distribution, and then evaluate the Inverse Cumulative Distribution function at that point. That is, pick a random number between 0 and 1, locate the point on the x-axis corresponding to that value, and then evaluate the function at that point.

Although the curves in figures 5.10, 5.11, and 5.12 appear to be smooth and continuous, and even though mathematically they may be continuous functions, in practice we are using a digital computer which uses only discrete numbers. The generation of a random number from a CDF involves a table lookup procedure. While it is possible to program functions that interpolate between table rows, it is usual to simply use the value stored in the table.

When random numbers that follow distributions that have closed form representations are needed, calculating them is an option. When there is no closed form, or where the data comes from observations, table lookup is used. If it is necessary in order to increase the accuracy of the distribution, interpolation between values listed in the table can be performed. Interpolation can be performed on-the-fly for each sample generated, or it can be done in a pre-processing stage which results in a higher resolution table that is used for lookup directly.

Figure 6.13 shows a portion of the lookup table for the Inverse Normal CDF.

	Inverse
Cumulative	CDF
Probability	Function
0.8849	1.20
0.8944	1.25
0.9032	1.30
0.9115	1.35
0.9192	1.40

FIGURE 6.13

If the uniform value selected is greater than or equal to 0.8944 and less than 0.9032, the associated value of the function, that is, of the random variable being selected, will be 1.25, and so forth. The smoothness of the generated data depends on the resolution of the table holding the inverse CDF.

In general, the relationship between a discrete CDF and its inverse is as illustrated in figures 5.5 and 5.14.

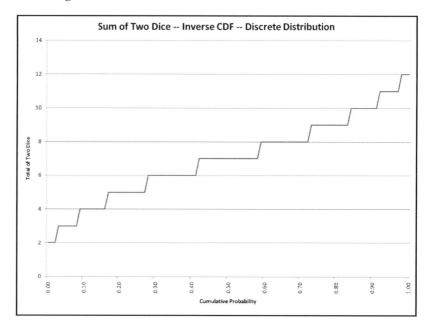

FIGURE 6.14

High Quality Random Numbers

Having a source of high quality uniform random numbers is critical to Monte Carlo simulation.

Monte Carlo simulations became practical, and we can say invented, in the late 1940s to help design and analyze weapons. The earliest electronic digital computers were being developed at that same time, and the two technologies developed together.

Truly random numbers can be obtained from physical processes. Examples include: flipping coins, tossing dice, or measuring the amount of time between receiving counts of radioactive decay. Mathematically generated pseudo-random numbers have two advantages and one disadvantage over truly random numbers.

- They are easier to obtain.
- They are reproducible, which is important if the simulation run is to be repeated.
- They may not be sufficiently random.

Monte Carlo simulations often need billions of random numbers. Early methods performed multi-word arithmetic and used the bits that overflowed from the operation. A common technique in current use that is similar uses modulus arithmetic and is called linear congruent generation.

Computational random number generators begin with a single number, called a seed, and compute a random number based on an algorithm and that seed value, then continue generating additional random numbers using the previously generated ones as the seeds. Other methods begin with similar techniques, but combine several independent series to produce more nearly random uniform numbers.

One of the issues related to generation of random numbers is the length of the period over which they repeat. Short repetition periods can cause problems when the simulations based on them do not cover all of the possible results with equal likelihood.

Note that there is no randomness at all – given the same starting seed value, the pseudo-random sequence is completely determined. This can be used to advantage when simulation runs are repeated using the same sequence of random numbers, but using different parameters for the model.

A method in current popular use is called Mersenne Twister, a generalized feedback shift register method. It has a period length on the order of 2^19937 and passes most tests of randomness. AmiBroker has a Mersenne Twister function, called randomMT. Many statistical analysis platforms, including R, have Mersenne Twister functions. There are Mersenne Twister add-ins for Excel, some of which are free. One can be found at: http://www.ntrand.com/ and another at: http://www.riskamp.com/mtrand.php.

Given an endless flow of uniform random numbers in the range 0.0 to 0.9999, inverse cumulative distribution functions describing the data to be used in the simulation, a description of the desired simulation, a computer, and analysis tools such as Excel or a dedicated Monte Carlo program, we can perform Monte Carlo simulations.

MONTE CARLO SIMULATION OF PLAYING ROULETTE

In the United States, there are 38 numbers on a roulette wheel. They are 1 through 36, 0, and 00. Half of the numbered locations are red, the other half black, 0 and 00 are green. Even money bets can be made on whether the ball will land in an even location or an odd one; the low half (1 through 18) or the high half (19 through 36); red or black. All even money bets pay 1 for 1. When the ball lands in either 0 or 00, all those even money bets lose, regardless of which way the bet was made. Given any even money bet, say red, if 38 spins are made and the ball lands in each of the 38 locations one time, 18 bets will win and 20 will lose. There will be 18 results of +1 and 20 results of -1. The expectancy of each bet is 18/38 – 20/38, or -4.26%. The table of bet outcomes, if displayed in a sorted list, would 20 -1s, followed by 18 1s. The corresponding pdf is shown in figure 6.15.

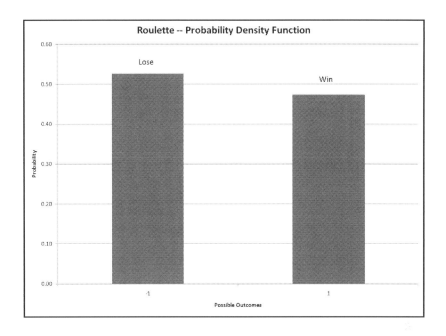

FIGURE 6.15

The CDF is shown in figure 6.16.

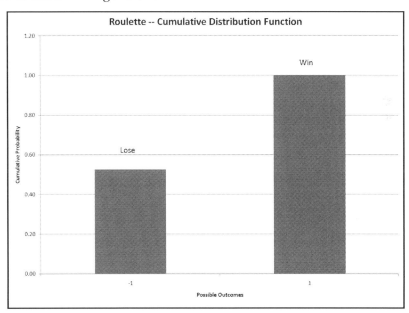

FIGURE 6.16

And the Inverse CDF is shown in figure 6.17.

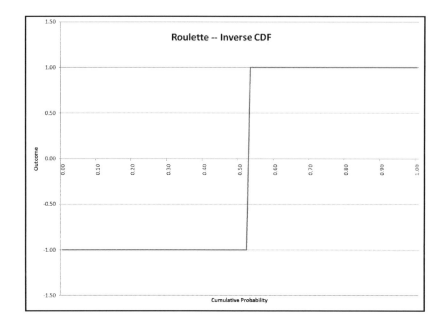

FIGURE 6.17

The table that will be used is much simpler than the chart of the inverse CDF suggests. It is shown in figure 6.18.

Cumulative Probability	Outcome
0	-1
0.5263	1
1	1

FIGURE 6.18

When using Excel to manage the Monte Carlo simulations, random variables will be drawn from Inverse CDF using the Excel LOOKUP function. The steps are:

1. For each random variable needed, generate a uniform random number between 0.00 and 0.9999. Call it r.
2. Lookup begins in the first row of the left column of the Inverse CDF table, goes down until the next entry is greater than or equal to r.

3. Lookup goes one column to the right and returns the value in that cell as the random variable from the desired distribution.

In this example, every uniform random number between 0.0 and 0.52629999 will return -1, all those 0.5263 and above will return +1. Be careful. It is easy to select a value that is off by one row. See figure 6.19

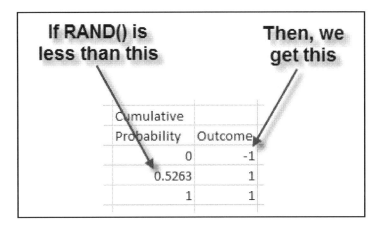

FIGURE 6.19

The value of the random variable returned represents the payoff the player receives. For each $1.00 bet, he loses $1.00 52.63% of the time and wins $1.00 47.37% of the time. His expectancy is -5.26%.

BETTING SYSTEMS

The casino roulette game is heavily biased in favor of the casino. The negative expectancy of the bias tells us the degree of the bias. But people play anyway, hoping to either have a run of good luck or to use a betting system that will insure a profit.

CONSTANT BET SIZE

Assume the player begins with $100 and makes $1 bets until his bankroll is entirely lost. What does the equity curve look like?

Since the expectancy is -0.05263, the player can expect to lose $0.05263, on average, for every $1.00 bet. His initial $100.00 will be gone, on average, in 1900 plays. Since the order of the winning bets and losing bets is random, the sequences differ. Figure 6.20 shows the equity for one sequence. This one makes $1.00 bets and is out of money by about bet 3200.

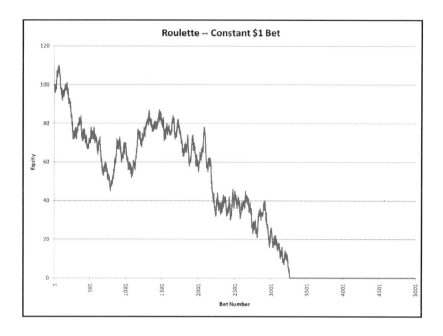

FIGURE 6.20

It is possible, just from the luck of the table, to be ahead for a period of time. Figure 6.21 shows a sequence that stays positive for about 1700 bets, and does not go broke until about bet 3100.

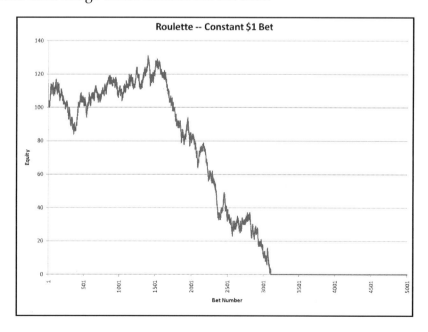

FIGURE 6.21

Other sequences lose quickly, as can be seen in figure 6.22.

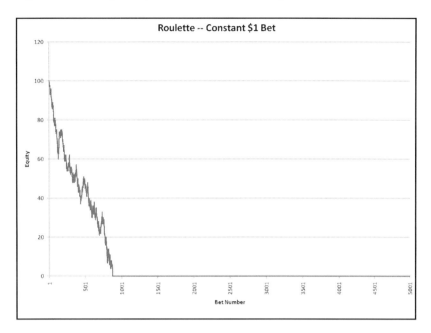

FIGURE 6.22

All three of these sequences follow from the same distribution and the same betting system. 997 more runs were made – 1000 runs in total – each of 5000 bets. In about 10% of the 1000 runs the player was never ahead. About 5% of the 1000 runs, the player was ahead by 30% or more. All 1000 had lost all of their initial bankroll before bet number 5000.

MARTINGALE BETTING

Martingale betting systems increase the size of the bet after a loss. They are based on the assumption that sequences of losing bets eventually end. An initial bet is made, say $1. After every win, the bet size is reset to $1. After every loss, the bet size is doubled. When a win finally occurs, the bet is just the right size to make up for all of the losses, plus give a profit of $1. On average, the player wins $1 for every win. Since the percentage of winning bets is 47.3, the player's equity rises about $0.473 for each bet made. After 1000 bets, the player expects to be ahead about $473. The problem arises when there is a losing streak so long that the player does not have enough cash to make the size bet required to continue the sequence. He bets everything he has left on one last play, and either recovers somewhat or is bankrupt. Figure 6.23 shows an example.

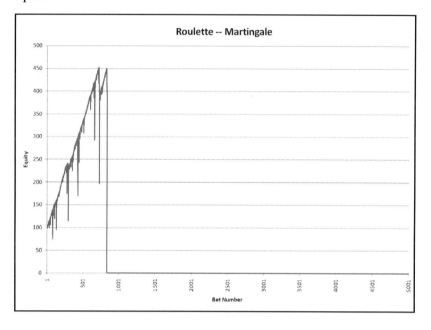

FIGURE 6.23

It is possible to have a fantastically good run of luck, as figure 6.24 shows.

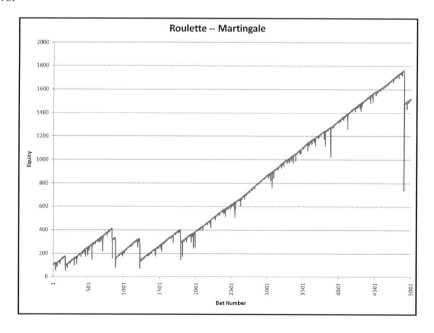

FIGURE 6.24

On average, the player has lost everything by about play 173. Casinos do not fear players using Martingale systems because one of two conditions will cause the player to be unable to complete the betting sequence at some point:

1. The player has a limited bankroll and cannot afford to double the previous losing bet.

2. The casino enforces two limits to bet size on every table – the minimum bet and the maximum bet. The base 2 logarithm of the ratio of these two defines the number of times the player is allowed to double, without regard to his bankroll. For example, a table might have a $1 minimum and $500 maximum. The ratio is 500. The 9th doubling will require the player to bet 512. Whenever there is a string of 9 or more successive losses, the player cannot continue the sequence. For a binary distribution with a losing rate of 0.5263, there will be, on average, 3 runs of 9 or more successive losses every 1000 plays.

Even when the player is winning, Martingale systems require taking larger and larger risks in order to win the same $1. The reward to risk ratio is very low, and the player will eventually go bankrupt.

Anti-Martingale

Anti-martingale betting systems increase the size of the bet after a win. They plan to capitalize on the hope that luck has "runs." Figure 6.25 shows a typical equity curve where the bet size is increased by 10% after each win, and reset to $1 after each loss.

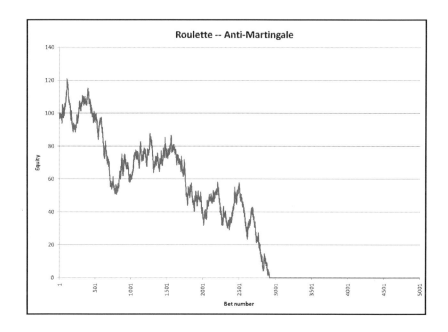

FIGURE 6.25

Whether the evidence comes from the mathematical formulas or from the simulations and charts, there are several truths apparent:

1. Systems that have a negative expectancy eventually go bankrupt.
2. No betting system can transform a system with a negative expectancy into a winning system.
3. There is a great deal of variation in the behavior of any given system, even when that system has well defined parameters that are kept constant over a large number of runs.

GOLDILOCK'S CASINO

In order to compare the results of a system that has a negative expectancy with one that has a positive expectancy, we will imagine Goldilock's casino. The croupier at the roulette wheel is instructed that every time the ball lands in either 0 or 00, all players who are betting even money bets win. The expectancy changes from -0.05263 to +0.05263. There are now 20 wins and 18 losses for every complete set of 38 possible outcomes, the formula is 20/38 – 18/38 which equals +0.05263. Systems that have positive expectancy result in gains, on average. There will still be variation. The mean tells us the expectancy; the standard deviation tells us the variation. A distribution that has only two states, a success and a failure, is a Binomial or Bernoulli distribution. If the amount won for a success is the same as the amount lost for a failure, only one parameter is required to describe the distribution – the probability of a win, called p. The probability of a win in this example is 20/38 or 0.5263. The probability of a loss is called q, and is calculated as $1 - p$. q has a value of 0.4737. The mean of n Bernoulli trials is the product, np; the variance is npq, making the standard deviation the square root of npq. Given a run of 5000, the expected number of wins is 5000 times 0.5263, or 2631. The standard deviation of the number of wins is .5263 times .4737 times 5000, or 1246. The expected gain over a run of 5000 is 2631*1 – 2369*1 or 262 times the size of each individual bet. The expected gain can be calculated another way – the expectancy times the number of bets – which is 0.05263 * 5000 or 263.15. In 1000 runs of 5000 bets each, the average gain found from the simulation is 264.7. Since the mean is over two times the standard deviation, the results over many test runs will be very consistent. In trading systems, we generally find the standard deviation to be two to four times the mean, resulting in considerably more variation from run to run. Any trading system that has a positive expectancy and a mean greater than about half the standard deviation is both profitable and low risk. Figure 6.26 shows the equity for a typical run of 5000 bets.

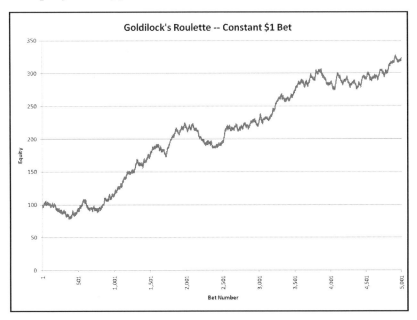

FIGURE 6.26

Of the 1000 runs each beginning with $100, 1 ends with less equity than it began, 5% end with less than $254, the average ends with $364, and 5% end with more than $482. 5% of the runs had a peak to valley equity drawdown of less than 10.8%; 5% of the runs had a drawdown of more than 38.1%. See figure 6.27.

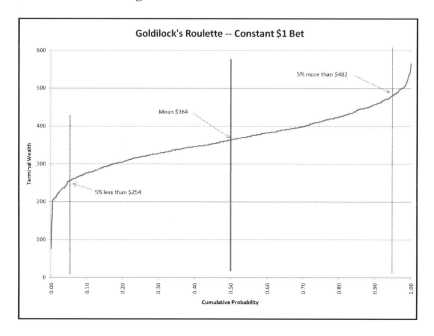

FIGURE 6.27

If a system has a positive expectancy, changing the size of the bet can, and usually will, change the growth rate of the equity. For systems like Goldilock's roulette, the Kelly formula gives the amount, as a percentage of current equity, to bet on each play to maximize the final equity – the terminal wealth – of the account. Using the variable b to represent the ratio of the amount won on a winning play to the amount lost on a losing play, the optimum bet size is: $(b * p - q) / b$. Filling in the values of 1, 0.5263, and 0.4737 for b, p, and q, respectively, the result is 0.0263. The interpretation is to bet 2.63 percent of equity on each play. Over a 1000 run simulation, on average, the final equity was 174 times the initial equity; and the peak equity was 232 times the initial equity. Figure 6.28 shows the equity curve from a typical run using that percentage. Note the change from linear to logarithmic scale for the equity amount.

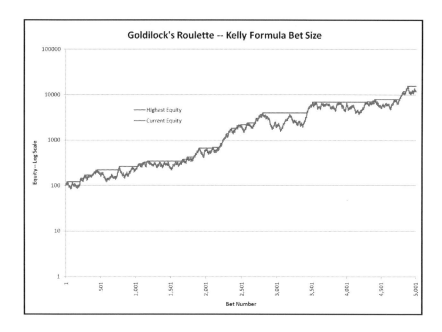

FIGURE 6.28

Some of the runs can be spectacularly good, as shown in figure 6.29.

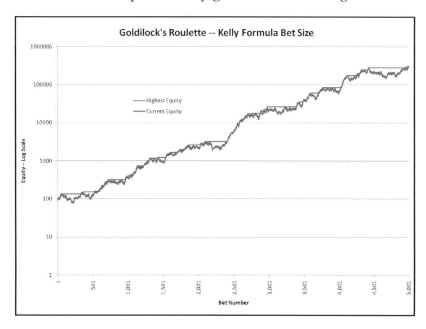

FIGURE 6.29.

Others very poor, as shown in figure 6.30.

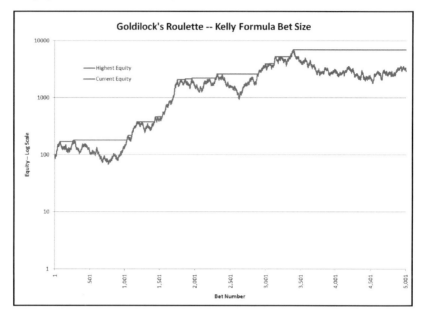

FIGURE 6.30

All three of these examples are equally likely. You have no way of knowing in advance which sequence your day at the casino will follow. The distribution of final equity for all 1000 runs is shown in figure 6.31. Over 10% of the runs showed final equity at least 1800 times the initial equity, which distorts the right side of the chart.

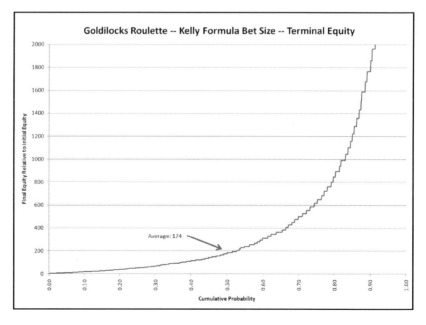

FIGURE 6.31

The big surprise comes when examining the peak to valley drawdowns. The average drawdown is 65%, only 5% of the runs had a drawdown less than 50%, and 5% of runs had drawdowns of 84% or greater. Figure 6.32 shows the distribution of drawdowns.

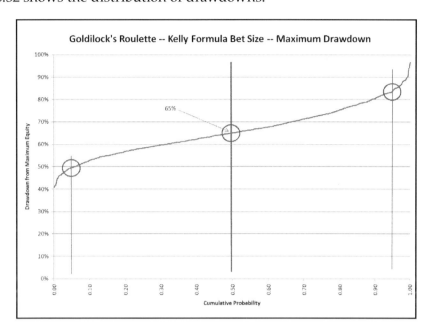

FIGURE 6.32

Refer back to figures 5.28, 5.29, and 5.30 and note that the system is in a drawdown a high proportion of the time. These levels of drawdown are unacceptable to most people. Position sizing methods that capture the huge increases in final equity typically experience very high drawdowns.

As we move from distributions we know well, such as the one that we find in the roulette example, to ones that we are very much less sure of, such as trading results, we need a better way to quantify our reward and risk profile.

Because we cannot tell which sequence our one single equity curve will follow, we must anticipate that it might be one with an unacceptably high drawdown. Then we will choose parameters that limit our exposure to that drawdown.

We will be reframing our goals in terms such as: "what position size and / or trading account size should be used to maximize return while risking at most a 5% chance of a peak to valley drawdown of 30% or more?"

In a series of runs, the bet size was reduced from 2.63 until the risk of a serious drawdown was low enough. The bet size required for risk limitation in this example turned out to be 0.60. Figure 6.33 shows the drawdown curve.

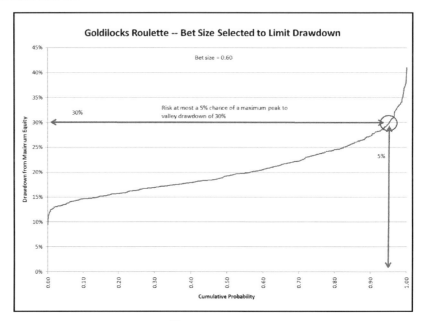

FIGURE 6.33

And in doing that, the distribution of the terminal equity changes as shown in figure 6.34.

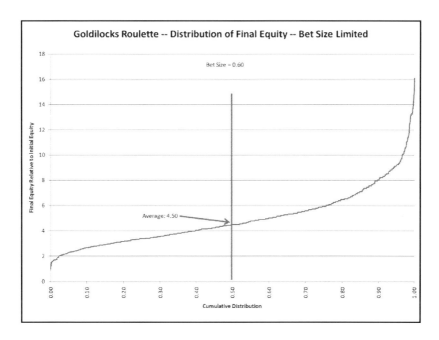

FIGURE 6.34

In limiting risk of a large drawdown to a 5% chance of a 30% draw-down, the average final equity dropped from 174 to 4.5. The reason for the large drawdowns and need to scale back so far in order to hold maximum drawdown to a reasonable level is the frequent occurrence of long sequences of large losses. This can be anticipated by looking at the pdf of the distribution of the wins and losses in figure 6.15. As we will see in more detail in the description of the characteristics of trading systems, having a high percentage of large losing trades causes this behavior.

How Good is the Simulation?

The simulation is based on a distribution of data. That distribution is either a list of closed trades or a list of day-to-day equity changes. The closed trades come from the trading system. The trading system is a combination of logic and data, and the synchronization between the two. The accuracy of the simulation has two major components

- The system
- Random variation

You cannot control the random part. Be as confident as you can about the system part. That confidence comes from using out-of-sample data to produce trades. The data should be representative of conditions you expect in the future. If your macro economic model suggests that the issue you are trading will be generally rising, then generate the trade list used to build the simulation using an out-of-sample period that is rising. If you believe the issue will be generally falling, then generate the trade list using an out-of-sample period that is falling. If you are in doubt, then use a generally flat period, as has been done for this book. The more accurately you are able to forecast the future, the better the resulting simulations will be.

But don't worry too much about the macro model. It is generally safe to use a flat period to create the distribution to create the simulation. If your view of the future becomes more positive, you can adjust the point on the maximum drawdown distribution curve you use to set the position sizing to be more relaxed. If your view of the future becomes more negative, be more conservative. Using the distribution curves is discussed in more detail in Chapter 7 on objective function. As we will see in later chapters, the health of the trading system will be continually monitored. If the logic and the data slip out of sync, there will be indicators to tell you to take the system offline until the situation is resolved.

Chapter 7

Objective Function

Deciding how to run our trading business is an exercise in decision making under uncertainty.

Life is a never ending stream of such decisions. Serious ones – what profession to choose, whether to marry and to whom, where to live. Trivial ones – what breakfast cereal to eat, what color to paint the walls, clean shaven or bearded. We get a lot of practice making the easy decisions, the cost of a poor decision is low, there are many opportunities to change our mind and try alternatives. The consequences of making a poor decision in the hard situations are greater, we have fewer opportunities to start over, the importance of being right is greater.

Whether we go through a formal process or just follow our gut, we make decisions by weighing positive benefits against negative costs. In the broad sense, both benefits and costs include multiple factors – monetary, convenience, pleasure, prestige. In the final analysis, everything is combined into a single metric – an objective function – whose value we attempt to maximize.

All of us involved in trading are asking the same questions.
- What trading system should I use?
- Is it working or broken?
- How much profit can I make?
- How much risk am I taking?

There are many non-monetary factors in choosing a trading system.
- The amount of time it requires to use it.
- The ease of understanding it.
- The amount of experience or judgment needed.
- Any account restrictions.

There are many monetary factors.
- Profit.
- Loss.
- Tax implications.

And some that seem to fall in between.
- Consistency of results.

In the end, we need a single-valued metric. Not all of us reach the point of formalizing the definition and calculation of that metric, but I suggest a candidate.

1. Decide how much working capital you will devote to your trading business. Some of that will be needed to pay for equipment, data, rent, supplies, education. Some will be the trading account. In this book, the trading account begins at $100,000.

2. Select a time horizon for the evaluation of the system. It must be long enough in both number of trades and number of days so that the variety of possible results can be considered. It must be short enough to imagine a project with a completion. In this book, I use a four year time horizon, then let the time determine the number of trades that take place in that time.

3. Decide how much of the trading account you are willing to lose before stopping. This is the *ruin* absorbing barrier. It can be measured either from the initial balance or the highest equity. There are examples of both, but I use a limit of 40% drawdown from highest equity in most cases.

4. Decide how much is "enough." If continued indefinitely, all systems eventually go bankrupt. If your account has grown enough, you should consider banking your profits and stop trading. This is the *retire* absorbing barrier. In some examples, the retire barrier is set so high that it is seldom reached. In others it is set to a relative wealth of 10.0. Having $100,000 become $1,000,000 requires a relative wealth of 10.0.

You have three stopping points:

1. A time horizon.
2. A ruin limit or ruin absorbing barrier.
3. A retire goal or retire absorbing barrier.

The simulation ends with whichever one happens first.

This does not mean that you must never trade after four years, or that you cannot recapitalize and begin again. What it does mean is that all scenarios can be evaluated by a common set of measurements.

There is a considerable amount of judgment in setting your criteria. When you were choosing an objective function to use in the system design, you included factors such as trading frequency, holding period, profit per trade. Those are reflected in the list of closed trades that you are using for your simulation.

When you are choosing your objective function for this phase, there are two major factors.

1. The percentage point on the distribution of the terminal equity.
2. The percentage point on the distribution of the maximum drawdown.

Refer to figure 7.1 which shows the distribution of profit or terminal wealth for a set of hypothetical data. The vertical axis is terminal wealth. If the retire absorbing barrier acted, there will be a flat portion at the high end. The horizontal axis is cumulative percentage of the distribution.

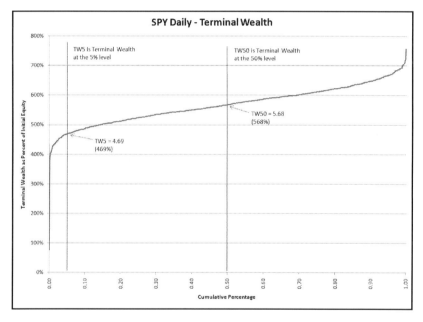

Figure 7.1

- 0.50 is the midpoint. Call it TW50—Terminal Wealth 50% level. The value of the curve at that point is the mean value of terminal wealth. In this example, TW50 is 5.68, or 568%.
- 0.05 is the 5% level. Call it TW5—Terminal Wealth 5% level. On average, if this system runs for many four year periods, one period out of every 20 the terminal wealth will be less than the value of the curve at the 0.05 level. In this example, the value of TW5 is 4.69, or 469%. The compound annual rate

of return, CAR, can be computed as:

$$CAR = 1 - \exp(0.25 * \ln(4.69)) = 47.1\%$$

- 0.95 is the 95% level. Call it TW95. On average, one period out of every 20 the terminal wealth will be greater than the value of the curve at this point. In this example, the value of TW95 is 6.68.

Most of the time, 90% of the time, 18 periods out of 20, the terminal wealth will be between TW5 and TW95. The better the trading system, the narrower this range will be.

Figure 7.2 shows the same information, this time as a probability density function, pdf. The areas to the left and right of the vertical lines represent the 0.05 and 0.95 levels. The standard deviation is 0.63.

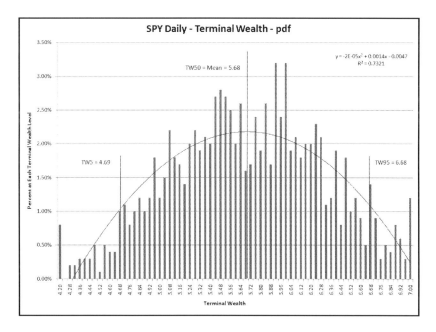

FIGURE 7.2

Figure 7.3 shows the drawdown as a percentage from maximum equity, and has the same interpretation as figure 7.1. If the ruin absorbing barrier acted, there will be flat a portion at the high end.

- 0.50 is the midpoint. Call it DD50. The value of the curve at that point is the mean value of maximum drawdown. In this example, DD50 is 10.0%.

- 0.05 is the 5% level. Call it DD5. On average, if this system runs for many four year periods, one period out of every 20 the maximum drawdown will be less than the value of the curve at the 0.05 level.
- 0.95 is the 95% level. Call it DD95. On average, one period out of every 20 the maximum drawdown will be greater than the value of the curve at the 0.95 level. In this example, DD95 is 20.4%

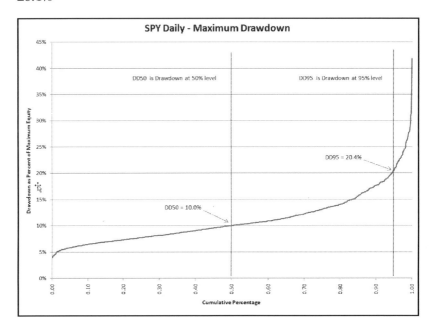

FIGURE 7.3

If only the averages are considered, those values can be read from the 0.50 points on each distribution curve. But it is a mistake to expect the result achieved in any period to always be the average.

The distributions for terminal wealth and maximum drawdown come as a closely linked pair. For a given trading system, the specifics of the distribution depend strongly on the position sizing in use. Changing the position sizing in an attempt to adjust one of the distributions will always affect the other. In particular, lowering the maximum drawdown will lower the terminal wealth. Raising the terminal wealth will raise the maximum drawdown. These relationships are examined more closely in later chapters.

Before you decide how aggressive to be with your position sizing, you must decide what levels you want to use on the terminal wealth and maximum drawdowns. Figure 7.4 shows a diagram that includes both the terminal wealth and maximum drawdown displayed in figures 6.1 and 6.3. Terminal wealth is on the vertical axis, maximum drawdown on the horizontal axis. The best combination is the upper left corner where wealth is highest and drawdown lowest. Avoid the areas at the right and bottom.

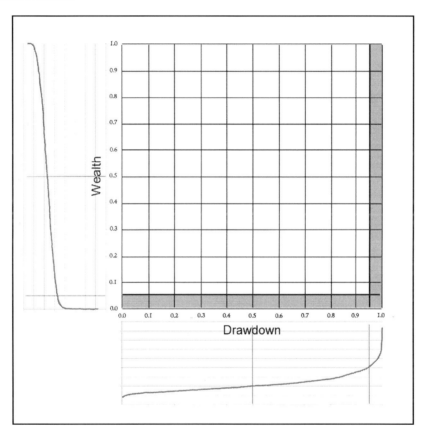

FIGURE 7.4

In figure 7.4, the areas are divided by lines located at 5% terminal wealth, TW5, and 95% maximum drawdown, DD95. Any run where the maximum drawdown exceeds the 95% level will be in the shaded area to the right of the vertical line; any run where the terminal wealth is lower than the 5% level will be in the shaded area below the horizontal line. The large square in the upper left is the area where wealth is above the 5% level and maximum drawdown is below the 95% level. Both of these levels are conservative, and 90% of the simulation results will fall into the large square. About 10% of the time either the wealth will be lower or the drawdown higher, or both, and the result will fall into the shaded area.

You need to choose your personal levels for minimum wealth and maximum drawdown. Relative wealth is final equity as a percentage of initial equity; maximum drawdown from highest equity is also a percentage. A ratio can be formed from two quantities that have the same units. Referring to figures 6.1 and 6.3, terminal wealth at the 0.05 level, TW5, is 4.69, which corresponds to a CAR of 47.1%. Maximum drawdown at the 0.95 level, DD95, is 20.4%. The ratio is 2.31. This ratio may be a useful objective function.

The interpretation is:

if you assume:

- The future performance of the trading system follows the simulation.
- The trader is willing to accept a 5% risk that maximum draw-down will be greater than 20.4%.

then:

- In 95% of four year periods, CAR will be greater than 47.1%, and terminal wealth will be greater than 4.69.

If the ratio is unacceptably low (it is unlikely that you would feel it is too high), then the position sizing must be changed, or the trading system improved, or both.

The resulting ratio is similar to the metric CAR/MaxDD, which is also called the MAR (Managed Account Reports) ratio. Since both CAR and MaxDD are taken at pessimistic points of the distribution, a ratio above 1.0 is exceptionally good.

Replace the 5% and 95% by values of your choosing. If you use 10% and 90%, you can expect to meet both goals 81% of the time; using 20% and 80%, goals will be met about 64% of the time. Importantly, using 50% and 50%, that is, using the mean results, joint goals will be met about 25% of the time. The metric—the ratio—will be higher, but the probability of a disappointing return or deep drawdown is increased.

UTILITY THEORY

John von Neumann and Oskar Morgenstern developed *expected utility theory* in 1944 along with their work in the theory of games. The application of their theory states that people would follow the expected value criterion. That is, they would view profits and losses in direct proportion to the probability of an event and the gain or loss associated with each. For example, assume someone is given a choice between a gift of $1.00 and a gamble where they win $200 with probability of 1% or nothing with probability 99%. The expected value of the gift is $1.00 and the expected value of the gamble is $2.00. By expected value theory, people would always take the gamble.

Utility theory breaks down when some people would prefer the sure thing to the gamble, or even one gamble to another, even though the preferred choice has a lower expected value. Other factors, such as how much money the person already has, the relative utility of $200 versus $1, how many times this game can be played, and the perception of low probability events all affect this and similar decisions.

Several alternatives have been proposed to explain why people deviate from acting in accord with expected utility theory. The most widely accepted is *prospect theory*, developed by Daniel Kahneman and Amos Tversky, both psychologists, in 1979. Prospect theory combines psychology with economic behavior. There are several excellent papers and books listed in the references if you wish to investigate this further. Among their findings:

- Given two equal choices, one expressed as a possible gain, the other as a possible loss, people prefer the possible gain.
- People prefer outcomes that are certain to outcomes that are merely probable.
- People are less willing to gamble with profits than with losses. This fits with traders who are quick to close profitable trades, but continue to hold losers.
- People look more at changes in wealth relative to some reference point rather than final levels of wealth.

Richard Thaler, an economist, working with Daniel Kahneman, developed the fields of *behavioral economics* and *behavioral finance* in about 1985, which add the study of framing, anchoring, and mental accounting behaviors.

An example of framing shows inconsistencies in people's thinking. If the reference point for a decision is defined such that the outcome is viewed as a gain, people will be risk averse. If it is defined such that the outcome is viewed as a loss, people will be risk seeking.

In summary, as gains increase, people value additional gains less. As losses deepen, people are proportionally less concerned about additional losses. This can be expressed as a mathematical formula and graphed. Figure 7.5 shows the graph that represents the utility function.

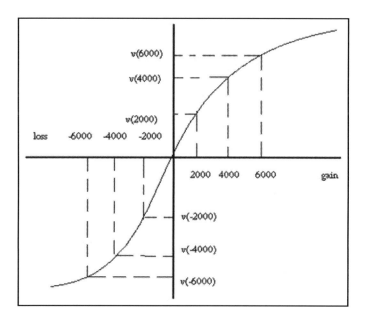

FIGURE 7.5

The interpretation of figure 7.5 is that as gains increase additional gains have less value. This can be seen in the upper right quadrant as the curve is concave downward and the line is trending toward becoming horizontal. Also, as losses increase additional losses become relatively less important. This can be seen in the lower left quadrant as the curve is concave upward and the line is trending toward becoming horizontal. Thaler discusses utility at length, and Gelman and Nolan give an exercise to help calibrate your own utility function.

Think carefully about your own attitude to gains and losses as you select the two percentage levels you will be using to guide position sizing for your trading system.

Chapter 8

Bar Length and Holding Period

PERIODICITY

The length of the data bar, holding period, and risk as measured by drawdown, are closely related. By length of the bar, I mean the period represented by each price bar. With modern trading system development platforms the length can be just about any that you can imagine. Traditional lengths are daily, weekly, and monthly. Each bar has four known price points – open, high, low, and close. Each bar has two known times – open and close. The opening price is the price reported at the opening time; the closing price is the price reported at the closing time. There is no information about the time at which either the high or low took place.

The data associated with a bar is determined by the reporting agency. As examples, it might represent the prices during the floor trading session of a commodity; all prices for transactions that took place during the normal trading hours of the New York Stock Exchange, whether those trades took place on the floor or on one of the other exchanges; or an arbitrary division of data for an issue that trades continuously, such as foreign exchange, FOREX, reported as daily.

With actively traded issues, the first reported price will probably have occurred very close in time to the time of the open. With less actively traded issues, the first reported price could have occurred any time in the bar, with no guarantee that it happened at the time the bar is defined to begin. In order to make any assumptions about the distribution of data within a bar, it is necessary to use bars of shorter length.

A trading system can be designed to use multiple bar lengths, such as weekly and daily, or daily and hourly. The longer length is typically used to determine broad characteristics, such as trend, and the shorter length to signal a trade.

For any given trading system, the length of the shortest bar sets some limits. A trading signal can be specified as to a time or a price. If there is fine enough resolution to the bars, the time can be a time of day, such as 10:05 AM. Otherwise the times available are the open and close of the bars, whatever time of day those happen to be. The price can be specified, such as $45.34. In those cases, signals will be generated and orders placed when something happens, such as the price rising to and then trading above the specified price. Otherwise the prices available are those at the open and close of the bars.

Figure 8.1 shows two representations of a price bar – traditional bar and candlestick – followed by two possible intra-bar price paths.

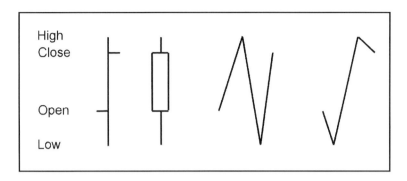

FIGURE 8.1

The number of transactions that can be specified for any single bar are limited:

- Enter a new position at the open, hold for the remainder of the bar.
- Enter at the open, exit at some specified intra-bar price.
- Enter at the open, exit at some specified intra-bar price, re-enter at the close.
- Enter at the open, exit at the close.
- Enter at some specified intra-bar price, hold for the remainder of the bar.
- Enter at some specified intra-bar price, exit at the close.
- Enter at the close.
- Exit an existing position at the open, be flat for the remainder of the bar.
- Exit at the open, take a new position at some specified intra-bar price.
- Exit at the open, take a new position at some specified intra-bar price, exit at the close.
- Exit at the open, take a new position at the close.
- Exit at some specific intra-bar price, be flat for the remainder of the bar.
- Exit at some specific intra-bar price, take a new position at the close.
- Exit at the close.

There is no guarantee that any of these orders will be executed. They all depend on having enough trading volume at the time and / or price specified. The orders with specified prices will be executed only when there is trading at the specified level – that is, the specified price must be within the low to high range for the bar. Just as orders can be created for specified intra-bar prices, they can be created for specified intra-bar times. Orders with specified times will be executed only when there is trading at that time, and there is no way to estimate the price.

It is not possible, given a single bar, to have any combination of actions where more than one action takes place at an intra-bar price.

In order to obtain the most accurate estimates of trading system performance, select the length of the data bar so that at most one action takes place within most bars.

The holding period is closely related to the length of the data bar. Systems based on daily bars hold one or more days; systems based on weekly bars hold one or more weeks; systems based on monthly bars hold one or more months.

RISK BASED ON BAR LENGTH

The holding period risk is also closely related to the length of the data bar. Assume a system takes a long position at the close of one bar and exits at the close of the next bar. The gain for that trade is determined by the difference between the entry price and the exit price. The risk is determined by the difference between the entry price and the lowest price while the position is being held. Similarly, the risk for a short position is the difference between the entry price and the highest price while the position is being held. The longer the bar length, the higher the intra-bar risk, For example, if a system is based on monthly bars, and position changes are made at the close of each month, the intra-month risk is entry price to intra-month low or intra-month high and can be significant.

We will examine potential performance of trading systems based on bars of several lengths, including yearly, quarterly, monthly, weekly, multi-day, daily, and hourly. The intention is to show the advantages and disadvantages of each, giving each reader information that will help him or her decide what bar length to use for analysis and to compare the potential return and risk associated with each.

How faithfully the future years mirror the past will only be known after the fact. Some people feel that the strong bull market in US equities that began in 1982 is unlikely to be repeated, at least not in the US. The twelve year period from 1998 through 2010 has produced little net change, as measured by major US indexes and their ETFs SPY (S&P 500), QQQQ (NASDAQ 100), and IWM (Russell 2000). Data for the simulations will be drawn from these ETFs from this period. As you replicate these simulations and extend them to reflect your own view of the future, you can use a different period or add whatever bias you think is appropriate.

In lieu of a trading system that makes trades with the frequency and profitability desired, we will use a technique of drawing a random result, then deciding whether the pseudo-trade represented by that result is a winner and gains that amount or is a loser and loses that amount. For each of the studies, results are for a holding period of one full bar length. Long positions only are taken at the close of a bar and exited at the next close. The sequence of close to close trades completely covers the time period studied. There is no loss of generality in taking only long positions. If the ETF rises over the next bar, a correct long position gains that amount, while an incorrect long position loses that amount. The same logic would apply to short positions.

Figure 8.2 contains a table of open, high, low, close quotes for SPY for a period in early 2010. The upper section is daily, the middle weekly, and the lower monthly.

In the studies in this section, we assume that a position will be taken at the close of one bar, with the exit at the close of the next bar of the same length. For example, using daily bars, a position taken at the close on January 29, point A, will be exited at the close on February 1, point B. Using weekly bars, a position taken at the close on Friday, January 29, point A, will be exited at the close on Friday, February 5, point C. Using monthly bars, a position taken at the close on the final day of January, point A, will be exited on the close of the final day of February, point D. The gain or loss is computed using the price at the close of the exit bar in relation to the price at the close of the entry bar. If the position is long, the drawdown based on closed trades is the percentage of drop from entry to exit, and the drawdown based on intra-trade price is the percentage of drop from entry to the lowest low in the holding period. If the position is short, the intra-trade drawdown is computed using the highest high in the holding period. Whether the position is long or short, intra-trade drawdown is always greater than or equal to the closed-trade drawdown. From the point of view of a conservative trader and also from the point of view of the margin clerk at the brokerage or exchange, intra-trade drawdown is the more important number. Even though a fund manager makes her position changes at the end of each month, if the client knows the position, the client will also be concerned about intra-trade drawdowns.

Daily		Open	High	Low	Close	
SPY	1/28/2010	110.19	110.25	107.91	108.57	
SPY	1/29/2010	109.04	109.80	107.22	107.39	A
SPY	2/1/2010	108.15	109.07	107.50	109.06	B
SPY	2/2/2010	109.26	110.59	108.88	110.38	
SPY	2/3/2010	109.88	110.48	109.51	109.83	
SPY	2/4/2010	108.98	109.03	106.42	106.44	
SPY	2/5/2010	106.56	106.88	104.58	106.66	C
SPY	2/8/2010	106.74	107.33	105.81	105.89	
SPY	2/9/2010	107.13	108.15	106.27	107.22	
SPY	2/10/2010	107.05	107.60	106.11	107.01	
SPY	2/11/2010	106.87	108.25	106.25	108.13	
SPY	2/12/2010	106.99	108.10	106.51	108.04	
SPY	2/16/2010	108.86	109.85	107.82	109.74	
SPY	2/17/2010	110.27	110.41	109.74	110.26	
SPY	2/18/2010	110.08	111.14	110.04	110.91	
SPY	2/19/2010	110.62	111.57	110.36	111.14	
SPY	2/22/2010	111.55	111.58	110.83	111.16	
SPY	2/23/2010	110.86	111.20	109.52	109.81	
SPY	2/24/2010	110.14	111.00	109.86	110.82	
SPY	2/25/2010	109.24	110.75	108.94	110.67	
SPY	2/26/2010	110.77	111.12	110.11	110.74	D
SPY	3/1/2010	111.20	112.00	111.17	111.89	
SPY	3/2/2010	112.37	112.74	112.00	112.20	
Weekly		**Open**	**High**	**Low**	**Close**	
SPY	1/29/2010	110.21	110.47	107.22	107.39	A
SPY	2/5/2010	108.15	110.59	104.58	106.66	C
SPY	2/12/2010	106.74	108.25	105.81	108.04	
SPY	2/19/2010	108.86	111.57	107.82	111.14	
SPY	2/26/2010	111.55	111.58	108.94	110.74	D
Monthly		**Open**	**High**	**Low**	**Close**	
SPY	1/29/2010	112.37	115.14	107.22	107.39	A
SPY	2/26/2010	108.15	111.58	104.58	110.74	D

FIGURE 8.2

Figure 8.3 shows candle charts for the month of February, 2010, corresponding to the quotes. The left section is daily, the middle weekly, and the right monthly. The points labeled A, B, C, and D mark the bars at which the trades are assumed to be taken.

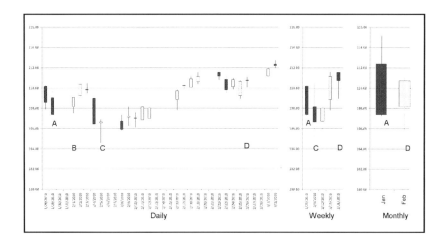

FIGURE 8.3

PROFIT POTENTIAL AND DRAWDOWN

An important question is how profit potential and drawdown are related to bar length and holding period.

A series of studies was run using bar lengths from one year down to one hour. Positions are taken at the close of each bar and held for exactly one bar. The profitability and drawdown depend on the accuracy of the trading system. A range of accuracies are used, from 50% to 70%. Accuracy lower than 50% is guaranteed to result in a losing system. Accuracies in the range of 55 to 60% are achievable and profitable. Accuracies of 65% and higher are excellent and extremely profitable.

For the ETF SPY, the period from 27 Feb 1998 to 31 Aug 2010 is net flat, beginning at 104.556 and ending at 105.31. Data for most of the simulations is drawn from this period. All of the studies cover a four year period, using however many bars are required.

MONTHLY DATA AND EXPLANATION OF THE CHARTS

To explain all of the charts, we begin with monthly bars.

Assume a trading system is based on monthly bars. At the end of each month, it forecasts whether the price at the end of the next month will be higher or lower, then takes either a long position or a short position. SPY is net flat for the period 27 Feb 1998 through 31 Aug 2010, with the prices of 104.8 and 105.3 at the start and end of the period respectively.

The 150 monthly data points for that period were used to provide the data for a series of Monte Carlo simulations. Each simulated period is four years. This means that a randomly selected set of 48 monthly data results are chosen from the 150 monthly data points available. The profitability of the system is represented by its prediction accuracy. For a relatively flat period, an accuracy of 50% should result in relatively flat performance. Higher accuracy will produce profitable results and lower accuracy will produce losing results.

Assume the system has a prediction accuracy of 60%. For each simulation run, a sequence of 48 months is chosen at random. A random decision is made whether the prediction for each of the coming month is correct or wrong. Using close to close price changes, the monthly gains are computed. Using close to either high or low prices, the risk is computed.

STRAW BROOM CHARTS

Figure 8.4 show the equity curves for ten four-year simulated periods. Equity is measured as a relative ratio of current equity to initial equity. There is one trade per month, so a sequence of 48 trades go into each 4 year result. On average, 60% of the 48 months will be winners and profitable; 40% will be losers. Depending on the trades chosen from the 150 available, and the sequence in which they were chosen, all paths are equally likely. Some result in little or no gain for the four year period; others result in a doubling of the account equity. These charts are called *straw broom* charts, because of their resemblance to the individual straws in a broom all beginning at the broom handle and expanding toward the tips. The dashed line is the average of the ten runs.

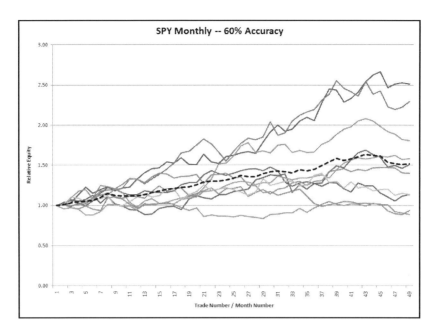

FIGURE 8.4

INTRA-TRADE DRAWDOWN

Figure 8.5 shows one of the four year equity curves.

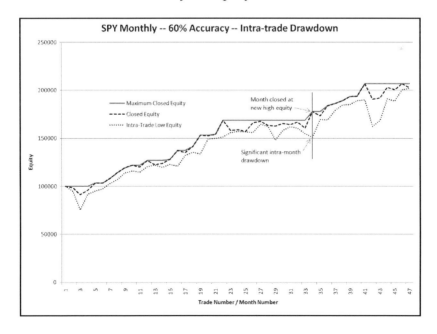

FIGURE 8.5

The solid line is the maximum equity, the dashed line is the close to close equity, and the dotted line is the low equity. Note the month at the vertical line at trade number 34. At the close of that month, the price was higher than at the close of the previous month, so the close to close equity shows a gain. But the price moved about 15% against the trade intra-month and at one point there was a substantial drawdown.

We know that risk increases in proportion to the square root of the holding period – a position held for one month, 21 days, has an expected risk that is 4.58 times the expected daily risk.

In addition, there is intra-trade risk. If the trader is willing to completely ignore intra-month prices, the risk profile would be determined by the close to close data. If the trader would adjust a position based on intra-month drawdown, then the data for the low equity line must be used. Figure 8.6 shows the scatter plot comparing the close to close change with the close to worst position change for each of the 48 months. When using monthly SPY data, the intra-month risk adds about 3 to 5% to the drawdown expected based on the close to close risk.

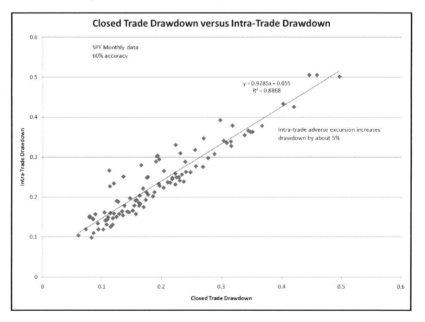

FIGURE 8.6

TERMINAL WEALTH

Figure 8.7 shows the terminal wealth for the distribution of 1000 simulation runs, each 4 years long. There are five lines. The top line gives the result when the accuracy is 70%. The next lines down are in order: 65%, 60%, 55%, and 50%. The terminal wealth is the ratio of final equity to initial equity. The vertical line at 0.50 marks the midpoint of expected results – half are expected to be higher and half lower. The top line, 70% accurate, shows the distribution of all 1000 simulation runs at that accuracy. It indicates that terminal wealth is about equally likely to be above or below 1.93. A compound annual rate of return, CAR, of 17.8% for four years gives a terminal wealth of 1.93.

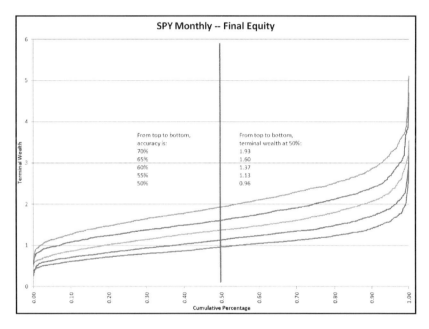

FIGURE 8.7

By looking at the left side of the chart, we see that there is a small chance that the account balance at the end of four years will be no greater than it was at the start. At the right side, we also see a small chance that it will have increased to at least three times. Terminal wealth drops as accuracy drops. As expected, at 50% accuracy, the midpoint of the distribution of terminal wealth is about the same as at the start, 0.96 per the simulation, meaning no net change in equity over the four years.

For this simulation, all funds available are reinvested in each new position, so this is the maximum terminal wealth that can be expected using monthly data without using additional leverage. Since trades are made at the market price on close, MOC, slippage is assumed to be zero; commission of $10.00 per round turn has been deducted.

DRAWDOWN CLOSE TO CLOSE

Figure 8.8 shows the close to close drawdown for the distribution of 1000 simulation runs, each 4 years long. Close to close drawdown measures only the percentage drawdown from the highest equity to date to the equity as marked to market at the end of each month. On this chart, intra-trade drawdown is ignored. Note that the order of the lines, from top to bottom, representing percentage accuracy is reversed from the final equity chart.

The top line is that for 50% accuracy, which has the highest drawdown. The midpoint of the distribution indicates that the expected drawdown from high equity will be about 29%. About 5% of the time, as indicated by the vertical line at the 95% position, drawdown will be greater than 53%.

When accuracy is 70%, the midpoint drawdown is expected to be about 12%, and about 5% of the time it will be greater than 28%.

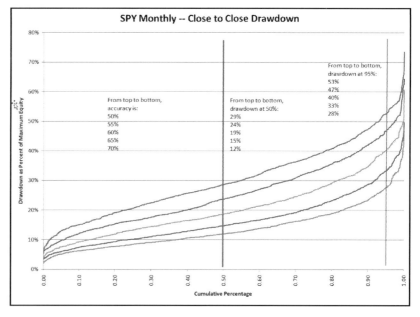

FIGURE 8.8

INTRA-TRADE DRAWDOWN

Figure 8.9 shows a chart similar to figure 8.8, taking the intra-trade drawdown into account. Note that the drawdown figures are about 3 to 4% greater when equity is marked to market throughout the month.

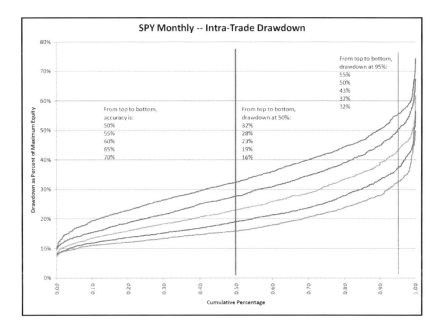

FIGURE 8.9

The next sections show the results of using bars of different lengths.

QUARTERLY DATA

This section shows the results when quarterly data are used. There are four data points per year, 16 positions in the four year simulation.

Figure 8.10 shows that the intra-trade drawdown increases compared to that found using monthly data.

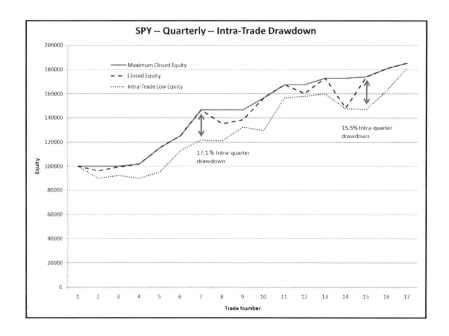

FIGURE 8.10

Figure 8.11 shows final equity, which is lower at all accuracy levels. A CAR of 10.0% over four years gives a terminal wealth of 1.46.

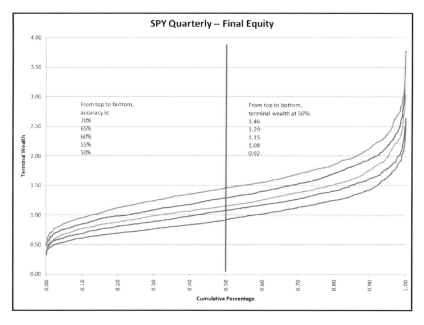

FIGURE 8.11

Close to close drawdown is shown in figure 8.12.

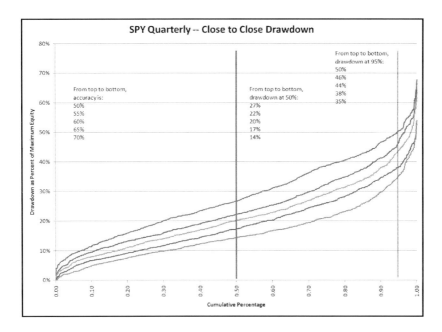

FIGURE 8.12

Intra-trade drawdown is shown in figure 8.13.

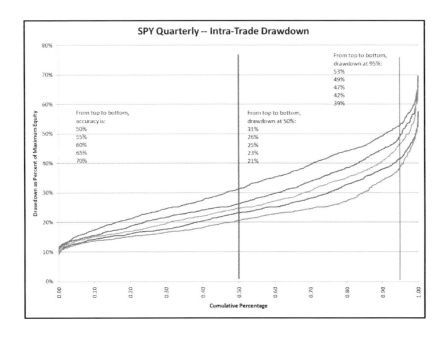

FIGURE 8.13

YEARLY DATA

This section shows the results when yearly data are used. There is only one data point per year, four in the four year simulation.

INTRA-TRADE DRAWDOWN

The intra-year drawdown is often in excess of 30%. Figure 8.14 shows one example.

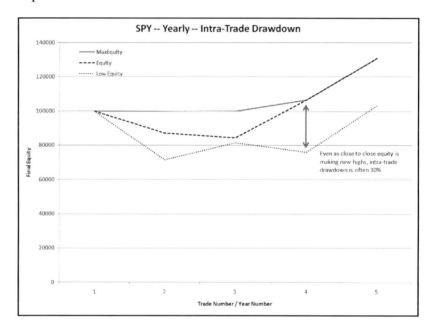

FIGURE 8.14

FINAL EQUITY

See figure 8.15 for final equity using yearly data. A CAR of 6.1% gives a terminal wealth of 1.27 over a four year period.

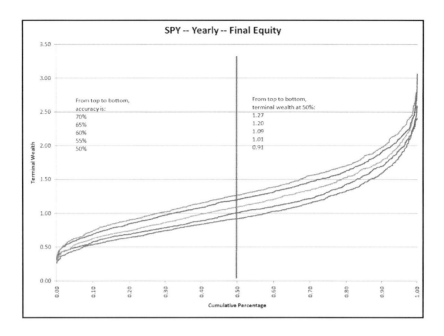

CLOSE TO CLOSE DRAWDOWN

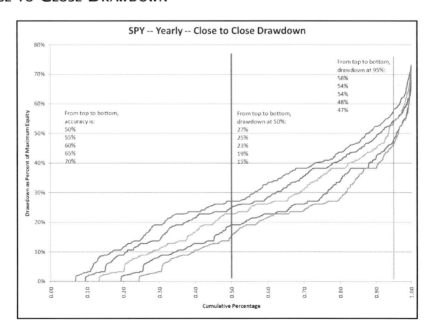

FIGURE 8.16

INTRA-TRADE DRAWDOWN

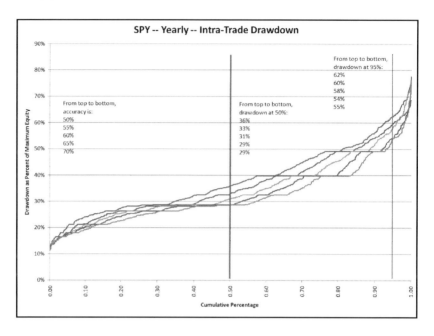

FIGURE 8.17

WEEKLY DATA

The flat period 27 Feb 1998 through 27 Aug 2010 contains 653 weekly bars that are used to establish the database. Each simulation is a sequence of 208 weeks to generate four-year sequences.

Intra-trade Drawdown - One Example

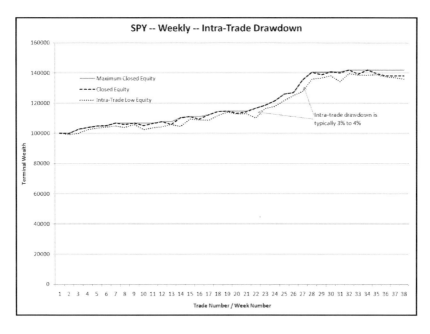

FIGURE 8.18

Final Equity

A CAR of 47.5% over a four year period results in a terminal wealth of 4.71.

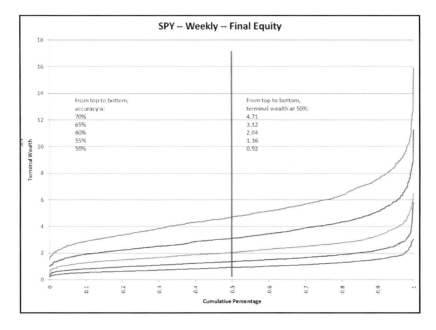

FIGURE 8.19

CLOSE TO CLOSE DRAWDOWN

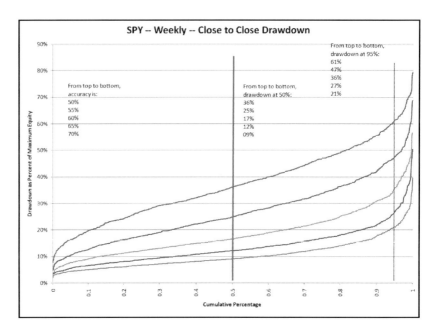

FIGURE 8.20

INTRA-TRADE DRAWDOWN

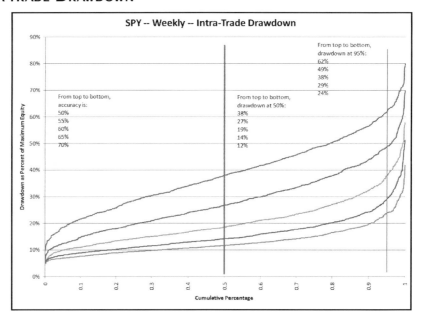

FIGURE 8.21

Daily Data

Final Equity

A CAR of 152% over a four year period results in terminal wealth of 40.76.

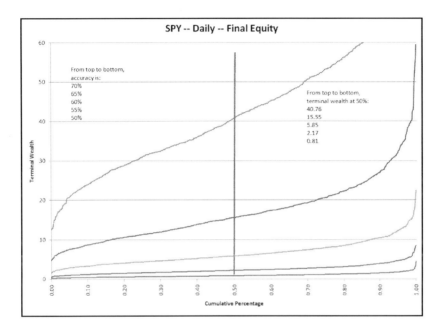

Figure 8.22

CLOSE TO CLOSE DRAWDOWN

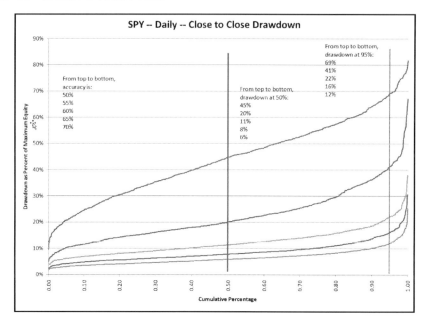

FIGURE 8.23

INTRA-TRADE DRAWDOWN

Intra-trade drawdown is about 1% higher than close to close drawdown.

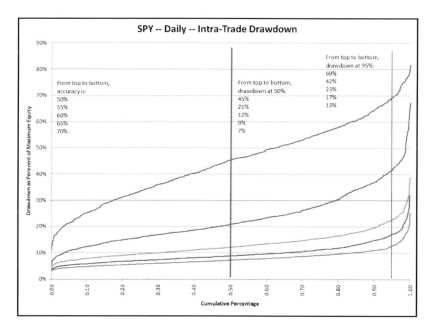

FIGURE 8.24

AREA MOST TRADERS WILL FIND POSSIBLE

Using daily bars with percentage accuracy between 50 and 64 percent.

FINAL EQUITY

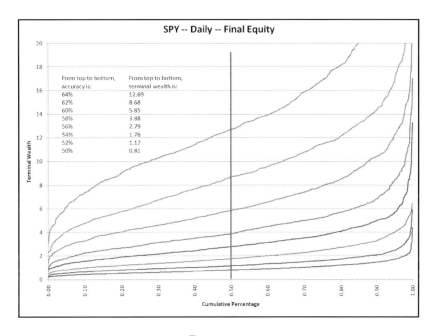

FIGURE 8.25

CLOSE TO CLOSE DRAWDOWN

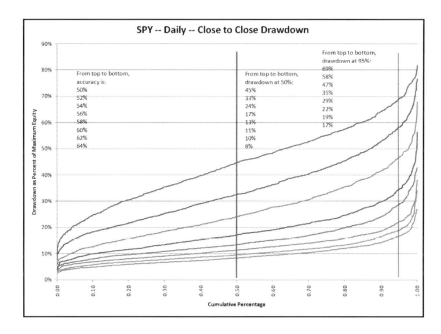

FIGURE 8.26

There is no need for the chart of intra-trade drawdown. The additional risk at all degrees of accuracy is about one percent.

RISING OR FALLING MARKETS

The data used for the simulations in the figures above assumes that the future will have characteristics similar to the 1998 to 2010 period – that is, an overall flat trend. A person who had reason to believe that SPY would be either rising or falling over the next four years would adjust the data used by selecting a period of time he or she thought representative. Simulations similar to those based on the flat period were run for periods of consistently rising markets, consistently falling markets, and very quiet markets. Final equity, close to close drawdown, and intra-trade drawdown are similar to these results for rising or falling markets.

BULLISH MARKET

The period from 30 Aug 2002 through 31 Oct 2007 was a strongly rising market. SPY started that period at a price of 91.5 and ended at 154.6. Figure 8.27 shows the final equity for four year simulations when the data was drawn from a period of rising market.

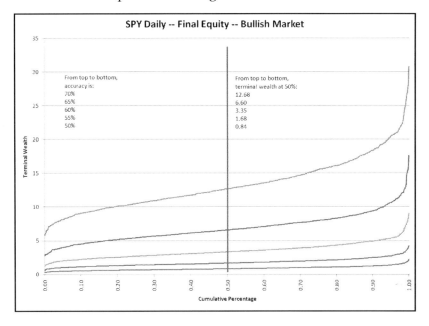

FIGURE 8.27

Figure 8.28 shows the Close to Close drawdown for the period of rising market.

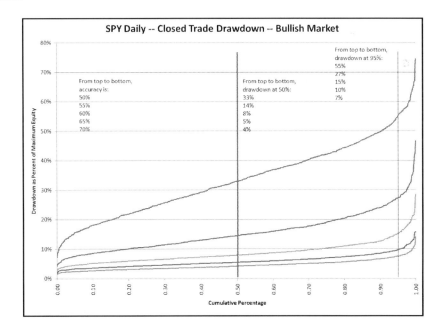

FIGURE 8.28

There is no need to show intra-trade drawdown – it is about one percent greater than close to close drawdown.

BEARISH MARKET

Results for bearish markets are similar in shape, but better in performance. An accurate prediction of the direction of the close of SPY in bear markets is very profitable. Figure 8.29 shows the final equity.

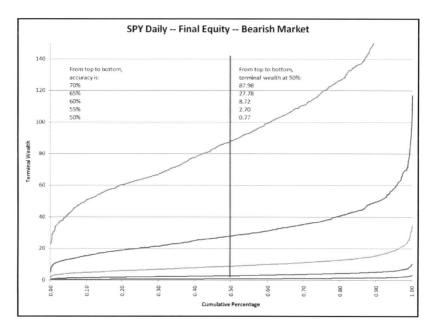

FIGURE 8.29

Figure 8.30 shows the closed trade drawdown.

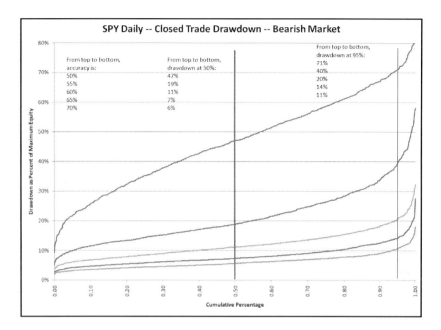

There must be enough volatility to profit from accurate forecasts. Very quiet markets produce low terminal equity and low drawdowns.

HOURLY DATA

Real-time data was collected for the period 1 Mar 2008 through 27 Dec 2010 and saved in hourly bars. The final bar of each day differs from the others in that it includes the overnight price change. Figure 8.31 shows the relative frequency of percentage changes from the close of one bar to the close of the next, with the last bars separated.

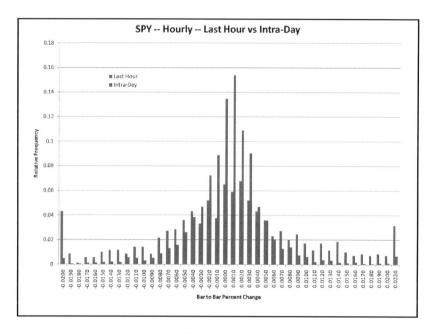

FIGURE 8.31

The very heavy tails are apparent in both distributions. Summary statistics are shown in Figure 8.32.

Last Hour			Intra-day	
Mean	-0.000053		Mean	0.000021
Standard Error	0.000422		Standard Error	0.000082
Median	0.000263		Median	0.000178
Mode	0.000000		Mode	0.000000
Standard Deviation	0.011098		Standard Deviation	0.005260
Sample Variance	0.000123		Sample Variance	0.000028
Kurtosis	3.092178		Kurtosis	15.884275
Skewness	-0.235225		Skewness	0.698794
Range	0.099747		Range	0.104096
Minimum	-0.051897		Minimum	-0.036542
Maximum	0.047851		Maximum	0.067553
Sum	-0.036895		Sum	0.088582
Count	693		Count	4152

FIGURE 8.32

INTRA-DAY VERSUS OVERNIGHT

There are clearly two very different distributions represented here. A trading system that uses the final bar and holds for a single bar is capturing the overnight change in price.

INTRA-DAY BARS

Figure 8.33 shows an example of the intra-trade drawdown when accuracy is 60% and intra-day hourly bars are used.

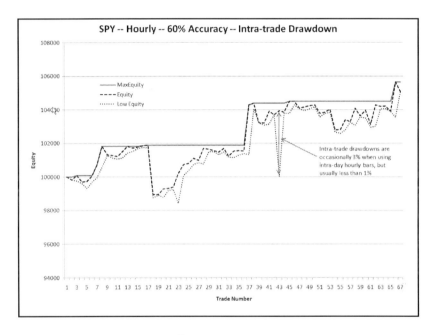

FIGURE 8.33

Figure 8.34 shows the correlation between the drawdown from maximum equity based on the close of each bar with the drawdown to lowest intra-bar equity. The accuracy of the signal is 60%. There are occasional intra-bar drawdowns of 3%, but the average is less than 1%.

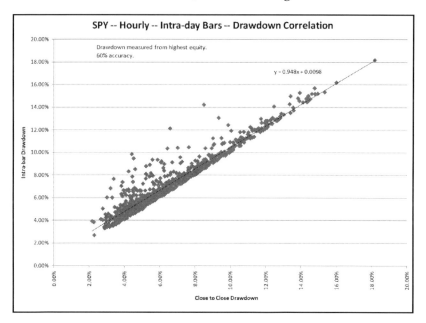

FIGURE 8.34

FINAL EQUITY

Assuming there is an average of one trade per day, each trade lasting exactly one one-hour bar, figure 8.35 shows the distribution of final equity for 1000 four year simulation runs. CAR of 36.3% for four years results in terminal equity of 3.45.

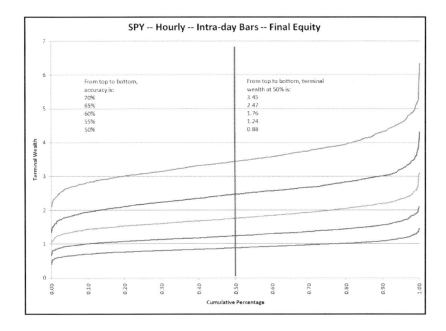

FIGURE 8.35

CLOSE TO CLOSE DRAWDOWN

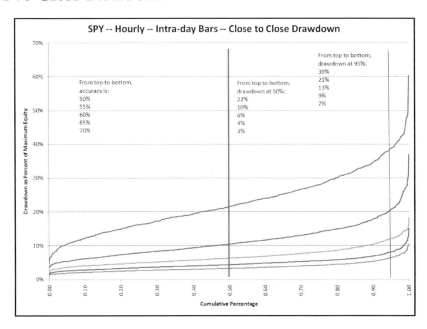

FIGURE 8.36

TWO TRADES A DAY

If the trader makes two trades per day rather than one, she will have 2016 trades in a four year period, compared with 1008 when a single trade is made each day. Figure 8.37 shows the final equity for these two systems, both at 60% accuracy. Terminal wealth is the geometric mean of each trade raised to the power of the number of trades. From that, we expect that doubling the number of trades will square the terminal equity; which it does – 1.76 squared is 3.10.

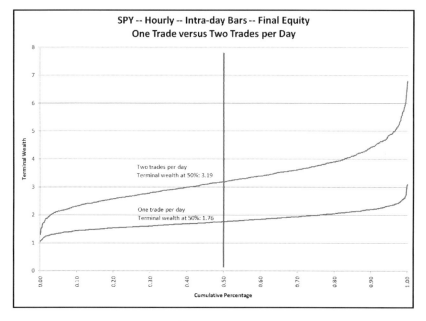

FIGURE 8.37

Interestingly, when the number of trades increases, the drawdown does not increase. Figure 8.38 shows the close to close drawdown for a single trade per day and two trades per day. The two distribution curves are almost identical. The drawdown at the 50% point is about 6% for both.

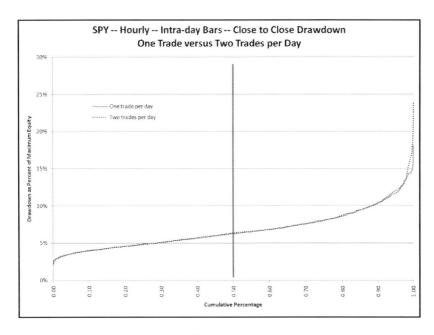

FIGURE 8.38

OVERNIGHT

Figure 8.39 shows the distribution of final equity using the set of bars that span the overnight period. Only one curve is shown – the one for 60% accuracy.

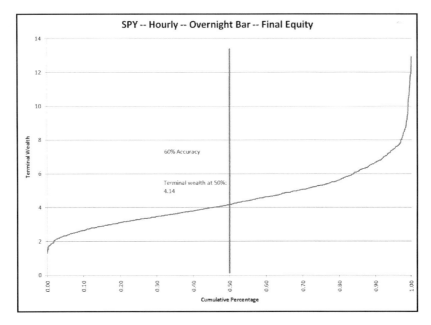

FIGURE 8.39

TRULY OVERNIGHT

The chart in figure 8.39 above does cover the overnight period, but also has a portion of the day session in each bar. To get a truer estimate of the value of trading the overnight session, a set of data was constructed using as its opening price the price at the close of the day session, and as its closing price the price at the open of the next morning's day session. This data, shown in figure 8.40, covers the same period that has been used for the hourly charts shown above – the charts can be directly compared. A CAR of 99.3% over four years results in terminal wealth of 15.77.

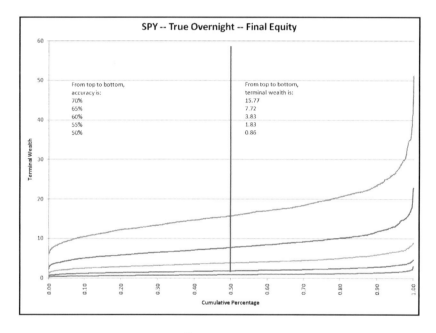

FIGURE 8.40

CLOSE TO CLOSE DRAWDOWN

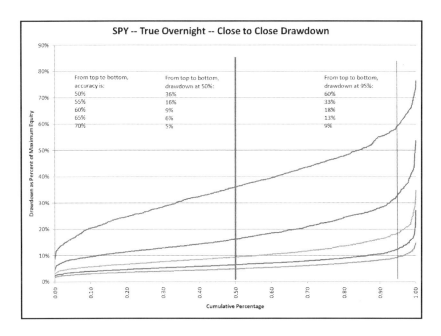

FIGURE 8.41

COMMISSIONS

The examples above assumed that an entire account was traded on each signal using SPY as the tradable vehicle. Commission costs have dropped sharply recently. Commission-free trading is available in some circumstances. Discount brokers handle trades of any size for a fixed fee or a percentage. I assume that any reader of this book is comfortable making trades online without broker assistance.

As of this writing, SPY is about $110. A $100,000 account would be trading about 900 shares. Some of current commission charges are listed below. These will rapidly become outdated, so check for current rates for each end of the transaction, then double to get the round turn rate:

eTrade	$9.99 for unlimited shares.
	($7.99 for frequent traders)
Fidelity	$7.95 for unlimited shares.
Interactive Brokers	$0.005 / share
MB Trading	$4.95 for unlimited shares.

OptionsExpress	$0.01 / share
OptionsHouse	$3.95 for unlimited shares.
Schwab	$8.95 for unlimited shares.
Scottrade	$7.00 for unlimited shares, market or limit order.
TD AmeriTrade	$9.99 for unlimited shares.
Thinkorswim	a division of TD Ameritrade
TradeKing	$4.95 for unlimited shares.
Zecco	$4.50 for unlimited shares.

Several of the brokerages listed charge no commission for trades in some funds and ETFs, provided minimum holding periods are met.

DAILY 60% VARYING COMMISSION

Figure 8.42 shows the effect of commissions.

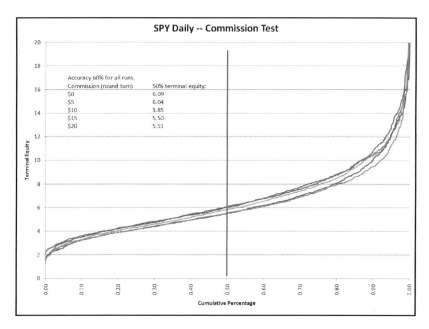

FIGURE 8.42

Five simulation runs, each using daily data and 60% accuracy, were made. Round turn commission was varied from 0 to $20. There are 1008 trades in each four year period. Final equity with zero commission was 6.09 times initial equity. The compound annual rate of return

(CAR) is 57.1%. Beginning at $100,000, final equity is about $609,000.

At $10 per trade, commissions reduced final equity by $10,080. The CAR corresponding to a terminal equity of 5.85 is 55.5%.

At $20 per trade, commissions reduced final equity by $20,160. The CAR corresponding to a terminal equity of 5.51 is about 53.2%.

As a rough gauge, for a $100,000 account, trading daily with 60% accuracy, every additional $5 round turn commission reduces terminal wealth by about 2%.

Drawdowns were not affected by commission setting.

SLIPPAGE

For studies made using yearly, quarterly, monthly, weekly, and daily, trades were made at the market price on the close of trading. SPY is the most liquid issue in the world and has a bid – asked spread of $0.01 almost any time of any day. SPY's price is in the range of $100 for the period studied. A spread of $0.01 on both the entry and exit would reduce the profit of each trade by 0.02%. The table in figure 8.43 estimates the effect of several levels of slippage when SPY is traded one per day at an accuracy of 60%. Slippage of $0.01 reduces CAR from 15.2% to 9.2%. Slippage of $0.02 reduces it further to 3.8%. Slippage of $0.03 reduces it to -1.8%, making the system unprofitable.

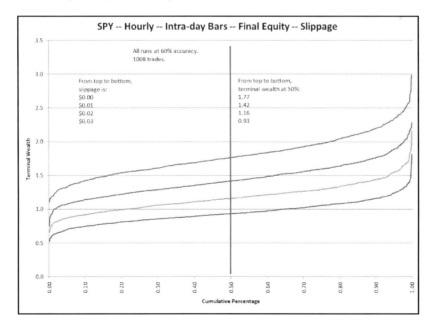

FIGURE 8.43

Increased slippage increases close to close drawdown as well, as shown in figure 8.44.

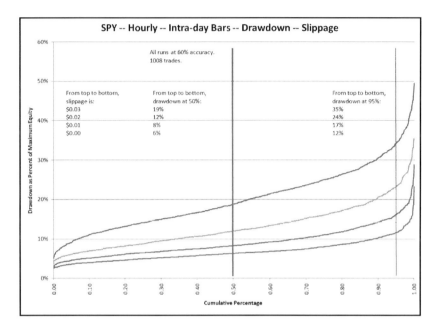

SPY -- Hourly -- Intra-day Bars -- Drawdown -- Slippage

All runs at 60% accuracy.
1008 trades.

From top to bottom, slippage is:	From top to bottom, drawdown at 50%:	From top to bottom, drawdown at 95%:
$0.03	19%	35%
$0.02	12%	24%
$0.01	8%	17%
$0.00	6%	12%

FIGURE 8.44

Intra-trade drawdown increases less than 1% over close to close drawdown.

SWEET SPOT

A partial summarization of results of the simulations is shown in the table in figure 8.45 and the chart in figure 8.46.

- Accuracy is at 60% for all runs.
- Round turn commission is $10 for all runs.
- Slippage is zero, except for Hourly 1 and Hourly 2, where it is $0.01.
- Terminal wealth is at the 50% level for four years, and is converted to compound annual rate of return, which is net of commission and slippage.
- Drawdown is close to close drawdown at the 50% level.
- Hourly 1 is trading hourly intra-day bars, 1 trade per day.
- Hourly 2 is trading hourly intra-day bars, 2 trades per day.

- 2 Day represents using bars 2 days in length. Detail charts are not shown.

- 3 Day represents using bars 3 days in length. Detail charts are not shown.

- 4 Day represents using bars 4 days in length. Detail charts are not shown.

The other periodicities are all close to close as described in their respective sections of this chapter.

	50% level Terminal Wealth	CAR	50% level Drawdown	Additional Intra-Trade
Yearly	1.09	2.20%	31%	8%
Quarterly	1.15	3.60%	25%	5%
Monthly	1.37	8.20%	23%	3%
Weekly	2.04	19.50%	19%	2%
4 day	2.15	21.09%	16%	1%
3 Day	2.63	27.35%	14%	1%
2 Day	3.35	35.29%	13%	1%
Daily	5.85	55.50%	12%	1%
Hourly 1	1.42	9.20%	8%	1%
Hourly 2	2.07	19.90%	9%	1%
Overnight	3.83	40.00%	9%	

FIGURE 8.45

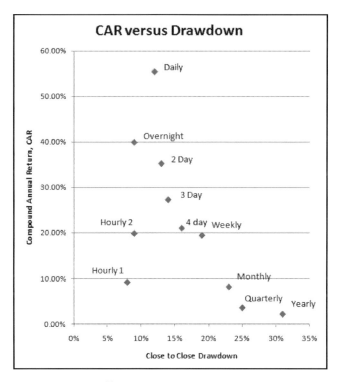

FIGURE 8.46

CONCLUSION

The results compare the reward, as measured by compound annual return, with the risk, as measured by close to close drawdown, for positions held in SPY for a range of holding periods. There is definitely a sweet spot in terms of bar length, holding period, close to close drawdown, and intra-trade drawdown.

Assuming a trading system is able to forecast the direction of the next bar with 60% accuracy, the maximum return with minimum drawdown comes with daily periodicity. Any of three options appear to be reasonable:

- Take a position at the close and hold until the close of the next day.
- Take a position at the close and hold until the open of the next day.
- Take a position at the open and hold until the open of the next day.

Intra-day trading can be profitable, but requires careful attention to drawdown and slippage.

Forecasting the direction of the close two or more days later reduces return significantly and slightly increases risk.

Using weekly data, even when the forecast of direction for the next week is 60% accurate, return has fallen and drawdown increased.

Monthly, quarterly, and yearly holding periods offer little return and very high risk.

Intra-trade drawdown increases significantly with holding period.

REALITY CHECK

If the retire boundary is set at 4.0 for a 4 year period of trading, what degree of accuracy is necessary to reach that goal for each bar length and holding period?

Figure 8.47 shows that information. The column headed TW5 shows the accuracy that will produce TW of 4.0 95% of the time. ITDD95 in the next column shows what the intra-trade drawdown at the 95th percentile will be when TW5 is 4.0. The column headed TW50 shows the accuracy that will produce TW of 4.0 50% of the time. ITDD95 in the next column shows what the intra-trade drawdown at the 95th percentile will be.

	% Correct necessary to have TW = 4.0			
	TW5	ITDD95	TW50	ITDD95
Daily	62%	20%	58%	30%
Weekly	75%	19%	68%	26%
Monthly	100%	15%	90%	16%
Quarterly	not possible		not possible	
Yearly	not possible		not possible	
Quarterly best result at 100% accurate				
	TW = 1.96	23%	TW = 2.66	23%
Yearly best result at 100% accurate				
	TW = 1.43	40%	TW = 1.89	40%

FIGURE 8.47

The conclusion is that it is not possible to achieve TW of 4.0 in 4 years unless the bar length and holding period is weekly or shorter.

These results are independent of whether the market is rising or falling. They depend only on the accuracy of predicting the direction of the price at the end of the next bar, then taking a position in that direction.

Asking for conditions that produce terminal wealth lower than 4.0 lowers the accuracy required, but does not change the conclusion.

SUMMARY

If you are seeking high terminal wealth, use daily bars (or intra-day bars) to forecast the close to close direction of SPY (or an equally attractive tradable issue) for one day in the future.

Avoid using bar lengths longer than weekly or holding positions longer than one week.

OVERNIGHT ANOTHER LOOK

This analysis is based on about 17 months of carefully analyzed intra-day data, 29 Jul 2009 through 3 Jan 2011, for ES, the S&P 500 futures contract.

Look at figure 8.48. Assume that at today's close, point X, you have perfect knowledge about whether tomorrow's close, point Z, will be higher or lower. Should you take the position at today's close or wait until tomorrow's open? That is, should you take the position at point X or point Y? Should you trade Market on Close, MOC, of the signal bar? Or Next Day Open, NDO?

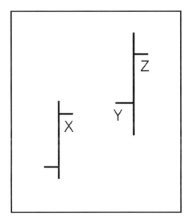

FIGURE 8.48

Figure 8.49 shows the proportion of gain that comes from each, trading with perfect knowledge.

- Positions taken at X and held to Z, Close to Next Close, result in final equity of 16.91.
- Positions taken at X and held to Y, Close to Next Open, result in final equity of 2.73.
- And positions taken at Y and held to Z, Next Open to Next Close, result in final equity of 6.19.

About 35% of the Close to Close gain comes from the movement in the overnight market. Note that the scale is logarithmic, and that 16.91 is the product of 2.73 and 6.19.

Also note that both the Close to Next Open and Next Open to Next Close equity curves are very smooth, indicating that there are very few surprises, and suggesting that it is generally safe to hold overnight when your system gives accurate forecasts of the direction for the next day.

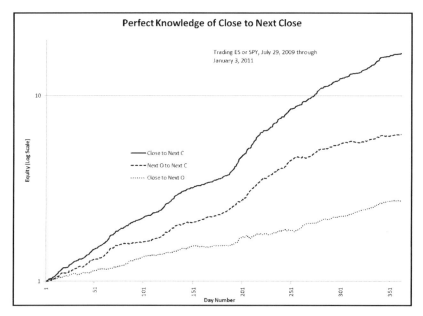

FIGURE 8.49

Figure 8.50 shows the correlation between price changes corresponding to trades held between points XZ and XY – today's close to tomorrow's close versus today's close to tomorrow's open.

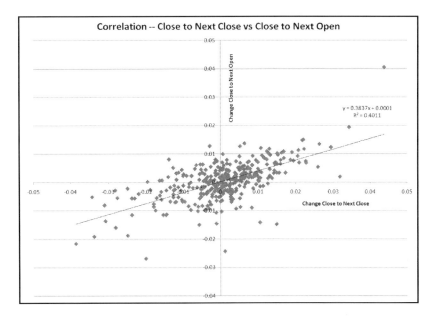

FIGURE 8.50

Figure 8.51 shows the correlation between price changes corresponding to trades held between points XZ and YZ – today's close to tomorrow's close versus tomorrow's open to tomorrow's close.

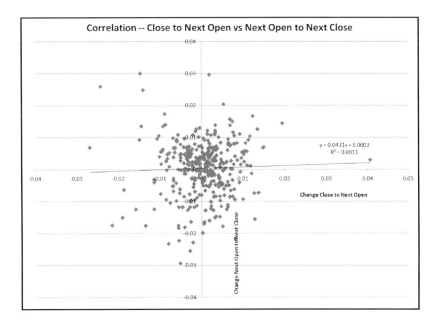

FIGURE 8.51

This chart shows that there is little correlation between the price change overnight and the subsequent price change in the day session. That is, if the futures move overnight, that does not suggest that the futures or associated equity will continue to move in the same direction.

ES AND SPY

Intra-day data was collected in 30 minute bars from 29 Jul 2009 through 3 Jan 2011, for both ES and SPY. There were a few periods, mostly half-days, when only one of the pair was being traded. Those periods were removed resulting in precisely the same bars for both series. The change from the close of one bar to the close of the next was computed for each series. Figure 8.52 shows the scatter plot and illustrates the very close correlation between the two series. The agreement is so close that the ES data used in the previous figures could be replaced with SPY data without altering the figures or the conclusions.

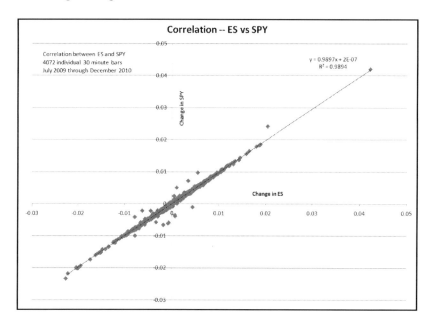

FIGURE 8.52

OTHER ETFs

Computation of the overnight and next day follow-through was performed for sixteen highly liquid ETFs, using data from 10 Mar 1999 through 22 Dec 2010 for all of them. In every case the equity curves were as smooth as those shown in figure 8.48 above. Figure 8.53 shows the series for SPY.

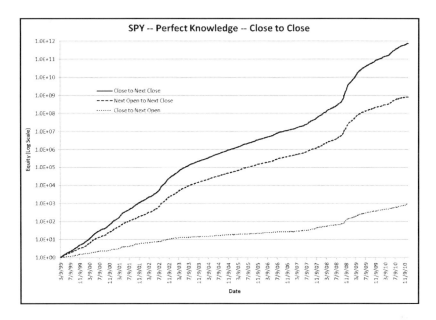

FIGURE 8.53

For the ETFs studied, the percentage of the total Close to Next Close change that happened overnight ranged from 20% to 48%, and averaged about 29%, as shown in figure 8.54. The remainder of the gain took place in the regular day session.

	Percent Change Overnight	Percent Change Day
DIA	24%	76%
EEM	42%	58%
GLD	48%	52%
IWM	20%	80%
QQQQ	21%	78%
SPY	25%	75%
TLT	42%	57%
XLB	26%	74%
XLE	24%	76%
XLF	26%	73%
XLI	28%	71%
XLK	29%	71%
XLP	27%	73%
XLU	22%	78%
XLV	25%	75%
XLY	28%	72%

FIGURE 8.54

OPEN TO OPEN

Some traders will compute signals for action at the Open. The same analysis shows that if there is an accurate Open to Next Open signal, both the day session and following overnight session will be profitable. Figure 8.55 shows the graph for SPY.

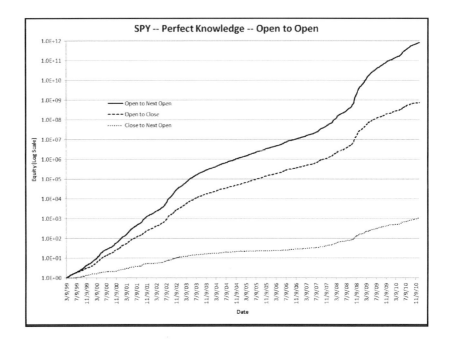

FIGURE 8.55

Figure 8.56 shows the percentage of the total Open to Open change that took place during the day session and in the following overnight session. For the ETFs studied, there is an average of about 30% follow-through overnight, with a range of 20% to 47%.

	Percent Change Day	Percent Change Overnight
DIA	75%	25%
EEM	61%	39%
GLD	53%	47%
IWM	80%	20%
QQQQ	76%	24%
SPY	75%	25%
TLT	59%	40%
XLB	75%	25%
XLE	76%	24%
XLF	72%	28%
XLI	68%	32%
XLK	69%	31%
XLP	71%	29%
XLU	74%	25%
XLV	70%	30%
XLY	71%	29%

FIGURE 8.56

CONCLUSION

If you have a system that gives Close-to-Close signals at the close of regular hours trading, there is a substantial benefit from taking the position at the close of the day that generated the signal, rather than waiting until the next day's open.

If you have a system that gives Open-to-Open signals for execution at the open of regular hours, most of the gain will come from the day session. On average, there will be follow-through and the night session will add to the gains of the day session.

Chapter 9

Tradables

What are the best issues to trade? Should I use leveraged ETFs?

MAJOR CONSIDERATIONS

As I read accounts of the problems traders and fund managers have had, they come down to three major concerns – liquidity, correlation, and leverage. There are several excellent books describing accounts of troubles in the financial industry listed in the reference section in the appendix.

When everything is right with the world, holding illiquid issues gives added return; having a portfolio consisting of several issues gives diversification; and using leverage increases return. When trouble arises, each causes its own problem and together they compound the difficulty. I recognize that it will be inconvenient, difficult, or impossible for many fund managers to follow my recommendations because of legal restrictions or client relations. Individual traders have more flexibility.

LIQUIDITY

I recommend that it should be possible to exit from any position at any time -- ideally in any minute of any day. Only tradable issues that can be purchased or, more importantly, sold through the trading day will be analyzed.

CORRELATION

The Capital Asset Pricing Model, together with the Efficient Market Hypothesis, suggest that portfolios consisting of multiple issues provide valuable diversification. During recent periods of market crisis, diversification has failed to provide the safety that was expected.

LEVERAGE

In later portions of this book we will examine position sizing techniques, including fixed fraction, that can be applied to tradable issues. In this section we will examine leveraged exchange traded funds where the leverage is built in to the fund. Futures contracts and options can also be used to increase leverage.

EXCHANGE TRADED FUNDS, ETFs

I find exchange traded funds, ETFs, attractive for several reasons:

- ETFs can satisfy almost any requirement for sector representation.

- ETFs trade through the day, compared with single trading opportunity and single price point for traditional mutual funds.

- ETFs give the opportunity to hold positions that are either positively or negatively correlated with the sector or broad market category they track.

- For some sectors and markets, leveraged ETFs provide convenient methods for increasing leverage in the trading account.

- ETFs appear to be ordinary securities in that they can be purchased in most accounts even though they may represent short and / or leveraged positions in equities, indexes, currencies, or commodities.

LIQUIDITY

Liquidity is defined as daily share volume times daily share price. The six month period from 8/1/2010 through 1/31/2011, using data supplied by Norgate Premium Data, was analyzed.

Figure 9.1 lists the number of stocks and ETFs that have average liquidity at various levels.

Daily liquidity at least	All Issues	ETFs
$1,000,000,000	20	7
$500,000,000	63	23
$100,000,000	404	65
$50,000,000	735	106
$10,000,000	1719	213
Total Issues	11841	976

FIGURE 9.1

Figure 9.2 lists the 100 most liquid ETF and common stock issues traded on exchanges in the United States.

Ticker	Close	Volume	Liquidity	Ticker	Close	Volume	Liquidity
SPY	130.74	166,962,208	20,225,955,840	JPM	45.93	28,255,500	1,463,811,328
AAPL	345.03	15,236,900	5,147,212,800	XOM	83.91	40,829,600	1,434,179,072
IWM	79.75	57,786,700	3,678,497,536	CSCO	21.47	40,519,800	1,374,107,264
QQQQ	57.05	76,952,896	3,385,684,992	LVS	49.09	31,054,200	1,309,541,888
EEM	46.92	105,876,000	2,624,127,232	INTC	21.48	60,971,000	1,263,208,832
BAC	14.31	211,978,400	2,477,014,784	F	15.89	178,894,304	1,171,310,080
C	4.90	392,371,200	2,200,509,440	XLF	16.74	63,879,700	1,154,954,240
GLD	130.80	15,363,700	1,987,301,888	EWZ	74.68	13,373,800	1,113,780,992
GOOG	611.04	2,745,300	1,569,991,296	FCX	57.04	48,860,200	1,026,672,384
MSFT	27.99	62,810,700	1,562,644,608	GE	20.80	68,304,304	1,016,602,560

Ticker	Close	Volume	Liquidity	Ticker	Close	Volume	Liquidity
EFA	60.85	25,762,500	993,284,480	XLE	74.34	20,427,600	852,964,416
WFC	33.44	31,359,000	985,566,912	RIMM	60.40	11,026,700	818,975,936
HPQ	46.52	14,488,500	980,480,192	SDS	21.94	37,361,600	800,652,928
TLT	90.45	11,508,400	966,475,648	PFE	19.22	134,506,208	793,979,840
BIDU	118.73	22,003,600	963,825,856	FAS	31.60	30,234,200	766,117,248
NFLX	212.90	4,094,400	960,184,960	IBM	163.56	5,831,300	759,828,736
GS	165.33	4,138,400	923,155,584	DIA	120.09	7,626,900	755,024,960
AMZN	172.11	5,085,900	922,818,112	FXI	42.84	18,007,400	731,786,944
ORCL	33.24	32,573,500	912,286,592	QCOM	55.08	17,000,000	730,694,336
POT	182.77	3,802,700	880,493,248	T	27.87	26,390,600	716,733,760

Ticker	Close	Volume	Liquidity	Ticker	Close	Volume	Liquidity
CVX	96.22	9,948,200	699,504,064	SSO	51.78	12,857,900	572,622,848
VWO	47.49	24,518,200	697,949,760	KO	63.05	8,014,000	560,161,984
PG	62.92	14,623,900	673,015,424	SLV	27.87	24,054,300	558,181,056
PBR	37.73	24,263,600	664,580,352	X	59.77	9,510,400	554,754,304
JNJ	60.63	14,780,500	656,963,776	CAT	98.01	7,553,400	549,285,056
SLB	89.64	10,033,100	618,715,648	GDX	55.44	11,419,600	542,552,448
WMT	56.33	12,851,600	610,858,944	OIH	154.71	5,683,800	529,897,120
VALE	35.62	19,074,200	610,519,104	IYR	58.23	10,015,600	523,048,256
VZ	36.27	16,351,300	603,176,832	COP	71.71	11,622,000	521,618,208
TNA	75.76	9,788,800	577,067,264	TZA	14.45	36,623,100	518,204,640

Ticker	Close	Volume	Liquidity	Ticker	Close	Volume	Liquidity
MRK	34.00	21,406,500	512,639,264	RIG	81.02	5,359,000	442,411,616
MCD	73.47	8,468,900	506,503,168	BP	47.98	20,934,400	440,513,376
MDY	170.43	3,876,900	502,245,952	XLI	36.75	13,750,600	433,449,664
EMC	25.24	23,851,700	497,737,312	XRT	47.06	11,525,000	429,098,496
HAL	45.51	15,635,600	496,960,640	ABX	48.26	12,297,500	420,021,696
TBT	39.41	17,315,200	487,219,232	PCLN	437.93	1,033,100	419,972,384
VXX	30.48	15,538,400	470,892,128	SNDK	46.49	12,848,400	419,578,496
V	70.70	6,362,200	464,361,504	PEP	65.05	7,138,100	398,674,528
FAZ	8.10	31,778,400	455,834,560	ABT	45.23	13,307,000	397,599,488
AXP	43.60	11,408,800	447,613,984	NEM	56.51	6,310,600	397,530,240

Ticker	Close	Volume	Liquidity	Ticker	Close	Volume	Liquidity
PM	57.72	6,181,300	390,590,368	MOS	83.88	7,021,100	368,686,368
MON	76.05	5,388,900	387,656,352	AA	17.32	55,766,600	366,142,912
CMCSA	23.40	15,260,200	386,758,368	QLD	89.06	4,329,100	357,983,904
OXY	98.93	6,718,400	384,786,976	IVV	131.24	3,190,700	357,246,080
CRM	131.64	2,178,000	383,428,416	BA	70.29	4,780,400	355,124,320
HD	36.99	9,623,200	378,563,232	APA	118.98	8,829,300	349,327,008
EBAY	31.64	14,481,400	378,542,912	TXN	35.00	11,582,700	347,546,464
MGM	15.09	19,639,800	371,684,064	GILD	38.50	8,828,900	346,052,800
MS	29.92	11,630,100	370,149,472	MET	46.96	5,964,500	331,077,728
DIS	39.88	9,283,000	369,536,064	XLB	39.47	16,032,100	330,931,456

FIGURE 9.2

Figure 9.3 lists the 80 most liquid ETFs.

Ticker	Close	Volume	Liquidity	Ticker	Close	Volume	Liquidity
SPY	131.15	134,584,896	20,160,700,416	SDS	21.79	17,082,600	789,964,416
IWM	79.87	39,532,700	3,681,240,064	FAS	31.12	16,102,800	759,351,936
QQQQ	57.38	47,585,000	3,392,535,808	DIA	120.69	5,191,300	754,445,056
EEM	46.50	76,698,096	2,643,584,768	FXI	42.87	10,429,400	724,314,240
GLD	131.66	15,214,300	2,006,472,192	VWO	47.06	11,580,900	702,678,464
XLF	16.61	62,246,300	1,153,713,536	TNA	76.19	6,610,200	577,672,384
EWZ	72.05	16,995,200	1,118,497,920	SSO	52.10	10,048,900	572,530,176
EFA	60.79	12,648,400	993,143,040	SLV	28.40	20,918,400	569,855,936
TLT	88.81	17,172,200	986,769,344	GDX	56.11	8,586,900	545,531,200
XLE	74.13	13,278,600	859,549,056	OIH	155.49	4,229,000	532,400,384

Ticker	Close	Volume	Liquidity	Ticker	Close	Volume	Liquidity
IYR	57.86	7,869,000	519,828,128	XLB	39.58	8,104,700	333,291,712
TZA	14.34	26,160,000	515,331,328	USO	37.34	17,271,500	328,487,360
MDY	171.61	2,139,900	507,046,016	SMH	35.81	7,554,600	288,113,248
TBT	40.89	21,876,300	499,754,240	XLK	26.69	7,567,600	241,796,736
VXX	29.21	17,896,500	472,201,600	XLY	38.21	4,876,000	230,354,064
FAZ	8.21	17,735,300	447,038,240	EWJ	11.35	46,256,400	212,768,928
XRT	48.11	14,047,800	434,336,512	UYG	71.02	1,839,200	209,336,880
XLI	36.78	8,689,400	432,161,952	XME	70.02	5,755,700	206,638,752
QLD	90.12	3,240,900	358,374,880	FXE	135.36	1,065,100	194,670,672
IVV	131.63	2,183,100	357,723,840	XLV	32.33	4,380,100	193,531,632

Ticker	Close	Volume	Liquidity	Ticker	Close	Volume	Liquidity
XLU	31.80	4,927,200	186,815,744	UNG	5.86	12,394,200	144,785,728
XLP	29.30	4,630,900	172,363,008	IWF	59.97	2,090,500	144,748,384
UPRO	231.27	531,300	170,046,480	RTH	106.86	419,700	138,666,016
QID	10.40	12,609,900	168,756,400	KBE	26.91	2,601,500	134,774,752
EWY	63.14	2,466,400	158,352,320	SH	41.97	1,452,600	132,705,624
EWT	16.01	6,422,900	156,923,152	IWO	89.58	1,526,200	130,678,488
SPXU	17.01	4,135,400	154,686,352	LQD	107.11	1,367,700	130,358,008
XOP	57.51	4,021,900	153,486,720	IWD	67.45	1,333,300	115,880,688
VTI	67.61	1,344,000	146,303,184	EWH	19.60	2,803,300	113,350,896
EWW	62.04	4,350,000	145,717,696	BGU	80.53	835,600	108,784,560

Ticker	Close	Volume	Liquidity	Ticker	Close	Volume	Liquidity
AGQ	138.20	957,600	105,719,264	EWA	25.86	3,328,500	91,377,344
IWN	72.29	1,766,700	105,564,032	ILF	51.43	1,861,700	90,919,944
TWM	11.90	6,345,100	105,510,792	AGG	104.26	1,116,600	90,664,504
VNQ	57.05	1,842,700	103,346,608	HYG	91.87	1,667,600	88,336,080
ERX	74.37	1,825,500	102,434,224	SHY	83.73	612,300	88,032,752
JNK	40.54	3,790,700	98,883,984	TIP	105.83	1,221,500	87,420,496
UUP	22.43	1,840,800	94,760,272	GDXJ	37.52	2,911,600	87,327,312
IEF	91.81	1,523,900	93,617,072	UWM	44.36	1,317,200	83,513,624
RSX	40.12	3,871,200	93,290,040	IJH	94.38	685,800	82,883,968
SKF	14.47	2,385,400	91,723,024	XHB	17.74	3,764,600	82,287,568

FIGURE 9.3

In keeping with my suggestion to "model something easy, trade something profitable", ETFs are good candidates to model.

The components of an ETF, particularly narrowly focused index ETFs, tend to have the same reaction to fundamentals, so their prices behave similarly. Having several issues combined allows the random changes in the price among the issues to cancel each other out – in keeping with the central limit theorem. The resulting price series is smoother than the prices of the individual components, and easier to model.

The internal structure obtained from analysis of the components also provides a valuable indicator for price movement in the ETF itself – similar to an advance-decline line for an exchange. Given a profitable trading system where the signals are derived from the ETF, there might be better issues to trade. Depending on your criteria, better might mean more profitable, more liquid, lower drawdown, higher beta.

There are two ways to select surrogates.

- One is correlation. Using your trading system development platform, set one price series to the ETF you have modeled. Have the development platform cycle through all the issues you think might be reasonable surrogates, calculate the correlation between each and the ETF, sort the results, and display a list. Correlation identifies the precision of the agreement in price movements, but not the magnitude.

- The second method also uses the trading system development platform. Using the price series of the ETF, generate perfect buy, sell, short, and cover signals. Cycle through all of the issues you think might make reasonable surrogates making the trades in the individual issues based on the signals from the ETF. The result will be a trading system report for each issue. Use an objective function or metric of your choice, such as compound annual rate of return (CAR), CAR / MDD, or expectancy, to rank them.

My trading system development platform of choice is AmiBroker. The AmiBroker code for these two programs is provided in the Appendix.

SPY was used to generate perfect signals for the period 1/1/2007 through 1/1/2011. Whenever SPY would be up the next week, take a long position in the surrogate; whenever SPY would be down, take a short position in the surrogate. The entire list of 1063 ETFs were tested individually. Using net profit as the metric, 300 of the ETFs produced higher profit over four years than SPY itself. Many of these have very low volume, so the test was rerun using the 105 ETFs that have at least $50,000,000 average liquidity over the past six months. 54 of the 105 were more profitable than SPY.

Figure 9.4 lists some surrogates for each of several ETFs. Do not get excited by the astronomical rates of return – they are completely un-realistic. But that is not the purpose of this study. Rather, it is to iden-tify issues that can be traded profitably when signals are generated by some ETF. The identification of the surrogates was done by comparing compound annual rate of return for each alternative. CAR may not be the metric you would choose. While CAR is high, drawdown is also high in some cases, so do your own analysis before deciding whether to trade any of the surrogates in place of the ETF used to generate the signal. For each ETF tested as the signal generator, there are five sur-rogates listed as the most profitable ETFs to trade in the same direction, five ETFs to trade opposite, five common stocks to trade in the same di-rection, and five common stocks to trade opposite. To trade in the same direction means to take a long position in the surrogate when the ETF generating the signal is long; to trade in the opposite direction means to take a long position in the surrogate when the ETF generating the signal is short. Note that although five places were reserved for stocks to buy when the ETF is short, none were profitable.

SPY	220	QQQQ	245	IWM	341	MDY	289
Positive ETF							
UYG	1969	UYG	1091	UYG	1682	UYG	1528
UWM	1166	UWM	1081	UWM	1540	UWM	1399
FAS	990	QLD	958	TNA	963	TNA	934
DIG	818	TNA	766	FAS	924	FAS	911
QLD	807	SSO	634	QLD	681	DIG	900
Inverse ETF							
SKF	1879	SRS	1182	SRS	2024	SKF	1659
SRS	1348	SKF	1125	SKF	1859	SRS	1528
TWM	1113	TWM	1054	TWM	1468	TWM	1325
FAZ	831	QID	988	FAZ	925	TZA	860
QID	790	TZA	711	TZA	920	FAZ	843
Positive Stock							
LVS	1351	LVS	1419	LVS	1229	LVS	1402
C	1149	MGM	813	MGM	1202	MGM	1149
MGM	918	F	683	C	929	X	917
BAC	855	SNDK	655	BAC	709	AA	892
AA	779	AA	628	X	655	C	875
Negative Stock							
None		None		None		None	

FIGURE 9.4

EEM	445	TLT	117	UUP	64	DBC	274
UYG	1270	SKF	281	DUG	206	DIG	626
UWM	948	TWM	267	FAZ	188	UCO	606
EDC	901	EDZ	234	TZA	159	USO	486
FAS	829	DUG	228	EDZ	155	ERX	451
DIG	783	FAZ	227	BGZ	134	XME	373
SKF	1295	UYG	287	ERX	234	DUG	533
SRS	1182	UWM	264	GDX	222	EDZ	350
TWM	912	FAS	257	DIG	203	TZA	257
FAZ	846	EDC	245	EDC	196	FAZ	221
TZA	708	DIG	242	FAS	196	BGZ	201
LVS	1211	None		None		FCX	508
MGM	934					PBR	495
VALE	823					MOS	431
FCX	807					X	337
C	803					APA	308
None		LVS	337	ABX	235	None	
		MGM	309	PBR	222		
		FCX	308	FCX	203		
		MOS	219	HAL	172		
		VALE	200	VALE	172		

FIGURE 9.4 CON'T

Figure 9.5 shows a number of asset classes, along with pairs of ETFs that can be used to take positions equivalent to being long and short the asset class.

Large Cap	Large Cap	Small Cap	Technology	Financial	Emerging
SPY/SH	DIA/DOG	IWM	QQQQ, XLK	XLF	EEM
SSO/SDS	DDM/DXD	UWM/TWM	QLD/QID	UYG/SKF	EDC/EDZ
BGU/BGZ		TNA/TZA		FAS/FAZ	
		BGU/BGZ			
Bond	Dollar	Real Estate	Commodity	Oil & Gas	Gold
TLT	UUP	IYR	DBC, XLE, XLB	XLE	GLD
TLT/TBT	UUP/UDN	URE/SRS	DIG/DUG	DIG/DUG	DGP/DZZ

FIGURE 9.5

All of the pairs listed have one issue that has a positive beta and will rise when the base ETF rises and one issue that has a negative beta and will rise when the base ETF falls. There are several advantages to using a pair of ETFs to trade a model of an ETF.

- Psychologically, it might be easier to exit a long position when a sell signal is generated if there is another ETF that can be used to take the trade. This is rather than continuing to hold the long position and waiting for the next buy signal.

- You can take advantage of the negative beta to profit when the ETF issues a signal to go short and falls in price. This is in comparison with going to cash or making a short sale.

- Taking both long and short positions gives twice the number of trades compared to taking long positions only. Equity growth depends on frequent compounding. Provided both the long trades and short trades are profitable, taking even marginally profitable short trades will improve the overall performance of the system.

Some of the pairs have a beta of 1.0 – such as SPY and SH. A one percent rise change in the base ETF results in an approximately one percent change in the ETF being traded. The change is approximate because the actual result may not be exactly the same as the designed beta, resulting in a tracking error.

Some of the pairs have higher betas. Using XLF as the base index, the beta of UYG is +2.0, the beta of SKF is -2.0, the beta of FAS is 3.0, and the beta of FAZ is -3.0. Assume a trading system using the base index results in a 20 percent annual rate of return. The terminal wealth after one year will be 1.20. When trades are taken using ETFs that have a beta other than 1.0, the terminal wealth will be 1.20 raised to the power of the beta. Using UYG and SKF, terminal wealth will be 1.44; using FAS and FAZ, terminal wealth will be 1.72.

UYG, SKF, FAS, and FAZ were all designed to track the financial sector. Figures 7.6, 7.7, 7.8, and 7.9 show the scatter diagrams for each of these ETFs. For each chart, daily changes in XLF are plotted along with daily changes for the ETF. A linear regression trendline has been fitted to the data points and the coefficient of determination, r-squared, computed. Note the coefficient of the "x" term in each regression equation. On figure 9.6, that coefficient is 1.7709. If UYG truly had a beta of 2.0, then that coefficient would be 2.0. The difference is the tracking error.

But the accuracy may be more important that the tracking. The correlation between the changes in XLF and UYG is 0.9918 and r-squared is 0.9836. Leverage decreases when tracking fails to meet the design goals. Drawdown increases when correlation drops. As you can see, correlation itself indicates only accuracy, and tells nothing about leverage.

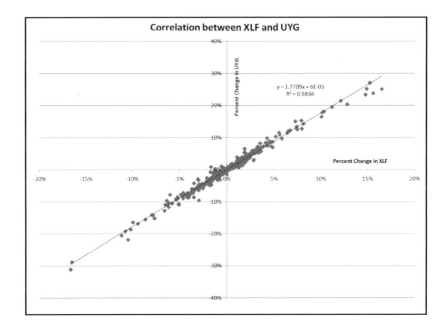

FIGURE 9.6

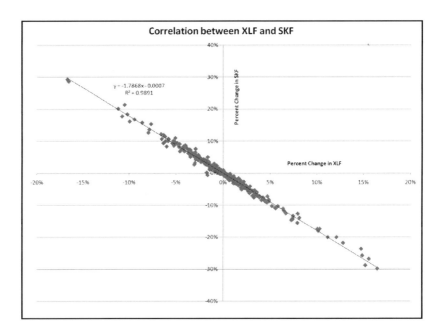

FIGURE 9.7

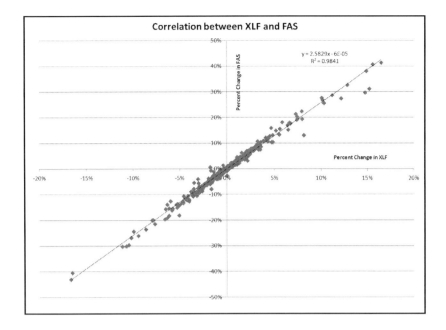

FIGURE 9.8

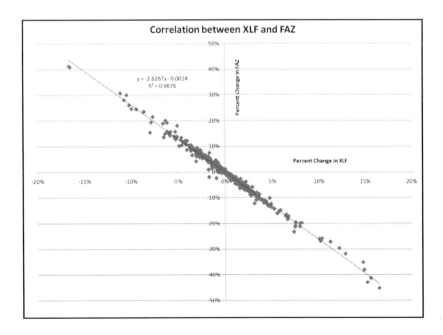

FIGURE 9.9

Leveraged ETFs, those that have beta higher than 1.0, are designed for holding periods of one day. In order to achieve the higher beta, they hold futures, options, and / or swaps. They are rebalanced daily and, over longer holding periods, are wasting assets. 3X is probably the highest leverage ETF that will be issued, and there is even a risk that a +3 beta ETF will be completely wiped out by a one day fall of more than 33.3%, or a -3 beta by a one day rise of more than 33.3%.

Results obtained when using leveraged ETFs can, and probably will, differ from those expected by assuming the leverage described in the ETF's prospectus. The difference could be tracking error, or wasting due to rebalancing, or both. Study your trading system carefully before using leveraged ETFs.

A series of simulations was run, each four years long, each based on a 60% correct prediction of XLF. The simulations differed in the beta used and the fraction of the trading account used to take each position. Beta of 1.0 traded XLF long and XLF short; beta of 2.0 traded UYG long and SKF short; beta of 3.0 traded FAS long and FAZ short.

Figure 9.10 shows the table of results.

		60% correct predictions for XLF				The upper value in each cell is TW5 / DD95.				
		Beta 1: XLF long / XLF short				The lower value is DD95.				
		Beta 2: UYG Long / SKF short				TW5 is the CAR for four years.				
		Beta 3: FAS long / FAZ short				DD95 is the maximum percent drawdown.				
		fraction used to trade									
		0.10	0.20	0.30	0.40	0.50	0.60	0.70	0.80	0.90	1.00
	1	0.789	0.813	0.875	0.921	0.997	0.982	1.015	0.989	1.027	0.993
Beta		0.080	0.157	0.220	0.286	0.338	0.397	0.453	0.518	0.551	0.596
	2	0.739	0.723	0.830	0.857	0.944	0.972	1.026	1.045	1.064	0.994
		0.140	0.267	0.371	0.478	0.562	0.620	0.689	0.764	0.795	0.831
	3	0.756	0.814	0.862	0.849	0.866	0.797	0.802	0.762	0.673	0.572
		0.205	0.370	0.513	0.630	0.728	0.814	0.868	0.908	0.937	0.957

FIGURE 9.10

The fraction used for each trade was varied from 0.1 to 1.0, the beta was varied from 1 to 3. Each cell contains two numbers. The upper number is the value of TW5 / DD95, the objective function described in Chapter 7. TW5 is the Terminal Wealth for the 5th percentile of the distribution – 95 percent of all four year periods, terminal wealth will be at least that great. TW5 is converted to a compound annual rate of return, CAR. DD95 is the drawdown at the 95th percentile of the distribution – 95 percent of all four year periods, drawdown will be no worse than that. DD95 is a percentage – the percent of the drawdown from the maximum equity.

REALITY SETS IN

Should this "system" be traded using a beta of 1, 2, or 3? XLF has high volatility and high liquidity itself, being number 6 in the liquidity list, and has +/- 2 and +/- 3 beta ETFs that are all in the top 80 of liquidity themselves. The question comes down to your risk tolerance, your return goals, and your ability to decide whether the system is working or broken. Here are some of the alternatives.

CONSERVATIVE – **XLF** ALONE WITH LOW DRAWDOWN

The second entry in the top row of figure 9.10 shows the results for trading XLF long / XLF short using 20% of the account for each position. Figure 9.11 shows the distribution of terminal equity.

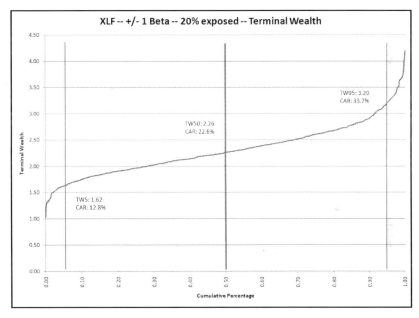

FIGURE 9.11

TW5 is 1.62, corresponding to a compound annual rate of return of 12.8%. TW95 is 3.20, corresponding to CAR of 33.7%. In 90 percent of four year periods, CAR is expected to be between 12.8% and 33.7%. Intra-trade drawdown is about 0.7% greater than closed trade drawdown.

Figure 9.12 shows the distribution of drawdown.

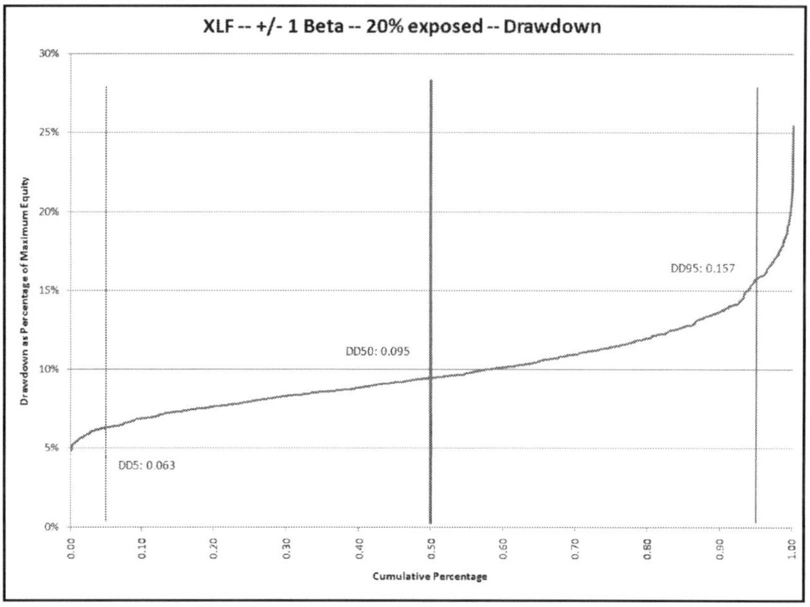

FIGURE 9.12

DD5 is 0.063, suggesting that maximum drawdown will be at least 6.3% at some point in 19 of 20 four year periods. DD95 is 0.157, suggesting that drawdown will be less than 15.7% in 19 of 20 periods. Referring back to figure 9.10, the lower number in the cell is 0.157 – DD95. The upper number in the cell is 0.813 – the ratio of TW5 to DD95 – the ratio of 12.8% to 15.7%. In 18 of 20 four year periods, provided the system continues to perform as it did when the data for the simulation was being developed, the ratio of CAR to MaxDD will be 0.813 or greater.

A trader with a $100,000 trading account who took a position either long XLF or short XLF with 20% of the current balance of the account would expect, on average, to see that account grow to between $162,000 and $320,000 in four years, and have a drawdown between 6.3% and 15.7% along the way. Possibly, but with low probability, final equity could be lower or higher, and drawdown could be lower or greater.

COMPARE BETAS

The sixth entry in the top row of figure 9.10 shows the result when the system is traded at a beta of +/-1, with 60% of the account used for each position. The maximum drawdown is 0.397 – that is, 39.7%, which is close to the 40% tolerance we will use for examples. Several simulations were run using the ETFs with betas of +/-2 and searching for the fraction that gave a similar DD95 value. The fraction is 0.32 and DD95 is 0.393. (If there was no tracking error, and the true beta of UYG and SKF was 2.0, the fraction would be 0.30.) Similarly, using 0.22 of the account (which would be 0.20 if the betas were truly 3.0) and the ETFs with betas of +/-3 gives a DD95 of 0.397. Three different trading methods result in the same DD95. Figure 9.13 compares the final equity. They are very similar.

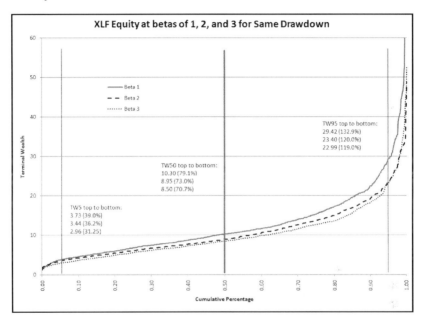

FIGURE 9.13

Figure 9.14 compares the drawdowns. For all three, DD95 is about 40%, DD50 is about 26%, DD5 is about 18%. Since all three methods have settings which result in similar values of DD95, the three are equivalent.

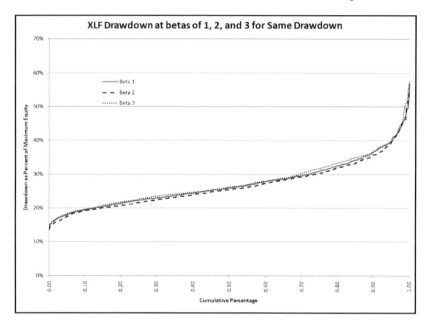

FIGURE 9.14

SWINGING FOR THE FENCE

The rightmost cell in the top row of figure 9.10 gives the results of using beta of +/-1 and using all available funds for each position. DD95 is about 60%. Since the TW5DD95 ratio is about 1.0, TW5 must be about 60% CAR. That is certainly an outstanding return, and it is the 5th percentile level so most returns would be higher. To increase the return beyond this, additional leverage is required. Using UYG and SKF with the beta of +/-2, TW5 rises to a CAR of about 83%. Using FAS and FAZ with the beta of +/-3, the highest TW5 occurs when 70% of available funds are used for each position. The highest TW50 occurs when all funds are used, but at these levels, drawdowns are in the 95% range and the system is not tradable.

Figure 9.15 shows the extremely high growth achieved by using FAS and FAZ using 90% of available funds for each trade. TW50 is 548. $100,000 becomes $54,800,000 in four years. The spread between TW5 and TW95 is very wide, from 9 to 38,188.

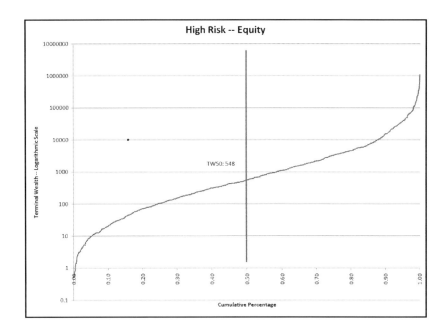

FIGURE 9.15

Figure 9.16 shows the distribution of the drawdowns.

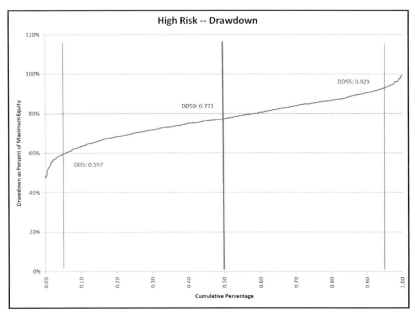

FIGURE 9.16

Figure 9.17 shows the equity curve of a single run over the course of 1008 days, one trade per day.

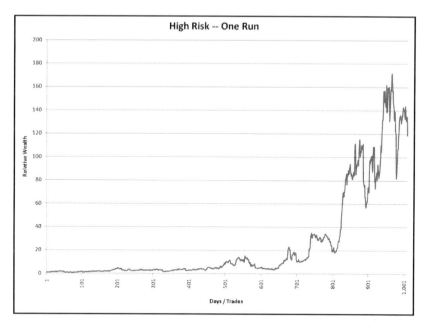

FIGURE 9.17

Based on the distribution of drawdowns, they are expected to be 60 to 90 percent. Figure 9.18 shows this specific set.

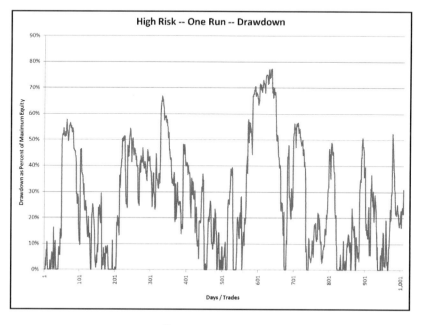

FIGURE 9.18

I can hear your comments. "To get this kind of equity growth, I'll put up with the drawdowns."

The problem isn't that the system can't overcome the drawdowns. The problem is knowing whether the system will continue to work as well in the future as it did in the past. How do we know it will continue to be 60% accurate? If there was a guarantee of the continued accuracy, there would be no problem. The drawdown limit we planned to observe was 40 percent. This system spends over 30 percent of its time in a drawdown of at least 40 percent, with spikes to the high 70s.

What is needed is some way to determine, based on the very recent performance, whether the system is working or broken. If it is working, we can hang on; if it is broken, we need to stop trading it. That is the focus of Chapter 11.

PORTFOLIOS

Traditional wisdom suggests creating a portfolio with several uncorrelated issues. Recently, the expected safety of uncorrelated issues has broken down. In recent periods of crisis when it is necessary to raise cash, reduce leverage, and sell poorly performing issues, those techniques have failed. There are several excellent books listed in the reference section of the Appendix detailing the problems. Without holding actual inverse issues, such as short positions, there are very few anti-correlated issues available. What had been uncorrelated and reasonably liquid in the best of times, becomes highly correlated and illiquid in the worst of times. People sell what they can, not necessarily what they prefer to sell.

If a manager wants to form a portfolio, I recommend not using the traditional approach.

Instead, pick one or more indexes or ETFs in asset classes where exposure is desired. Choose indexes that have ETFs with both positive and negative betas that track them closely. Figure 9.5 lists twelve good choices. For each index, develop a trading system for strictly that index that takes either long or short positions using ETFs. For example, to hold a position in real estate, model IYR, then trade URE and SRS. To hold a position in emerging markets, model EEM, then trade EDC and EDZ. To hold a position in financials, model XLF, then trade FAS and FAZ.

The index being modeled does not have to be highly liquid or even traded. Depending on the indicators used to generate the signals, it could be a computed index or even be a traditional mutual fund. It is the ETFs that are used to take the positions that must be highly liquid.

SUMMARY

- Build the trading system using whatever price series makes the design, testing, and validation of the system easy.
- Take positions either in the series used in the system, or in some issue closely related to it.
- Take positions only in highly liquid issues. You should be able to exit your positions on any given day; preferably in any given minute.
- Consider using ETFs to take both long and short positions.
- Leveraged ETFs might not track as well as planned by their creators, but their correlation with their underlying is generally excellent.
- There is little difference in the risk and reward profiles of using leverage to take positions in the underlying compared with using leverage through high beta funds.
- Develop several good systems, each for highly liquid issues, rather than create a portfolio.

Chapter 10

Position Sizing

Paul Tudor Jones, quoted in Jack Schwager's Market Wizards:

> I'm always thinking about losing money as opposed to making money. Don't focus on making money, focus on protecting what you have.

The goal of trading is to increase the balance of a trading account as much as possible without going bankrupt in the process.

The trading system you have developed gives buy, sell, short, and cover signals. It tells you when to buy and at what price. The trading system defines the profit potential and loss profile of the individual trades. Position sizing tells you how many to buy or short – how many contracts, how many dollars worth of shares, how many dollars worth of options.

Position sizing gives you the techniques for reaching your retirement goals – your retire absorbing boundary. Monte Carlo simulation gives you tools to measure the risk of losing a significant portion of your money.

Kelly Formula

Like several other interesting stories and developments, this one begins at the Bell Telephone Laboratories. In the early 1950s, John Kelly was working with Claude Shannon on problems related to transfer of information over noisy lines. He made use of an analogy that a bettor, receiving tips that were less than 100 percent correct, could maximize his wealth by making each bet in accordance with the probability that the tips were correct. Kelly published his research in the Bell System Technical Journal in July, 1956. The original title of the paper was to be "Information Theory and Gambling," but he changed it to "A New Interpretation of Information Rate" at the request of laboratory executives.

Edward Thorp described use of the Kelly formula in his famous book, *Beat the Dealer*, in 1962. Writing in "The Kelly Criterion in Blackjack, Sports Betting, and the Stock Market," a paper he presented at the 10th International Conference on Gambling and Risk Taking, Montreal, 1997, Dr. Thorp clearly identifies the key issue in achieving trading success.

> The central problem for gamblers is to find positive expectation bets. But the gambler also needs to know how to manage his money, i.e. how much to bet. In the stock market (more inclusively, the securities markets) the problem is similar but more

complex. The gambler, who is now an investor, looks for excess risk adjusted return. In both these settings, we explore the use of the Kelly criterion, which is to maximize the expected value of the logarithm of wealth (maximize expected logarithmic utility).

The criterion is known to economists and financial theorists by names such as the geometric mean maximizing portfolio strategy, maximizing logarithmic utility, the growth-optimal strategy, the capital growth criterion, etc.

In its simplest form, the Kelly formula is applied to a betting situation where the amount won for a winning bet is equal to the amount lost for a losing bet. The variable is the percentage of bets that are won.

If p is the probability of a winning bet, then the probability of a losing bet, q, must be 1-p. Beginning with Kelly, f has been used to represent the fraction of the trading or betting account to be placed on each bet. The Kelly formula states that the value of f that maximizes the logarithm of terminal wealth is:

$$f = p - q$$

The example often used is a gambling game where a toss of a ten-sided die wins whenever any number from 1 through 6 occurs and loses whenever 7 through 10 occurs. p is 0.60, q is 0.40, resulting in f being 0.20. That is, bet one-fifth of the funds on every throw.

Figure 10.1 shows the probability density function (or probability mass function) for this distribution of games. These conditions could also arise in a trading system. For example, an options buyer might pay $1.00 for an option with the plan to sell it when it doubles to $2.00. If his profit target is reached, his gain is $1.00. If it expires worthless, his loss is $1.00. If his predictions are 60 percent accurate, then his results are the same as those of the dice game.

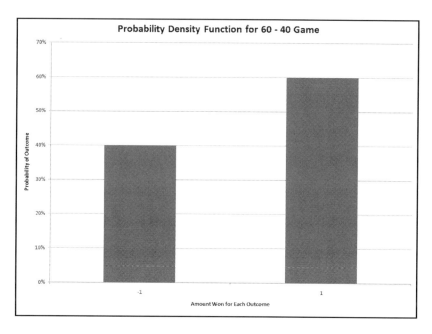

FIGURE 10.1

When f is set to the optimum value according to the Kelly formula, 0.20 or 20%, equity changes by a factor of 1.20 with each win and changes by a factor of 0.80 with each loss. On average, for a series of 10 plays, there will be 6 wins and 4 losses. Final equity or terminal wealth, TW, is the final balance of the account in monetary units. Terminal wealth relative, TWR, is the final balance in relation to the initial balance. TWR will be:

$$TWR = (1.20) \wedge 6 * (0.80) \wedge 4 = 2.986 * 0.410 = 1.224.$$

The average geometric return, G (in keeping with the notation of Thorp, Kelly, and Vince), per play necessary to produce 1.224 in 10 plays is:

$$G = (1.224) \wedge 0.1 = 1.0204.$$

That is, equity increases by an average of 2.04 percent per play.

Playing 100 times results in a terminal wealth relative of $(1.0204) \wedge 100$ = 7.534. This is the expected value—the value at the mean of the distribution.

On average, there would be 60 wins and 40 losses in each 100 plays. The mean number of wins for a binary distribution, which this is, is $n * p$, which is 60; and the standard deviation is the square root of $n * p * q$, which is 4.90. We expect the number of wins to be within plus or minus 4.90 of 60.0 about 68 percent of the time.

One standard deviation below the mean there will be 60.0 – 4.9, or 55.1 wins; and therefore 44.9 losses. With these values, TWR is computed to be 1.027. One standard deviation above the mean there will be 64.9 wins and 35.1 losses, and TWR is computed to be 54.616.

Figure 10.2 shows the results of 5000 simulations, each of 100 plays. The agreement is very close. One standard deviation below the mean is .3413 z-score units below the mean, or TW16. At TW16, TWR is computed to be 1.027 and is 0.986 from the simulation. One standard deviation above the mean is TW84. At TW84, TWR is computed to be 54.616 and is 53.08 from the simulation. TW50, at the mean, is computed to be 7.534 and is 7.489 from the simulation.

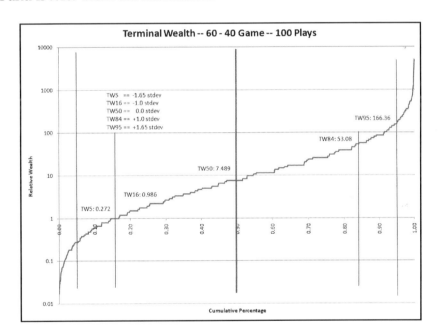

FIGURE 10.2

From this we learn:
- The simulation produces accurate results.
- If this was used as a trading system, the distribution of final equity shows that results are far too inconsistent for it to be practical.

The simulation can be used to determine the optimal value for f. Figure 10.3 shows the results of testing f values from 0.10 to 0.30. Rather than terminal equity, the geometric holding period return, G, is used as the metric. Given a final relative value for the equity after 100 plays, the geometric holding period return is that number such that, when raised to the 100 power, produces the final equity.

Comparison is made for three simulations – 100, 1000, and 5000 runs. The value of G at the midpoint of the simulation result, TW50, is recorded and plotted.

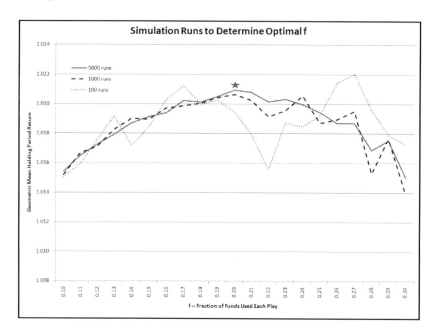

FIGURE 10.3

From this we learn:

- The curves become smoother as the number of runs increases. This illustrates the central limit theorem and the law of large numbers at work.

- From the curve for 5000 runs at each point, the maximum appears to be at an f value of 0.20, as expected (at the star).

- If an individual was testing this by throwing a ten-sided die and recording the running total of equity, he would need at least 1000 runs, each of 100 throws, 100,000 throws in total, to begin to identify the correct sweet spot on the curve.

- If an individual was trading this system, he would need 100,000 trades to accurately identify the correct sweet spot.

Figure 10.4 shows five individual series, each of 100 plays of the 60 – 40 game. An individual planning to trade a system with these characteristics must be prepared for a great deal of variation in results.

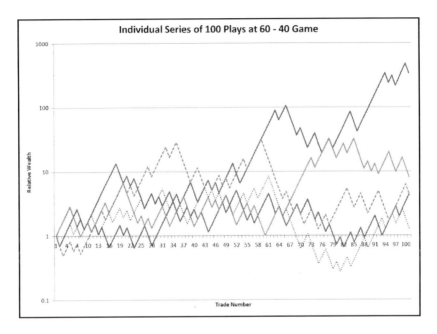

FIGURE 10.4

It is possible to expand the Kelly formula to account for a ratio of amount won per win to amount lost per loss other than one to one.

And it is possible to mathematically compute the values of critical parameters, such as the optimal fraction, for some known distributions that have well known characteristics, such as the binomial distribution.

But, rather than discuss theory in more detail, we will focus on some practical aspects of position sizing using real data and using simulations.

POSITION SIZING PRELIMINARIES

To determine the position sizing methods you will use for your own trading, you must begin with:

- A trading system with a positive expectancy.

- A trading account.
- Two monetary goals:
  - Your ruin boundary. The figure at which you will admit defeat and stop trading.
  - Your retire boundary. The figure at which you will retire and stop trading.

You will use position sizing to:
- Maximize terminal wealth relative, TWR.
- Hold maximum drawdown to a reasonable level.
- Minimize the amount of time to reach your TWR target.

The variables:
- Features of the trading system:
  - Expectancy.
  - Variance, standard deviation, and semi deviation.
  - Trading frequency.
  - Percent winners.
  - Profit factor.
  - Profit ratio.
- Initial account balance.
- Drawdown percentage acceptable.
- Wealth goal.
- Definition and size of trading unit.

The method:
- Choose the size of the position on each trade.
- Increase leverage during profitable periods and decrease leverage during losing periods.
- Monitor trading in real time to determine whether the trading system is working or broken.
- Take the system offline when it appears to be broken.

DATA

The techniques described here can be used to study the effects of position sizing techniques using any distribution of data. The data can be either closed trades or changes in equity. If closed trades, it can be in monetary units or in percentages. If changes in equity, they can be for any period of time, such as daily or weekly. Whatever the data is, it can be represented by a statistical distribution. Theoretical distributions, such as the normal distribution, can be used. Or the distribution can be hypothetical data that you make up to fit your own requirements. If the data is closed trades, they can be actual trades, paper trades, trade results from out-of-sample runs, trade results from in-sample runs, or hypothetical trades.

In order to allow the simulation to accept data from any of these sources, it will be pre-processed into one of two formats:

- A list of values. Each value will be either a percentage change or a profit and loss in dollars. If the data is closed trades, each value is the percentage gain or loss from a trade. If the data is changes in equity, each value is the percentage gain or loss from that period or a profit and loss in dollars.

- An inverse cumulative distribution function in the form of an Excel table.

The Appendix has a series of "how to" examples that describe and illustrate the method for producing the required format given any initial distribution. There are also examples for converting from any distribution format to any other.

In addition to the simulation program used in this book, there are several commercial programs that perform position sizing. Examples include Stator, Equity Monaco, and Market Systems Analyzer. Contact information is in the reference section of the Appendix. All of these programs require that the data be a list of values.

DATA QUALITY

I cannot emphasize too strongly the importance of using the highest quality data. If you plan to implement position sizing using real money, the simulations used to determine the parameters and to estimate the drawdown and profit that can be expected must use out-of-sample data. Data that is hypothetical, that is drawn from a standard statistical distribution, or that comes from in-sample test runs will result in misleading simulations. If hypothetical or standard distribution data is used, you will already be aware of the limitations.

The greatest danger comes from use of data from in-sample test runs. In-sample data has no value in estimating future performance of a trading system. Use of in-sample data will seriously overestimate future profitability and underestimate risk. It will suggest position sizing parameters that are far too aggressive. Trading a system developed using in-sample data will almost certainly result in serious loss of money.

RISK

There are two risks associated with trading a system.

ACCOUNT RISK

Account risk is that portion of your trading account you are willing to risk, that is, to lose, on any single trade. One percent is a value often recommended. If you have a trading account with a current balance of $100,000 and plan to hold account risk to 1%, each trade should risk no more than $1,000. Do not confuse risk with position size. You can take a position larger than $1,000. It is the loss should that trade be a losing trade that is limited to $1,000.

Among the parameters you set is the ruin level at which you will stop trading. Compute the dollar amount of your account, and the account risk associated with it, at the lowest level the account balance can reach before you stop trading. If your ruin limit is 0.40, and your initial account balance was $100,000, your account could be as low as $60,000. Compute the dollar amount of your account risk at this level of funding.

Account risk is determined by your risk tolerance and the number of risk units needed to continue trading through series of losing trades. Think back to the discussion in Chapter 5 where blackjack professionals are advised to have a bankroll of several hundred to 1000 times their basic bet.

TRADING SYSTEM RISK

Trading system risk is determined by the buy and sell logic, along with the issue being traded. Given a series of trades, there are several metrics that measure the risk:

- Maximum loss among all trades.
- Maximum loss over a sliding window of recent trades.
- Average loss among all trades.
- Average loss over a sliding window of recent trades.

- Maximum maximum adverse excursion, MAE, among all trades.
- Maximum MAE over a sliding window of recent trades.
- Average MAE among all trades.
- Average MAE over a sliding window of recent trades.
- Standard deviation of profit and loss among all trades.
- Standard deviation of profit and loss over a sliding window of recent trades.
- Standard deviation of losing trades, called semi-deviation, among all trades.
- Semi-deviation over a sliding window of recent trades.

The most conservative measure of risk is maximum MAE among all trades. But, since the biggest drawdown is always in the future (as guaranteed by the random walk process and diffusion equations), even this figure may be too conservative.

In the final analysis, it does not matter as much as it would appear to. Select a metric that is easy to compute and seems reasonable and representative of trading system risk to you.

Whatever metric is chosen will assist you in setting the parameters for the simulation, the results of which will be a distribution of terminal equity and a distribution of maximum drawdown, from which you will make a subjective decision.

If you are thinking of your account risk as a percentage, say 1%, also think of your trading system risk as a percentage. If your choice of metric is two times the average MAE, and that turns out to be 2.5% of the entry price for the ETF being traded, 2.5% is the trading system risk. In a step that will be explained in a moment, both the percentages will be converted to dollar amounts.

If you are thinking of your account risk as a dollar amount, say $600, think of your trading system risk as a dollar amount. For a system that trades corn that might be $900 per contract.

Be cautious. You are guaranteed to have your biggest loss when you have your biggest position. Since there will invariably be a sequence of losing trades, the total for the sequence must not exceed the drawdown limit. Using your own set of trading statistics, estimate the percentage of trades that are losers. Compute the number of trades that will be made in a four year period. Use the binary distribution to estimate the maximum number of consecutive losing trades over that period. Use that information to help you determine your risk.

Basic Unit

Consider what is being traded. Compare the account risk with the trading system risk. Based on this relationship, decide on the size of a single basic unit.

Futures

If you are trading futures, including stock indexes, interest rates, currencies, and commodities, the basic unit is one contract; because you cannot trade less than one contract.

Stocks or ETFs

Stocks and ETFs can be traded in any number of shares. Since they rise and fall in price, and can change price significantly when split, using a fixed number of dollars works better than a fixed number of shares. Choose a round number less than or equal to your account risk, say $600.

Since this is the risk, not the position size, compute the position size of the ETF that can be used in a trade without violating the account risk. The largest the trading system risk can be is also $600. 2.5% of what position size gives $600? Divide the $600 by the trading system risk, 2.5%, to get $24,000. This is the largest position that can be taken without violating the risk parameters you have decided to use. If the ETF is SPY, trading at about $110 per share, $24,000 will buy 218 shares, which seems reasonable. Adjust the dollar figure up or down as you wish and pick any round number $24,000 or less to be your basic unit. $10,000 might be a good choice. Your $100,000 trading account then has 10 basic units of $10,000 each.

There are trade-offs to the size of the basic unit. Keeping the unit size small makes it easier to make fine adjustments in position size. On the other hand, trading smaller sized units will result in frictional costs being a higher percentage.

Options

An option contract is for some number of shares or futures contracts.

Multiply the cost of a single option you typically trade by the number of shares or contracts it represents. Analyze the types of options trades you make, and adjust the trading system risk accordingly. Then decide whether you want to treat these trades as if they are contracts or shares.

SUMMARY

You will have an account risk, a trading system risk, and a basic unit. You must have an account with enough funding in it to be able to trade at least one basic unit when the account is at its lowest balance. Depending on the issue being traded and the size of the account, you will find combinations that cannot be traded by small accounts.

In most cases, you will find that you cannot buy all the shares you have funds to cover while keeping the total trading system risk below the account risk. Using the figures selected above, with $60,000 you can buy 545 shares of SPY, but the trading system risk would be $1500 which is larger than the $600 account risk limit. The largest position you can take without violating the risk constraints is 218 shares. Trading the number of basic units where trading system risk equals account risk is 1 to 1 leverage. Any larger position is using leverage. In this example, buying all the shares you can afford is 2.5 to 1 leverage.

Using the position sizing techniques, you will begin trading a single unit or a small number of units. As profits increase the size of the trading account, additional units will be added and leverage will be increased.

POSITION SIZING TECHNIQUES

Position sizing works because a profitable and stable trading system:
- Develops confidence that the system performs as the validation tests suggested it would.
- Uses profits made from trades to increase the trading account balance and fund positions of increased size.

When losses occur, reduce your leverage.

When either of your boundaries is reached, stop trading.

CONSTANT AMOUNT

On each signal, buy (or short) a single trading unit. One unit is some constant number of futures contracts, or some constant dollar amount of shares.

Trading a single unit is probably not a practical method for achieving retirement, because the time required to reach the goal is too long.

But trading a single unit is important because it establishes the baseline that will be used to monitor the health of the system and to insure that it continues to be both profitable and stable. No matter which position sizing method you eventually use, you will regularly refer to this baseline data.

In order to create the baseline results, the data used for the simulation must be unleveraged and the trading uncompounded. Each of the trades or equity changes that make up the list that feeds into the position sizing program must represent trading a single unit.

VOLATILITY WEIGHTED POSITION SIZE

When portfolios consisting of several issues are traded, it can be desirable to balance the sizes of the positions so that average daily marked-to-market equity changes are similar across all issues. One method of achieving this is to compute the average true range or standard deviation of recent price changes of each issue. Determine the relative changes among those, and give each a weighting such that the dollar changes are approximately equal for all the issues in the portfolio. This defines the single unit for each issue, and position sizing proceeds from there.

If a portfolio is desired, I recommend first selecting the asset classes or sectors to be represented.

For each sector or asset class:
  • Select an index or ETF to be the basis for that sector.
  • Create a single trading system for each sector, taking signals from the ETF that is the basis.
  • Implement the system by taking trades in ETFs, either long-only or long-short ETFs.
  • Determine position sizing based on the community account.
  • Monitor and manage each system independently.

This is not a portfolio in the traditional sense of rotating holdings based on some indicator such as relative strength. Rather, it is a group of trading systems that each trade independently, but use a common funding account.

Having multiple systems, whatever combination of logic and data series they use, whether they trade different issues or the same issue, gives the advantage of more compounding events per unit of time. One system that trades SPY about one trade per week compounds 52 times a year. Five such systems, each with one trade per week, compounds 260 times a year.

MARGIN REQUIREMENT

Margin is sometimes recommended as a component of the position sizing calculation. It is certainly a limiting factor, but it is not appropriate for use in the position sizing.

Margin requirements are set by the exchange that lists the contract or security and guarantees counterparty compliance on all trades. Brokers may, at their option, increase the amount of margin required. If a position sizing method computes a position size that would cause the trader to take a position so large that the product of the number of units and the margin exceeded the account, then margin would be a limiting factor. But that would be unusual.

FIXED FRACTION

Using the fixed fractional approach, a fraction is chosen, say 0.15, the trading account equity is multiplied by that fraction, and a position of as many shares or contracts as can be funded is taken. Unless you wish to do so, it is not necessary to trade shares in increments of the basic unit. As the account balance grows, the additional funds allow larger positions to be taken.

Ralph Vince popularized fixed fractional position sizing, including calculation of that fraction that maximizes terminal wealth – optimal f. All of his books are excellent and are recommended reading. Mr. Vince points out the effects of trading at a fraction other than optimal f. Trading higher assures ruin. Trading lower than optimal f reduces return geometrically while reducing drawdown only arithmetically.

The approach we use does not search for optimal f, but rather for the fraction that optimizes your individual objective function. As described in Chapter 7, I suggest an objective function formed as a ratio of reward to risk, where reward is the compound annual rate of return that is likely to be achieved most years, and risk is the maximum drawdown that is unlikely to be exceeded most years. Several simulation runs will be made, the charts are examined, and the fraction chosen. The fraction chosen using this process will always be below optimal f.

When using fixed fraction, the search is for the fraction, f, that will maximize your objective function.

FIXED RATIO

The fixed ratio approach uses previously booked profits to fund increased position size. A variable, named delta, larger than the size of the basic unit, is chosen. As profits are accumulated, the number of basic units is determined by the number of deltas of profit. Trades are made in increments of the basic unit.

Ryan Jones popularized this method in his book *The Trading Game.*

Using Jones' terminology, delta is the number of dollars profit that must be booked in order to increase the number of units traded by one. Delta must be greater than trading system risk or the system will be unstable.

As profits accumulate, the number of basic units being traded grows. As losses occur, the number shrinks. In the standard implementation, the profit required to increase is the same as the loss required to decrease. An alternative is to have the delta required to increase the number of units larger than the delta required to reduce the number. This reduces leverage faster than it increased and helps retain profit when the system enters a drawdown.

The simulation approach is to vary the size of delta, examine the resulting terminal wealth and drawdown distributions, and choose a value that maximizes your objective function.

When using fixed ratio, the search is for the value of delta that will maximize your objective function.

GENERALIZED RATIO

If you do Internet research for position sizing, you will read postings giving opinions of fixed fraction versus fixed ratio. Some of them are heated. There is a common mathematical relationship between constant size, fixed ratio, and fixed fraction, which is often overlooked in the discussions and is not important enough to explain here. If you focus on reaching your retirement goal with minimal risk of ruin, you will find both methods useful, and those discussions will not have an effect on your position sizing decisions.

PRACTICAL ISSUES

Using methods described by Ralph Vince and Ryan Jones in their books, it is sometimes possible to compute the optimal fraction or the optimal delta. When computation is not possible, it is possible to have a position sizing program search for them. I do not recommend doing either for two reasons:

1. Values that are optimal according to the theory will be too aggressive and will lead to higher drawdowns than are acceptable.
2. Those values will be a single number – typically the mean. It is dangerous to focus on the mean without taking the variability into account as well.

I recommend a different approach. One that uses the limits each trader sets for him or herself regarding the goal and drawdown tolerance. One that displays the distribution of the terminal equity and drawdown, rather than a single number, and shows the trader the range of values and the likelihood of success or failure.

The values for the retire boundary and the ruin boundary are the personal choices of the trader. The values can have a significant effect on the position sizing. Which points on the terminal wealth and maximum drawdown curves are chosen, and how they are combined into an objective function, are personal decisions. These are all subjective decisions that should be made after careful study of many simulation results and thoughtful examination of personal goals and risk tolerance.

DESIRABLE CHARACTERISTICS OF TRADING SYSTEMS

POSITIVE MATHEMATICAL EXPECTATION

The trading system must have a positive expectancy. In general, the higher the gain per trade, the better. But while having a positive expectancy is a requirement, in itself that feature is not sufficient.

Low Standard Deviation

The more consistent the trading results are, the safer it is to use aggressive position sizing. Standard deviation appears in the denominator of metrics such as t statistic and Sharpe ratio. Reducing the standard deviation increases those metrics.

Consider using Semi-deviation

When computing the standard deviation of a group of data, all deviations from the mean are penalized. Most traders welcome positive deviations (profits) and penalize negative deviations (losses). When calculating the standard deviation, if a trade near the mean is replaced by a large winning trade, the standard deviation increases. If the standard deviation appears in the denominator of a positions sizing algorithm, that means that winning trades are penalized.

The semi deviation uses the same algorithm as the standard deviation, but replaces every winning trade with a value of zero. Consequently, only losing and break-even trades are penalized.

High Accuracy

George Soros is widely quoted as saying, "it doesn't matter how often you are right or wrong - it only matters how much you make when you are right, versus how much you lose when you are wrong."

This quote is frequently used, particularly by trend followers who hold for long periods, to suggest that traders need not attempt to have a high winning percentage. The statistics show quite the opposite – it is much easier to have an account grow rapidly and to a high balance when the winning percentage is high. It is also much easier to diagnose systems that have a high winning percentage to tell when they are broken.

Frequent Trading

Wealth at the end of a period of time depends on two values – the average geometric return for each trade, G, and the number of compoundings, n. Increase n whenever you have an opportunity. The equation is:

$$TWR = (G)^n$$

Trading systems that trade frequently tend to have short holding periods. Having a short holding period is an additional advantage because it reduces the exposure to drawdown. Refer back to Chapter 8 and note that, compared with holding one day, holding one week adds 8% to expected drawdown (7% due to close to close exposure, plus 1% due to intra-trade exposure), holding one month adds 13%, holding one quarter adds 17%, and holding one year adds 26%. (These apply to SPY. Leveraged ETFs and common stocks will be higher.)

MONITORING THE SYSTEM

In order to be profitable and avoid serious drawdowns, the system must have a positive expectancy the entire time it is being used. Using walk forward runs and other tests to validate a system during its development are very important. Monitoring the system while it is being traded is equally important.

Systems are combinations of logic and data series. As designed, the logic detects patterns in the data that precede profitable trading opportunities. The patterns are the signal portion of the data; everything else is noise, even if it contains valuable patterns that could be detected by some other logic. Periodically the data will change enough so that the logic and data fall out of synchronization, causing first lower profitability, then losses. The data may change again so that the logic and data return to synchronization and profits return. Or the system may not recover on its own. The baseline for system performance is the single unit trading data. It is used to provide data for the statistical tests that will help decide whether the system is working or broken.

Advice is sometimes given that drawdowns are exactly the right time to increase position size. That advice is exactly wrong. All broken systems begin with periods of lower profits, then losses. It is impossible to tell whether the losses are temporary or permanent. The safest response to a system that is performing poorly is to take it offline. Be aggressive when profits are increasing; be cautious when profits are decreasing.

Examples

Limit Drawdown

If the maximum drawdown limit is 40 percent, how can position sizing be used to maximize terminal wealth?

Three position sizing techniques are compared:

- Fixed Fraction

  Use a fixed fraction of the current account equity for the next position. Vary the fraction, seeking maximum terminal wealth while holding maximum drawdown to 40 percent of maximum equity.

- Fixed Ratio

  Establish the dollar size of a trading unit. If a futures contract is being traded, pick a number consistent with trading one contract. If it is an ETF or equity, pick a convenient number, say $10,000.

  Establish a dollar amount for a variable named delta, say $1,000. Delta can be any size, but is usually several times the trading system risk. Trades are taken in multiples of the trading unit.

  Begin by trading one unit. Compute accumulated profits. As profits increase, increase the number of units. As profits decrease, decrease the number of units. Vary delta, seeking the maximum terminal wealth while holding maximum drawdown to 40 percent of maximum equity.

- Fixed Fraction in Units

  Use the fixed fraction method, but trade only multiples of a trading unit. Vary the fraction, seeking maximum terminal wealth while holding maximum drawdown to 40 percent of maximum equity.

Drawdown is not a single value, it is a distribution. As described in Chapter 7, Objective Function, I recommend selecting a percentile, say the 95th, at which to measure drawdown. Call this DD95. When done this way, drawdown will be no more than 40% in 95% of the four year sequences.

Similarly, terminal wealth is a distribution. Measuring it at the 5th percentile estimates the gain that can be expected 95% of the four year sequences. Call this TW5.

The ratio of TW5 to DD95 is a useful metric by which to compare alternative position sizing techniques and their parameter values.

Results from a real trading system are used to illustrate. The system uses mean reversion logic. It buys after prices drops and sells short after price rises. The data represent 280 closed trades over a four year period, 2007 through 2010. The data is out-of-sample and net of commission and slippage. The issue traded is XLF, the S&P financial sector ETF.

Figure 10.5 shows the percentage gain for each of the 280 trades as a histogram. If the vertical axis was in percentage, this would be a probability density function or probability mass function. The chart title says "unmodified" because it will be used as a basis for some other studies later in this chapter.

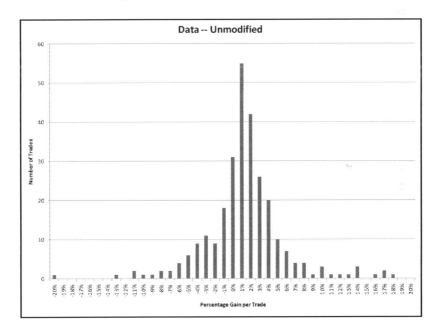

FIGURE 10.5

Sorting the trades and plotting the sorted array gives another perspective. See figure 10.6.

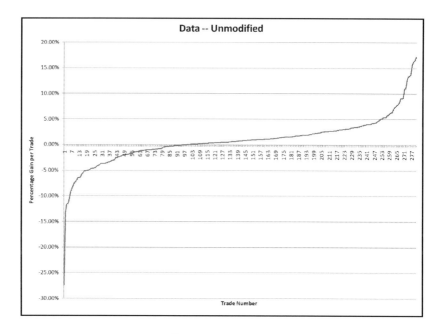

FIGURE 10.6

Figure 10.7 shows the descriptive statistics for the trades.

Unmodified	
% Profit	
Mean	0.0080
Standard Error	0.0027
Median	0.0077
Mode	-0.0099
Standard Deviation	0.0459
Sample Variance	0.0021
Kurtosis	6.8738
Skewness	-0.3303
Range	0.4463
Minimum	-0.2744
Maximum	0.1719
Sum	2.25
Count	280

FIGURE 10.7

The first tests used all available funds for every trade. A Monte Carlo simulation selected trades at random from the 280 and generated ten equally possible equity curves, as shown in Figure 10.8. The time period is four years. Some runs show final equity about double initial equity, others much higher. Some are smooth, others have considerable variation.

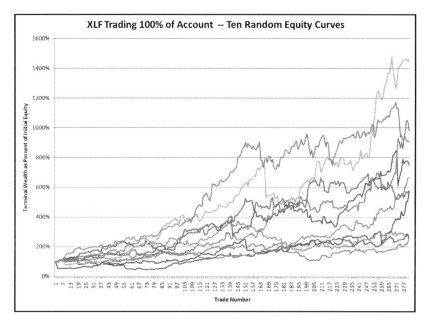

FIGURE 10.8

The four year equity was simulated 1000 times. Figure 10.9 shows the distribution of terminal equity. At TW5, the 5th percentile, a level very likely to be exceeded, TWR is 1.99—approximately a doubling—and the CAR to produce that is 18.7%. At TW50, the mean, TWR is 7.15 with a CAR of 63.5%. At TW95, a level unlikely to be exceeded, TWR is 23.72 and CAR is 120.7%. Based on equity growth alone, the system is very profitable.

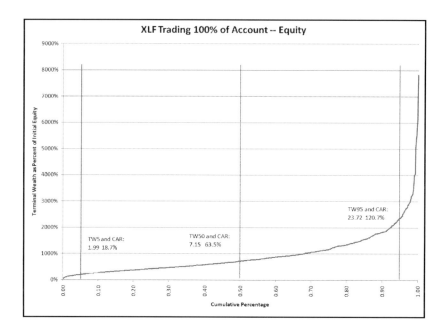

FIGURE 10.9

Figure 10.10 shows the distribution for the drawdowns. DD5, the 5th percentile, shows that most periods the drawdown will be at least 20%; At DD50, the mean drawdown is 36%. At DD95, the 95th percentile, a level unlikely to be exceeded, drawdown is 57%.

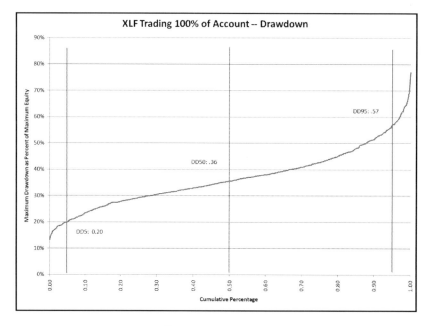

FIGURE 10.10.

Approximately 35 percent of the time, drawdown exceeds 40%, with extreme values over 70%. The system will not be able to guard against all extreme drawdowns. There are too many factors that can happen in the future to be certain. The level of the distribution of drawdowns rises and falls as the position size is increased and decreased. By reducing the size of each position the distribution drawdown is lowered and maximum drawdown at any chosen percentile can be held to a chosen level.

Additional sets of simulation runs were made using each of the three position sizing methods. The parameters of the positions sizing method were varied until the drawdown at the 95th percentile was no greater than 40%. Figure 10.11 shows the comparison of the drawdown distribution curves for the three methods, and shows they are aligned at the DD95 point.

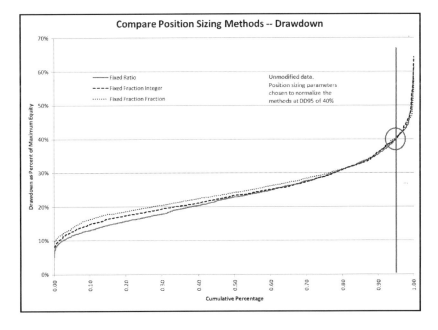

FIGURE 10.11

The close agreement between the two variations of the fixed fraction, plotted as the two dotted lines, indicates that there is no significant difference between those two techniques. Use whichever one is appropriate for the system being traded. There is a slightly lower drawdown for the fixed ratio method.

Given the parameter values that produced the drawdown curves in figure 10.11, the terminal wealth of each was computed and is plotted in figure 10.12. When maximum drawdown is held to 40%, fixed fraction significantly outperformed fixed ratio. Note how the fixed ratio results are well below fixed fraction for the entire left side of the chart, converging at about the 80th or 90th percentile.

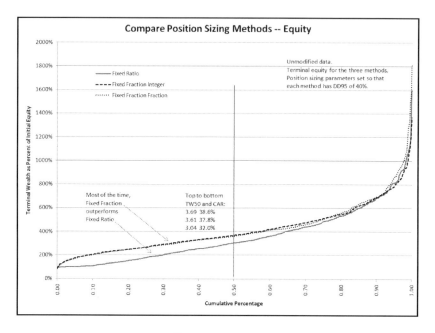

Several more runs were made to verify that relationship holds across the entire range of parameters. Figures 8.13 and 8.14 show the drawdown and terminal wealth distributions when maximum drawdown is held to 20%. The shapes of the curves and relationships among them are the same as the 40% maximum drawdown curves. And fixed fraction outperforms fixed ratio.

When position sizing parameters are set using maximum drawdown as the limit, reducing the maximum drawdown also reduces CAR. TW50 is reduced from 3.61 in figure 10.12 to 1.92 in figure 10.14, and the corresponding CAR values are 37.8% and 17.7%. The proportional changes on the equity curves vary with the percentile point, but TW values and CAR values drop to about 40 to 50%.

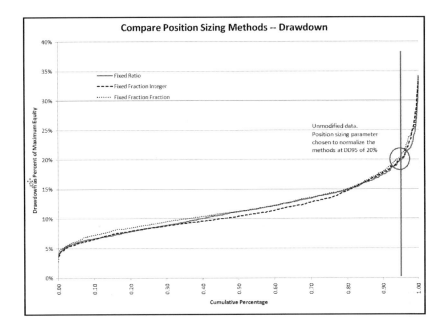

FIGURE 10.13

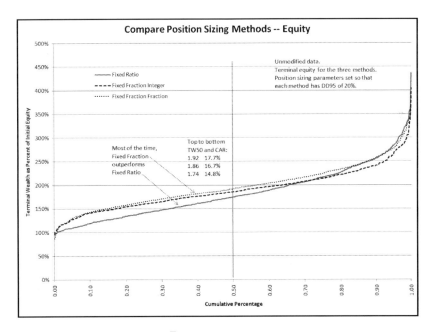

FIGURE 10.14

LIMITING LOSING TRADES

Refer back to figures 8.5 and 8.6, and note that there are several very large losses. Limiting the magnitude of the losses on losing trades is very important.

To illustrate, three modifications were made to the original data.

The first replaced the five worst trades by the average of the five worst trades. The mean, the expectancy, is unchanged and the standard deviation is barely changed.

The second modification replaced the 44 worst trades by the average of the 44 worst trades. The mean remains unchanged and the standard deviation is lower.

The third replaced all 96 of the losing trades by the average of the 96 losing trades.

Figure 10.15 shows all six charts.

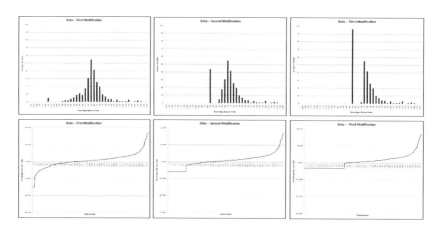

FIGURE 10.15

Figure 10.16 shows the descriptive statistics for the three sets of modified data. Note that the mean is unchanged and the standard deviation dropped slightly.

First Modification		Second Modification		Third Modification	
% Profit		*% Profit*		*% Profit*	
Mean	0.0080	Mean	0.0080	Mean	0.0080
Standard Error	0.0027	Standard Error	0.0026	Standard Error	0.0024
Median	0.0077	Median	0.0077	Median	0.0077
Mode	-0.1497	Mode	-0.0595	Mode	-0.0326
Standard Deviation	0.0452	Standard Deviation	0.0428	Standard Deviation	0.0402
Sample Variance	0.0020	Sample Variance	0.0018	Sample Variance	0.0016
Kurtosis	3.7534	Kurtosis	2.2834	Kurtosis	2.8889
Skewness	0.0856	Skewness	0.7874	Skewness	1.3716
Range	0.3216	Range	0.2314	Range	0.2045
Minimum	-0.1497	Minimum	-0.0595	Minimum	-0.0326
Maximum	0.1719	Maximum	0.1719	Maximum	0.1719
Sum	2.25	Sum	2.25	Sum	2.25
Count	280	Count	280	Count	280

FIGURE 10.16

Two sets of simulation runs were made. One keeping the maximum DD95 at 40%, the other at 20%. For each set, four series of runs were made, one for each of the four data sets -- original unmodified, first modification, second modification, third modification. Each of the three position sizing methods was tested for each case. Giving 24 runs in all. The objective function, TW5DD95 was computed for each run and is shown in figure 10.17.

	TW5DD95 Metric							
		DD95 Normalized at 20%				DD95 Normalized at 40%		
			First	Second	Third		First	Second	Third
		Original	Modification	Modification	Modification	Original	Modification	Modification	Modification
Fixed Fraction - Any Fraction		0.33	0.38	0.52	0.68	0.35	0.40	0.53	0.68
Fixed Fraction - Integer Units		0.31	0.38	0.49	0.67	0.37	0.40	0.47	0.74
Fixed Ratio		0.12	0.13	0.19	0.33	0.00	0.01	0.02	0.09

FIGURE 10.17

Several insights can be drawn from the results:

- Fixed ratio performs poorly. Almost every equity distribution for fixed ratio showed that 10 to 20 percent of the time there was no equity growth over the four year period. At the upper end, fixed ratio's performance was better than fixed fraction, but that comes at the risk of poor performance in some periods. And there is no way to predict in advance which is coming next.
- Fixed fraction using any fraction and fixed fraction using inte-

ger multiples of the basic unit perform essentially the same.

- Reducing losses for losing trades improved results significantly no matter which position sizing method was used.

ABSORBING BOUNDARIES

One of the recommendations is to set a goal for account growth and stop trading when that goal is met. Since the terminal wealth distribution curves report only the final values, there is no information about the performance during the four year period.

The simulation was set up to note the equity and drawdown after every trade. Two user-settable variables contain values for the retire boundary, say 4.0, and ruin boundary, say 0.40. If the account grow to four times its original balance, no further trades are made. If the drawdown reaches 40% of maximum equity, no further trades are made. Whatever the account balance and drawdown are at that point are carried through to the end and reported as final values.

Figure 10.17 shows the effect on maximum drawdown of limiting drawdown to 40% and capping terminal wealth at 400%.

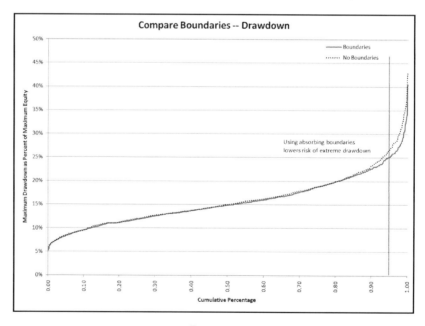

FIGURE 10.17

Figure 10.18 shows the effect on equity of limiting drawdown to 40% and capping terminal wealth at 400%.

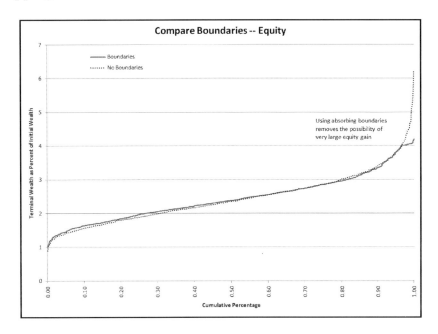

FIGURE 10.18

Try this with your specific system. Some systems benefit more than others from this technique.

TRADE FREQUENTLY

The number of trades, n, is the exponent in the growth equation.

$$TWR = (G)^n$$

If you know the geometric mean of your trades, G, you can compute how many trades, m, it will take to reach your retire goal (Goal).

Assume G = 1.02 (2% per trade), Goal = 4.0.

$$m = \frac{\log(Goal)}{\log(G)} = \frac{1.386}{0.0198} = 70$$

$$(1.02)^{70} = 4.00$$

Knowing how many trades, review how many trades the system gives per year, on average, say 20. It will take 70 / 20 years, or 3.5 years, to get

70 trades and reach your goal.

If the system trades only 12 times per year, it will take 70 / 12 years, or 5.8 years to get 70 trades and reach your goal.

It is certainly worth while increasing the number of trades as much as your trading style and circumstances can tolerate. As mentioned in Chapter 8, Bar Length and Holding Period, taking one trade a day gives an excellent ratio of profit potential, number of trades, and manageability. Manageability includes being able to trade with a minimum of time in front of the real-time data feed. One method of trading once every day is to analyze conditions just before the close of the regular session of trading, take a position at the close, take profits in the overnight session or during the next trading day, and repeat at the next day's close.

Depending on the percentage of the trading account that being committed, which is often less than half, it may be possible to run two completely separate systems. Alternatively, include the code for both systems in one trading system module and consolidate the signals.

If there are multiple systems giving signals and they are cherry-picking so there are many fewer signals than days, trades tend to come in bunches. In this case, the data used to feed the simulation should be daily equity changes taken from test runs where all of the systems are included. The correlation, or lack of correlation, will be maintained in the equity data, but would be lost if only the trade results from each system were used.

TRADING FREQUENCY OR LEVERAGE

Assume you have a system that trades infrequently, say 2 times per month, and it is well behaved when traded at a low fraction, say 0.125. Should effort be made to increase the frequency, perhaps by developing additional systems with the same characteristics or trading additional markets? Or should the existing system be traded with increased leverage, that is, with a higher fraction?

A series of simulations were run with frequency at 2, 4, 8, and 16 times per month; and with fraction at 0.125, 0.25, 0.50, and 1.00. Three results are reported for each run:
- CAR at TW50, the midpoint of the distribution.
- Drawdown at DD50, the midpoint.

- TW5DD95, the metric of system performance likely to be met about 90% of the time.

Figure 10.19 shows the spreadsheet summary.

		Fraction			
		0.125	0.25	0.50	1.00
Frequency					
CAR at TW50	2	0.045	0.091	0.190	0.413
	4	0.091	0.189	0.414	0.980
	8	0.191	0.418	1.000	2.910
	16	0.420	1.011	3.036	14.490
DD at DD50	2	0.009	0.017	0.034	0.070
	4	0.011	0.022	0.044	0.086
	8	0.013	0.025	0.050	0.099
	16	0.015	0.030	0.058	0.118
TW5DD95	2	1.96	2.10	2.16	2.27
	4	3.79	4.22	4.73	5.34
	8	7.96	8.97	10.07	14.85
	16	16.29	19.87	29.49	63.77

FIGURE 10.19

Look along the diagonal at combinations that might be expected to be equivalent.

In the block of data for CAR at TW50, Frequency 4 / Fraction 0.125 versus Frequency 2 / Fraction 0.25. Both have results of 0.091. Throughout the CAR block, fraction and frequency can be traded off equally.

- 4/0.125 == 2/0.25
  0.091 == 0.091
- 8/0.125 == 4/0.25 == 2/0.50
  0.191 == 0.189 == 0.190
- 16/0.125 == 8/0.25 == 4/0.50 == 2/1.00
  0.420 == 0.418 == 0.414 == 0.413

In the block of data for drawdown at DD50, that same pair results in 0.017 versus 0.011. Throughout the DD block, drawdown is lower by increasing frequency than by increasing leverage.

- 4/0.125 < 2/0.25

  0.011 < 0.017
- 8/0.125 < 4/0.25 < 2/0.50

  0.013 < 0.022 < 0.034
- 16/0.125 < 8/0.25 < 4/0.50 < 2/1.00

  0.015 < 0.025 < 0.044 < 0.070

In the block of data for the ratio of TW5 to DD95, that metric is much better when frequency is increased rather than increasing leverage by the equivalent amount.

In general, increased frequency is preferred to increased leverage, given a choice between one or the other. If a trading-system / leverage-technique combination has such high leverage that the ruin boundary is reached, increasing the leverage will not improve the performance. Increasing the trading frequency will increase the overall performance in two ways—increased CAR and decreased drawdown. The system will be more profitable, and it will pull back from the ruin boundary.

Summary

Use your own data – real data or data you want to analyze. If you are planning to trade based on results of simulations, use only out-of-sample data to select your method and parameters.

There are two risks—account risk and trading system risk. The relationship between them is important.

Defining and measuring trading system risk is difficult. Fortunately, having an accurate specific value is not necessary.

Use your own definition of a retirement goal and of a ruin limit. Quit while you are ahead.

Keep track of two series.

- The equity in the trading account, including gains and losses trading using position sizing.
- The equity and trading statistics using a single unit. This is the data used to determine whether the system is working or broken.

Terminal wealth is a distribution, not a single point. Consider the consistency of profits as well as the average.

Drawdown is a distribution, not a single point. Consider consistency and be aware of the severity of the deepest drawdowns.

Simulations help determine position sizing parameters without relying on theory or calculations of optimal values.

The fixed fraction method of position sizing outperforms the fixed ratio method in most cases.

Characteristics of trading systems that produce high terminal wealth with low drawdown are:

- trade frequently
- high expectancy
- high accuracy
- limited losses

Check system health regularly. Reduce leverage during drawdowns.

Given a choice between increasing frequency of trading or increasing leverage, increase frequency.

Chapter 11

Is It Broken?

One of the most important aspects of trading a system is determining whether it is performing satisfactorily or is broken. Answering that question requires a comparison between recent performance and something else. Applying analytical techniques to comparisons requires application of statistics.

STATISTICS

Statistics is defined as the collection, tabulation, analysis, interpretation, and presentation of quantitative data. The goal of statistics is to gain understanding from the data. There are two phases of statistics, both of which are important to traders:

- Descriptive statistics. Deals with description and analysis, such as employment statistics or baseball statistics.
- Inferential or inductive statistics. Attempts to draw conclusions about a larger population of data from a smaller sample of data. Tests hypotheses about the relationships between samples and populations. Since the conclusions and inferences cannot be stated with certainty, the language of probability is often used. Probability is a formalism for quantifying uncertainty.

THE QUESTIONS

You have a system that you have been trading, or watching, and you have some recent performance results from it. You want to know whether the system is working as you expected and is safe to trade, or it is broken and should be taken offline. This chapter discusses this question.

The questions most often asked regarding trading systems relate to its profitability:

- Has the accuracy declined?
- Has the mean of some metric such as expectancy declined?
- What statistical distribution does a sample of data come from?
- Is there a difference between the statistical distributions of two samples of data?
- Has the distribution of the recent data changed from that of earlier data?
- Is there serial correlation in the trade sequence?

- Is the system broken?
- Are the changes such that the trading system should be taken offline?

These are all questions that require comparisons – typically comparing recent results with baseline results, perhaps comparing with random results or theoretical results.

POPULATIONS AND SAMPLES

A population is a set of objects or data with something in common – a population of people, of daily temperatures, of closed trades from a trading system. In general, we cannot itemize all of the members of a population, but we can list some of them – a subset that is called a sample. The individual data values of the sample are known and can be used in calculations. A measurement that describes a population is called a parameter. A measurement computed from a sample of a population that is used to estimate a parameter of that population is called a statistic, or, when there is no ambiguity, it is also called a parameter or a metric.

Inferential statistics are used to infer properties of populations based on samples drawn from them. Two theorems or laws provide the justification:

- The law of large numbers – states that the average of a large number of measurements of some metric taken from samples will be close to the expected value of that same metric for the population, and will tend to become closer as the number of measurements is increased.
- The central limit theorem – states that the mean of a sufficiently large number of independent random variables, each with finite mean and variance, will be approximately Normally distributed.

The theorems rely on the assumption that individual events – random variables – that make up the sample are independent and identically distributed (iid).

Independence of a process implies that the process is memoryless. Past outcomes provide no information about future outcomes.

Being identically distributed means that each random variable in a sample has the same probability distribution as the others.

SAMPLE SIZE

There is a trade-off. Larger samples are needed to see the effects of smaller differences. The more data points used in the calculation of the statistic, the higher the confidence. But, the more data points, the longer the lag between the point at which the system changes and the point at which the statistic is telling you that it is significant. The better your system is working, the easier it is to tell when it is broken.

PERIODICITY

The data points used for the analysis are equity values recorded periodically or profits from closed trades. If, as I recommend, trading is frequent and holding periods are short, these will be very similar.

The periodicity of the data must match the periodicity of your actions. If equity values are being used, you must be willing and able to exit open trades whenever the test shows the system should be taken offline. If the system is a rotational system that is reevaluated at the end of every month and no changes will be made mid-month, it is of no value to compute the statistics on any time scale more frequent than monthly. Review the charts showing drawdown versus periodicity and holding period. To apply statistical methods to determine whether the system is broken, monthly or less frequent data is inadequate.

INTRAOCULAR IMPACT TEST

One of the best tests is the Intraocular Impact Test. Plot the data. If the result hits you between the eyes, then it is significant.

Kidding aside, always plot your data. That is the first step to understanding it.

DESCRIPTIVE STATISTICS

We begin with a review of terms and definitions.

Data used by statistical tests can be classed as:
- Nominal, where each data item fits into a category that has a name, but there is no numeric value or rank associated. Examples include win/loss, red/green/blue, male/female, blonde/brunette/redhead/bald, trending/range-bound.
- Ordinal, where each data item has a numeric rank. Examples

include thermostat setting low/medium/high, finishing position in a race, relative attractiveness of a trading opportunity
poor/good/bet-the-farm. Although each element of ordinal
data has a numeric score associated with it, do not do arithmetic using those scores – that is almost always inappropriate.

- Interval, where ordinal data has numeric values that are
equally spaced. Examples include number of minutes
to walk a mile 7/8/9/10/11/12, salary to the nearest $5000
$20000/$25000/$30000/$35000.

- Numeric, where each data item has an arbitrary numeric value
(that may be integer or real). Examples include gain per trade,
number of bars held.

Mean The mean is a measure of central tendency of a sample of data.
It is the arithmetic average. The mean is the first central moment of
a distribution. It is computed by adding the values of all of the data
points in the sample, and dividing by the number of data points, n. The
symbol for the mean of a sample is $\overline{x}$, pronounced x-bar. The mean of
the sample is an estimate of the mean of the population. If the mean of
the population is known, its symbol is μ, pronounced mu. The mean of
a finite sample is computed as:

$$\overline{x} = \frac{\sum_{i=1}^{n} x_i}{n}$$

Median   The median is a measure of central tendency of a sample
of data. It is the middle value in the sorted list of data values. Median
is less affected by extreme values than mean. Median is used to describe ordinal, interval, or numeric data.

Mode The mode is a measure of central tendency of a sample of data.
It is the most frequently occurring value. If that value is unique, the
sample is called unimodal; a distribution with more than one mode is
said to be bimodal, trimodal, or in general, multimodal. Mode is also
used to describe the general appearance of numeric data, as in unimodal or bimodal.

Variance   The variance is a measure of the variability of the data. The variance is the second central moment. The variance is the square of the standard deviation. The variance, s^2, of a finite sample is computed as:

$$s^2 = \frac{\sum_{i=1}^{n}(x_i - \overline{x})^2}{n-1}$$

where $\overline{x}$ is the mean of the sample.

Standard deviation   The standard deviation is a measure of the variability of the data. The standard deviation is the positive square root of the variance of a set of data.

Skew Skew, or skewness, is a measure of the shape of the distribution – the degree to which the distribution is lopsided. Skew is the third central moment of a distribution. The skew, S, is computed as:

$$S = \frac{\frac{1}{n-1}\sum_{i=1}^{n}(x_i - \bar{x})^3}{\sigma^3}$$

where n is the number of data points, and σ is the standard deviation.

Distributions that have longer tails to the left than the right are left skewed and the skew value of those distributions is negative. Distributions that have longer tails to the right are right skewed and the skew value is positive. The skew value of a Normal distribution is 0.

Kurtosis   Kurtosis is a measure of the shape of the peak and tails of the distribution – the extreme values. Kurtosis is the fourth central moment of a distribution. Increasing kurtosis is associated with the movement of probability mass from the shoulders of a distribution into its center and tails. Distributions with sharp peaks and fat tails, such as changes in prices of securities, have high kurtosis and are termed leptokurtic. The kurtosis, K, is computed as:

$$K = \frac{\frac{1}{n}\sum_{i}^{n}(x_i - \overline{x})^4}{\sigma^4}$$

where n is the number of data points, and σ is the standard deviation.

A Normal distribution has kurtosis value of 3. (Excel, and some other statistical analysis packages, compute kurtosis using the formula given here, then subtract 3, report the result and call it excess kurtosis. Thus, if you use Excel's Data Analysis package to compute the descriptive statistics of data that fits a Normal distribution, the reported value for kurtosis will be 0.)

OTHER MOMENTS

All samples of data have a mean and a median. All samples with two or more data points have a variance, skew, and kurtosis. Higher degree moments are defined, but are not commonly used. In general, a statistical distribution is not completely determined by its moments (but it is completely determined by its characteristic function).

Samples that follow the Normal distribution are completely determined by their mean and variance – the skew is always 0, and the kurtosis is always 3. It is not meaningful to talk about a Normal sample with skew other than 0 or kurtosis other than 3 – that sample is not Normal.

DEGREES OF FREEDOM

The number of degrees of freedom of a statistic computed from a sample is the number of independent pieces of information on which the statistic is based. A data set contains a number of observations, n. That is, there are n individual pieces of information which can be used to estimate parameters such as the mean or standard deviation. In general, each parameter being estimated uses one degree of freedom. The difference, n minus the number of parameters being estimated, is df, the number of degrees of freedom associated with the statistic.

DESCRIPTIVE STATISTICS IN EXCEL

To compute all of the basic descriptive statistics using Excel, use the Data Analysis menu, and choose Descriptive Statistics. Daily changes in SPY from February 1998 through August 2010 were analyzed with the results shown in figure 11.1.

PeriodGain	
Mean	0.000098
Standard Error	0.000247
Median	0.000527
Mode	0
Standard Deviation	0.013879
Sample Variance	0.000193
Kurtosis	9.3932
Skewness	0.2689
Range	0.2436
Minimum	-0.0984
Maximum	0.1452
Sum	0.3073
Count	3147

FIGURE 11.1

This data is definitely not Normal. Skewness of 0.2689 indicates a longer tail to the right; excess kurtosis of 9.3932 indicates many more data points in the tails than would be expected.

The minimum day to day change is a loss of 9.84%, which gives a z-score for that point of -7.07. The maximum day to day change is a gain of 14.52%, with a z-score for that point of 10.48. If the sample came from a Normal distribution, the probability of a data point with a z-score of either +5 or -5 would be 0.0000002868 – less than 1/3 of a time per million. The 3147 data points have 6 below -5 and 4 above +5. If the distribution was Normal, it would take 150,000 years of daily data to have 11 points farther away from the mean than plus or minus 5. The single point at z-score of 10.48 would occur once in 10^24 years – a very long time, considering the universe is probably about 1.3 * 10^10 years old.

Figure 11.2 shows the distribution of changes of 2 percent or less. All data points greater than 2% are consolidated into the tall bars at the ends.

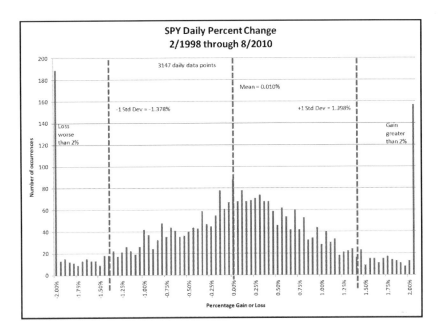

FIGURE 11.2

INFERENTIAL STATISTICS

A statistical hypothesis test is a method of making decisions using experimental data.

Statistical hypothesis testing is divided into two methods:

- Frequentist testing is the classical method developed in the 20th century by people such as Sir Ronald Fisher. It is the method taught in most secondary school and undergraduate statistics courses. Described loosely, frequentist methods gather all of the data, compute frequencies and probabilities, and then apply the methods.
  According to the frequentist view, the probability of an event occurring in a particular trial is the frequency with which it occurs in a sequence of similar trials.

- Bayesian methods are more subjective, take observed results into account, and modify probabilities as data is acquired. According to the Bayesian view, the probability of an event is the degree of belief that a person has that it will occur, given all relevant information currently known to that person.

Except for the section near the end of this chapter outlining the Bayesian concepts and practices, methods discussed in this section of the book are traditional, frequentist methods.

There is a significant amount of subjectivity involved in applying statistical tests. Decisions include:

- Choice of appropriate data.
- Representation of the data, including scaling, transformation, distribution, parameters.
- Choice of the appropriate statistical test.
- Choice of the level of statistical significance.
- Interpretation of the results.
- Action based on the results of the test.

A result is called statistically significant if it is unlikely to have occurred by chance. There is no certainty. The best we can hope for is a high degree of confidence. As with any decision involving risk, the chance of an occurrence of an event, the effect that event will have if it does occur, and the tolerance for risk, must all be taken into account.

Hypothesis Testing

The area of statistics that covers the question we are asking about the health of trading systems is hypothesis testing. A hypothesis is an assertion about the model. Two hypotheses are required. H_0, the null hypothesis, and H_1, the alternative hypothesis. The two hypotheses together must account for all possibilities.

For example:

H_0: The mean trade result is less than zero.

To cover all possibilities, H_1 must be:

H_1: The mean trade result is greater than or equal to zero.

If we draw a horizontal line and mark the area represented by H_0, then all the remainder of the line must be represented by H_1. If the area represented by H_0 begins at some point and continues all the way to the infinite limit in one direction, then H_1 is in one piece and must cover from that point to the infinite limit in the other direction. Since H_1 covers only one extreme, a one-tailed test will be used.

If the area represented by H_0 is a single point, or a range that does not extend to either infinite limit, then H_1 is in two pieces and must cover both extremes, and a two-tailed test will be used.

The testing procedure assumes that the null hypothesis is true. We begin by stating a null hypothesis – usually a statement we hope will be false. That is, we want to be able to reject the null hypothesis. If we are comparing the recent results to random results, the null hypothesis might be: "recent trading results are equal to or worse than random." And then the alternative hypothesis would be: "recent trading results are better than random." At the conclusion of the statistical calculations, we hope to be able to say: "we reject the null hypothesis." Since there are only two hypotheses, and together they cover all possibilities, that implies that the alternative hypothesis is more likely. Since there is no way to be 100 percent certain about rejecting H_0, we also choose some level of confidence that we apply to the statement, say 95%. A more complete conclusion would be: "with 95% confidence, we reject the null hypothesis" or equivalently "at the 5% level of significance, we reject the null hypothesis." Strictly speaking, we cannot say that we accept the alternative hypothesis. The statistical tables, and the commonly used statement of results, use the smaller figure. We say "at the 5% level" or "at the 1% level" to imply 95% confidence or 99% confidence. There is never certainty, only increased levels of confidence. The purpose of all of the statistical tests is to fill in the percentage number – nothing more.

Why can't we "accept the alternative hypothesis?" Because there might be an explanation that is not included in the null hypothesis. For example, a dry sidewalk confirms that it has not recently rained; a wet sidewalk cannot confirm that it did rain, because it might be wet from a sprinkler.

Our null hypothesis might be "the mean trade result is less than or equal to zero." Which makes our alternative hypothesis "the mean trade result is greater than zero." If the null hypothesis is rejected at the 5% level, it is not necessarily true that the mean trade result is greater than zero. It might be that the mean trade result actually is less than zero most of the time, but for the data used in the test, it is greater – just by random chance. This creates a Type I error, which is explained below.

THE PROCESS

The process of using statistical analysis to decide whether a trading system is broken, and, if so, what action to take, is:

1. State a null hypothesis that the system is broken in some way, relative to some benchmark. We hope that is wrong. Because if it is wrong, that gives confidence that the system is working.
2. Gather data. Account equity data or closed trade data for the system; benchmark data to make the comparison.
3. Decide on the level of confidence, say 5%.
4. Select a statistical test, say the t-test.
5. Compute the test statistic and the p-value.
6. Using a table or formula, determine how likely that test statistic value occurs.
7. Take action of either trading the system or taking it offline, as required.

WHAT IS A P-VALUE?

P-values are used to test hypotheses. Nothing more.

The p-value is the probability that the data would be at least as extreme as those observed, if the null hypothesis were true.

A small p-value implies that the observed data is unlikely unless the null hypothesis is false.

Use some judgment when evaluating the results. A p-value of 0.051 is essentially the same as a p-value of 0.049.

TYPE I AND TYPE II ERRORS

There are two possibilities regarding the null hypothesis – H_0 is true or H_0 is false. And there are two possibilities for our actions – reject H_0 or accept H_0. Figure 11.3 shows a diagram with these possibilities.

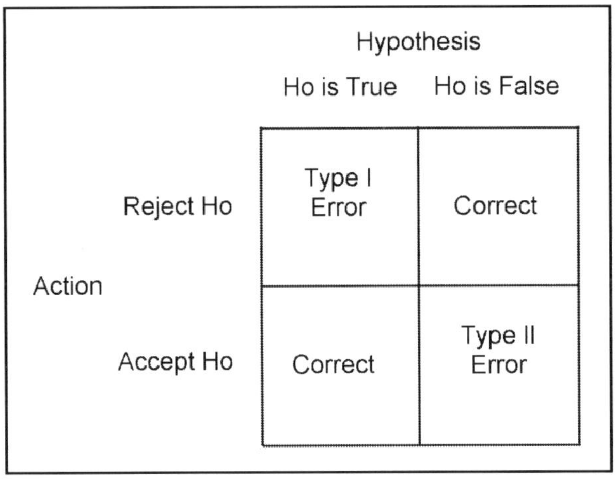

FIGURE 11.3

In two cases, the action is correct, and in two cases it is wrong. Rejecting a true null hypothesis is called a Type I error. The percentage of the time this happens is known as alpha, α. As the confidence level is increased, the probability of committing a Type I error is decreased. Accepting a false H_0 is called a Type II error. The percentage of the time this happens is known as beta, β. There is not a simple relationship between α and β, but reducing α usually results in increasing β.

In terms of the trading system, there are two possibilities for the state of the system – it is either broken, H_0, or working, H_1. And two possibilities for our actions – we either trade it, reject H_0, or take it off line, accept H_0. Figure 11.4 shows a diagram labeled with the trading system question.

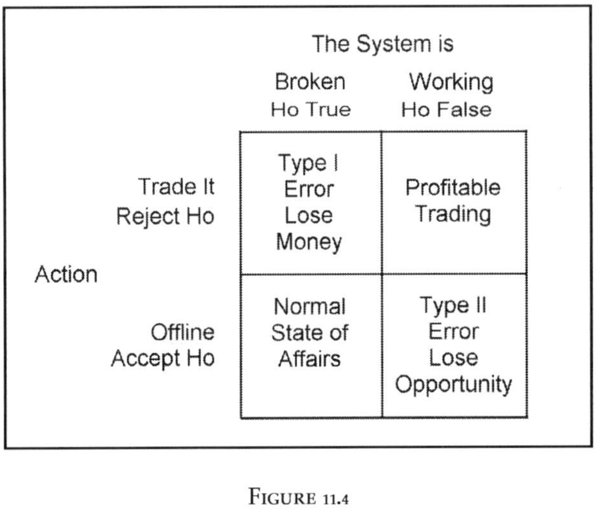

FIGURE 11.4

The four possibilities are:

1. H_0 is true, the system is broken, but we reject H_0 and continue to trade it. This is a Type I error and it is the expensive one – it results in losing trades.

2. H_0 is false, the system is working, and we correctly reject H_0 and continue to trade it. We are trading a working system and making profits.

3. H_0 is true, the system is broken, and we correctly accept H_0 and take it offline. We are not taking trades using a broken system. This is the normal state of our affairs – there are millions of trading systems that do not work, and we are not using any of them.

4. H_0 is false, the system is working, but we accept H_0 and take the system offline. We are not taking trades, but the system would be producing profits. This is a Type II error, but not an expensive one. We lose opportunity, but not money.

What Test Will Tell Us What We Need to Know?

The test to be used is determined by considering all of the issues mentioned above – what question we want answered, what data is available, what test is appropriate, how definitive a conclusion is required?

There are many statistical tests that might be applied. Some rely heavily on assumptions about the data, such as that it must follow the Normal statistical distribution. Some rely on knowledge of parameters of the distribution, such as mean or standard deviation. If the values of the parameters are not known, it may still be possible to use the test, but at reduced confidence as estimates are made of those parameters. Some work equally well on any data without regard for its distribution. Some are easily computed, others complex. Some are easily and unambiguously interpreted, others not so.

The sections that follow discuss some of the tests that are commonly suggested in the trading literature. Some of these tests are appropriate and helpful; some are appropriate, but either fail to give the needed information or are better suited to answer some other question; some are inappropriate, but included here because they are often mentioned.

They fall into a few general categories:

*   Correlation and serial dependence

- Accuracy
- Comparison of means
- Goodness of fit

THEORY VERSUS PRACTICE

An experimental statistician was overheard telling a theoretical statistician "in theory, theory and practice are the same, but in practice, they are different".

We are asking "is the data we have profitable enough?" and "is the system broken?"

Most of the time we are interested in getting confidence levels in one of three areas:

- The difference between two means.
- Whether two samples came from the same distribution.
- The correlation between two data series.

A theoretical statistician, or an applied statistician working in a different field, might be interested in whether data being studied came from a specific theoretical distribution. The one case where this might be of interest to a trader is determining whether a data sample follows the Normal distribution, before using a test that assumes normality. But, since we seldom have control over the distribution of the data we are working with, our primary interest is determining whether the results we have are reliable.

SOME HYPOTHETICAL DATA

Data used in some of the discussions to follow comes from a hypothetical trading system.

This system trades an ETF that represents a major market index. It makes some calculations in the few minutes before the close of trading every day, gives a signal to be either long or short as of the close, and exits some time the next day – at a profit target, at a price limiting the loss, or at the close. It is always in the market, and holds its position for one day. It has been 60% accurate, but appears to have fallen out of sync and is no better than random—50% accurate. Since this is a simulated system, the point at which the accuracy drops (instantaneously) from 60% to 50% is known. Several statistical techniques will be used to detect when the accuracy changed, and to determine whether the system is broken so badly that it should be taken offline.

Each data point represents a closed trade, and the numeric value is the percentage gain for that trade. The amounts of the gains and losses are random. The early period, from the beginning of the data through trade 111, has a win to loss ratio of 60%. Starting with trade 112, that ratio is reduced to 50%. Figure 11.5 shows the trade by trade gain.

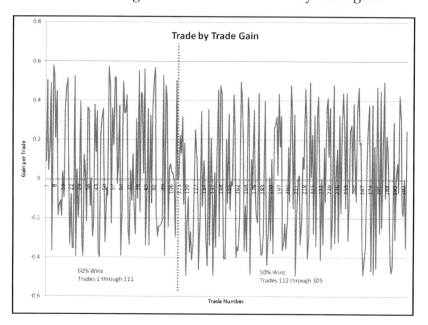

FIGURE 11.5

CORRELATION AND SERIAL DEPENDENCE

Pearson product-moment correlation   Correlation measures the degree to which two or more variables change with respect to each other. There are several methods of computing the correlation coefficient, r, all of which result in a number between -1 and +1. The most common is the Pearson product-moment method which works well when used with numeric data that is reasonably Normal. Other methods, such as Spearman's rank correlation, are available for use with discrete numeric and ordinal data. Perfect correlation, r = 1, indicates that change in one variable is matched by a corresponding change in the other. When r = -1, a change in one variable is matched by an opposite change in the other. The correlation coefficient measures only the degree to which the variables change, and cannot suggest whether one change causes the other change.

In Excel, the function CORREL computes the Pearson correlation.

There are several variations of formulas. One is:

$$r = \frac{\sum_{i=1}^{n}(x_i - \bar{x})(y_i - \bar{y})}{(n-1)s_x s_y}$$

Where $\bar{x}$ and $\bar{y}$ are the sample means, and s_x and s_y are the sample standard deviations.

The square of the correlation coefficient is known as the coefficient of determination, R^2. When r is computed as a result of a linear regression, it has the same interpretation as Pearson's correlation. For the regression, R^2 represents the portion of variability accounted for by the regression equation, or the line that best fits a scatter plot of the data. Note that r is sensitive to outliers.

Autocorrelation is correlation between values of the same variable at different times – between the value now and the value some number of bars or trades ago. Autocorrelation is a measure of serial dependence. The autocorrelation coefficient can be calculated by substituting lagged data pairs into the formula for the Pearson correlation coefficient.

If autocorrelation is found, either in the raw data or in the residuals of a regression, then the data points that comprise that sequence are not independent. The best action is to revise the trading system, adding logic to take the serial correlation into account.

Spearman Rank Correlation   Spearman rank correlation is the equivalent of the Pearson correlation, but applied to ranked variables. Begin with raw scores X_i and Y_i, convert them to ranks, x_i and y_i, and take the difference between the ranks, $d_i = x_i - y_i$. If there are no tied ranks, then the correlation, ρ, is given by:

$$\rho = 1 - \frac{6\sum_{i=1}^{n}d_i^2}{n(n^2 - 1)}$$

If tied ranks exist, use the formula for the product moment correlation based on ranks. Each of the tied ranks is given the average of all its tied partners.

To convert numeric data to rank data, sort the raw numeric scores into ascending order. The position in the sorted order is the rank.

RUNS TEST

The runs test can be used to decide if a set of data is random and to test for serial dependence. The runs test operates on nominal data that comes from a binomial distribution – one where there are only two outcomes. If the original data is numeric, it must be converted into categories. For example, every positive gain becomes a "W" and every negative gain becomes an "L". The number of runs, r, follows the Normal distribution. The test statistic for the runs test is z-score.

The runs test uses a data series of length n. The number of runs, r, is counted. A run is a sequence consisting of similar values. The number of Ws and the number of Ls are also counted.

If the data has strong positive serial correlation, wins tend to follow wins, losses tend to follow losses, there will be a low number of runs, and a low z-score. If the data has a strong negative serial correlation, wins and losses tend to alternate, there will be a high number of runs, and a high z-score. If there is no strong serial correlation, sequences of wins and losses will be random, and the z-score will be neither consistently low nor consistently high.

For example, the sequence WWWLLWLWWWWLLWLWWLWWW is 20 data points long, has 11 runs, 13 Ws, 7 Ls.

$n=20$, $r=11$, $W=13$, $L=7$.

Statement of the hypotheses might be:

H_0: The sequence appears to be random.

H_1: The sequence appears to exhibit serial correlation.

The test statistic is the z-score, computed as:

$$\text{Define} \quad mean = \frac{2 * W * L}{n} + 1$$

$$\text{Define} \quad stdev = \sqrt{\frac{(mean - 1)(mean - 2)}{n - 1}}$$

$$z = \frac{r - mean}{stdev}$$

For this example:

$$mean = \frac{2*13*7}{20} + 1 = 10.1$$

$$stdev = \sqrt{\frac{9.1*8.1}{19}} = 1.97$$

$$z = \frac{11 - 10.1}{1.97} = 0.46$$

Since r follows the Normal distribution, the critical levels of z are about ±1.65. 0.46 is not greater than 1.65, or less than -1.65, so this sequence is probably not unusual, and we cannot reject H_0.

Figure 11.6 shows the plot of the z-score of the runs in the 60% / 50% data.

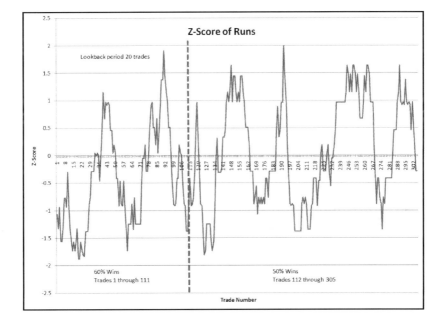

FIGURE 11.6

The percentage of winning trades changed abruptly from 60% to 50% at trade number 112. If the runs test would be helpful, it would show the z-scores to the left of the line at trade 112 to be different than those to the right. Positive serial correlation results when wins tend to follow wins, which should happen more often when 60% of the trades are winners. The area to the left of trade 112 does not show strong serial correlation. The area to the right of the line at trade 112 should show a random pattern, moving above and below zero, and seldom beyond 1.5 in either direction – which it does.

It is appropriate to use the runs test. On the surface, the runs test appears to be well suited, since one of the metrics of a trading system is its accuracy. Additional tests with the winning percentage set higher than 60% do show convincing z-score patterns. At the accuracy levels of 60% and below, the runs test does not seem to be useful in determining whether a system is broken or when it happened.

ACCURACY OF TRADES

If a trading system has a historical accuracy of some level, say of 60 percent, there is a distribution of the number of winning trades that can be expected in a sequence of any length. Of course, the average number of winning trades in a 20 trade sequence when the winning percentage is 60% will be 12 trades. But knowing the distribution and, in particular, how few winning trades can be expected before concluding that the system is broken, is useful. A simulation was run that generated 1000 independent sequences, each 20 trades long, with accuracy percentages from 20 percent to 80 percent. Figure 11.7 shows the result. The lines represent inverse cumulative distribution functions (CDFs).

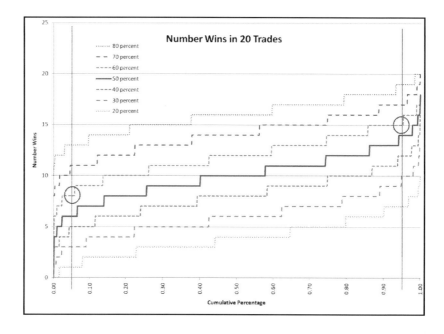

FIGURE 11.7

As expected, the higher the accuracy, the higher the percentage of a 20 trade sequence are expected to be winners. The dotted line with the circles near the ends is the line representing an accuracy of 60%. The two vertical lines that go through the circles are at cumulative percentage 5% and 95%. A system that has been 60% accurate does have a mean of 12 winning trades (the value of the 60% line at the point where cumulative percentage is 0.50) and will usually have between 9 and 15 winning trades in every 20. The left side of the chart shows how many winning trades would be unusually low. If it has a sequence of 20 trades has 8 or fewer winning trades, the system is probably broken and should be taken offline. If it has 16 or more winning trades, that is also unusual, but is not penalized.

Figure 11.8 shows a similar chart for sequences of 15 trades.

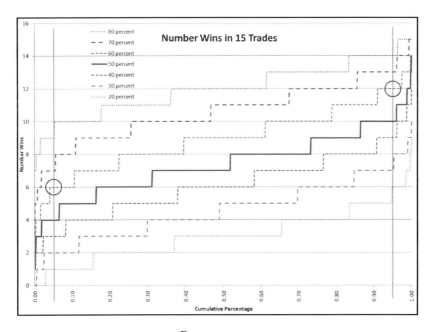

FIGURE 11.8

Figure 11.9 shows the distribution of the number of winning trades in 10 trades.

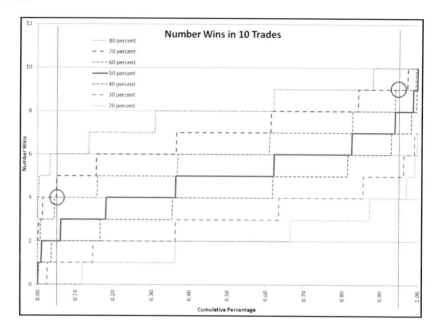

FIGURE 11.9

The ability to use these charts depends on having a high ratio of winning trades to losing trades.

It is relatively easy to detect that a system that has a high ratio of winners to losers has gotten out of sync. A system that has 60% winners can confidently be taken offline if there are fewer than 4 winners in the most recent 10 trades, fewer than 6 in the most recent 15 trades, or fewer than 9 in the most recent 20 trades.

On the other hand, systems with low ratios are more difficult to diagnose. If a system has only a 30% ratio of winners to losers, the trader can expect that in about 15% of every sequence of 10 trades there will be only one winning trade, but even this low number is not low enough to suggest that the system is broken.

The accuracy test is appropriate, and is useful when the trading accuracy is high.

BINOMIAL DISTRIBUTION

When the outcome of a process can take only one of two possible values, the process is called a Bernoulli process, and the results are described by the Binomial distribution.

A trading example is whether a trade is a winner or a loser, without regard for the amount of gain or loss.

A binomial distribution is characterized by a single parameter, p_0, the probability of success. Since the only other possibility is not success – failure – and the sum of the probabilities must equal 1, then the probability of failure is $1 - p_0$.

A single Bernoulli experiment can be represented by a graph, where the point at the left is the initial state before one of the two outcomes is determined, the two lines represent the two possible outcomes with labels indicating which happened, and the probability is given for each path. The branching continues with each path showing one of the possible outcomes of a series of experiments, all of which are identical and independent. Figure 11.10 shows the graph for a series of three successive trades, where each has a 60% probability of being a winning trade.

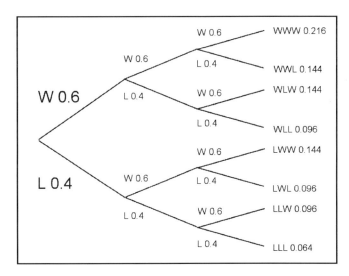

Figure 11.10

There are eight final results, each represented by one of the paths. The possible outcomes can be summarized as:

3 Wins	1 way Probability 0.216	
2 Wins 1 Loss	3 ways	0.432
1 Win, 2 Losses	3 ways	0.288
3 Losses	1 way	0.064

The distribution and probability of a particular ratio of winning trades to losing trades can be read from the results. For example, there are 3 different combinations that result in 2 wins out of a series of 3 trials, and the probability of having 2 wins is 0.432.

The probability of that combination can be computed using the binomial formula. The probability of x successes in an experiment of n trials where the probability of success is p_o is:

$$\binom{n}{k} p_0^k (1 - p_0)^{(n-k)}$$

where $\binom{n}{k}$ is the binomial coefficient. The binomial coefficient is the number of ways k items can be chosen from a set of n items. The coefficient can be computed using the relationship:

$$\binom{n}{k} = \frac{n!}{k!(n-k)!}$$

where ! is the factorial operator. n! is defined to be $1 * 2 * 3 * \ldots * n$ – the product of all integers up to and including n. 0! is defined to be 1.

The probability of 2 wins out of a series of 3 trials when the probability of a win is 0.6 is:

$$\binom{3}{2} 0.6^2 (1 - 0.6)^1 = 0.432$$

The binomial distribution is closely approximated by the Normal distribution for any fixed p, even if p is a small value.

The mean of a binomial distribution is np_o and the standard deviation is $\sqrt{np_0(1 - p_0)}$.

PRACTICAL APPLICATION

In the case of computing the number of wins in a certain number of trades when the percentage of trades that are winners is known, the binomial distribution can be used. This section compares use of the theoretical distribution with simulation. It replicates the 50 percent winner line in figure 11.7 which shows the number of wins in 20 trades.

The binomial distribution is the result of a binomial experiment. A binomial experiment has these characteristics:

- A fixed number of trials. 20, in this case.
- For each trial there are two outcomes. Win or Lose.
- The probability of success, p, is fixed. 0.50 in this case.
- The trials are independent.

Figure 11.11 shows the spreadsheet used to perform the calculations. Note that there are no calls to the random function. All calculations are deterministic.

	A	B	C	D	E	F	G	H	I	J	K	L	M
7			20										
8			Percent Win										
9			0.50										
10													
11		Wins	pdf	CDF	Wins		Cum Pct	Num Wins		C7: Maximum length			
12				0.0000	0		0	0		C9: Percent winners			
13		0	0.0000	0.0000	1		0.001	3		B13:B33 0 through 20			
14		1	0.0000	0.0000	2		0.002	4		C13: =BINOMDIST(B13,C$7,C$9,FALSE)			
15		2	0.0002	0.0002	3		0.003	4		C14:C33 Copy down			
16		3	0.0011	0.0013	4		0.004	4		D12: 0			
17		4	0.0046	0.0059	5		0.005	4		D13: =C13+d12			
18		5	0.0148	0.0207	6		0.006	5		D14:D33 Copy down			
19		6	0.0370	0.0577	7		0.007	5		E12: =B13			
20		7	0.0739	0.1316	8		0.008	5		E13:E32: Copy down			
21		8	0.1201	0.2517	9		0.009	5		E33: =E32			
22		9	0.1602	0.4119	10		0.01	5		G12: 0			
23		10	0.1762	0.5881	11		0.011	5		G13: = G12+0.001			
24		11	0.1602	0.7483	12		0.012	5		G14:G1012: Copy down			
25		12	0.1201	0.8684	13		0.013	5		H12: =LOOKUP(G12,D$12:E$33,E$12:E$32)			
26		13	0.0739	0.9423	14		0.014	5		H13:H1012: Copy down			
27		14	0.0370	0.9793	15		0.015	5					
28		15	0.0148	0.9941	16		0.016	5		Chart B13:D33			
29		16	0.0046	0.9987	17		0.017	5		Chart G12:H1012			
30		17	0.0011	0.9998	18		0.018	5					
31		18	0.0002	1.0000	19		0.019	5					
32		19	0.0000	1.0000	20		0.02	5					
33		20	0.0000	1.0000	20		0.021	6					
34							0.022	6					
35							0.023	6					

FIGURE 11.11

The calls to BINOMDIST create the column labeled pdf – the probability density function. Forming a cumulative sum of the values of the pdf create the Cumulative Distribution Function in the column labeled CDF. The graphs results from these two columns are shown in figure 11.12.

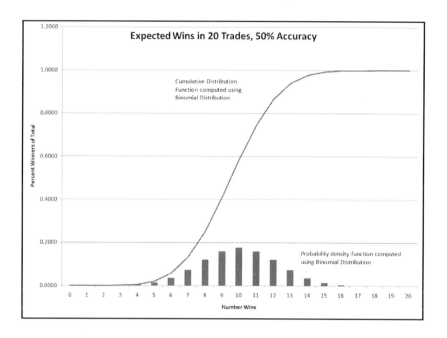

FIGURE 11.12

The inverse CDF is computed in columns labeled Cum Pct and Num Wins. The chart of those two columns is shown in figure 11.13.

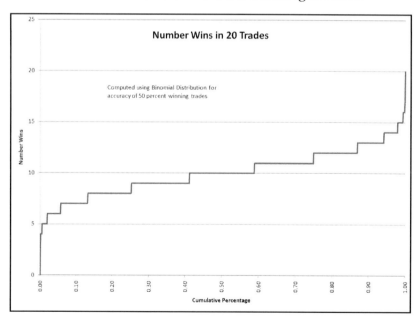

FIGURE 11.13

The line in figure 11.13 is the result of using the theoretical Binomial Distribution, and the line in figure 11.7 is the result of a Monte Carlo simulation. In this case, we could use either technique because we know which theoretical distribution should be applied and there is a closed form of that distribution that can be used to calculate the pdf, CDF, and Inverse CDF. When either we do not know the correct theoretical distribution, or there is not a formula for it, then the simulation is the technique used. Figure 11.14 shows the agreement between the two methods. If the agreement is not adequate, running the simulation with more data points will improve it.

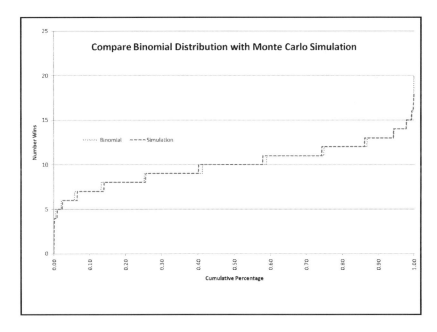

FIGURE 11.14

The Excel and Monte Carlo results can be verified using the binomial formula. For example, the probability of exactly 6 winners in a series of 20 trades when the probability of a winning trade is 0.50 is:

$$\binom{20}{6}(.5^6)(.5^{14})$$

(38760) (0.015625) (0.000061035) = 0.036964

which rounds to 0.0370 and agrees with the value in the table from Excel above.

Calculation and testing of z-scores is also possible and appropriate for binomial data. The standard definition of z-score for a specific number of wins, x, is:

$$\frac{x - np_0}{\sqrt{np_0(1 - p_0)}}$$

For a sequence of 20 trades, where the probability of a winning trade is 0.60, the z-score for having 8 winning trades is:

$$\frac{8 - (20)(0.60)}{\sqrt{(20)(0.60)(0.40)}} = -1.826$$

A z-score is significant at the 5% level if its absolute value is 1.645 or greater. The z-score of -1.826 suggests that it is probably safe to say that the winning proportion is no longer 60%.

COMPARISON OF MEANS

T-TEST

There are several varieties of t-test: one-sample, two-sample, and paired. In each case, the t-statistic, which follows the standard Normal distribution with mean 0 and standard deviation 1, is computed. There is a different t distribution for each sample size. Large values of t suggest the measurement is far from the mean, the p-value will be small, the test significant. For sample sizes above about 10 the t distribution closely approaches the z distribution; at about 30 they are nearly identical. A t-statistic of 3 corresponds to a z-score of 3, meaning a difference of 3 standard deviations from the mean, which occurs less than 0.3% of the time.

One-sample

A one-sample t-test tests the hypothesis that the mean of a sample is equal to a specific value, usually an estimate of the population mean, μ_0.

The statistic is:

$$t = \frac{\bar{x} - \mu_0}{\frac{s}{\sqrt{n}}}$$

where s is the standard deviation of the sample and n is the sample size.

The equation could be written more simply, but the term, $\frac{s}{\sqrt{n}}$, is the standard error of the sample mean and this form of the equation makes clear how the t-statistic relates to it. As related to a trading system, a one-sample t-test could be used to test whether the mean gain for an observed set of trade results differs from 0. The formula for that is:

$$t = \frac{\bar{x}}{s}\sqrt{n}$$

It is the ratio of the mean to the standard deviation, multiplied by the square root of the number of data points. This illustrates the importance of having:

- large mean
- small standard deviation
- large n

Two-sample

The unpaired t-test for two means tests the difference between the means of two samples of numeric data. In a trading example, an unpaired two-sample t-test could be used to test whether the mean gain for a set of recent results differs from the mean gain for a benchmark set of results. The formula is:

$$t = \frac{(\bar{x}_1 - \bar{x}_2) - (\mu_1 - \mu_2)}{\sqrt{\dfrac{s_1^2}{n_1} + \dfrac{s_2^2}{n_2}}}$$

where the terms indexed 1 and 2 represent the two samples. The number of degrees of freedom can either be calculated, as will be done by a package such as Excel, or use the smaller of n_1-1 and n_2-1. The radical term in the denominator takes the variance of both samples into account.

Paired

Paired tests are used when there are two treatments, two conditions, or a before and an after result. This is more applicable to controlled experiments than trading systems.

Use

The ability of the t-test to distinguish differences in the means of two samples depends very heavily on the variability of the data. Figure 11.15 shows three situations. The means of the two samples are the same in each situation, but the standard deviation varies considerably. In the first, it will be easy to show a difference. The second will be more difficult – there will be a lower level of confidence. The third may not be able to distinguish.

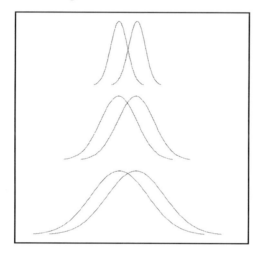

FIGURE 11.15

WHEN TO USE T-TEST

The t-test comparing two means assumes that both samples come from Normal distributions. When the data does come from approximately Normal distributions, and the t-test is an appropriate test, it will usually be a more conclusive test than other tests that do not assume the Normal distribution.

The t-test is reasonably robust and insensitive to deviations from the Normal distribution. Use the t-test when any of these conditions apply:

- The population distribution is normal.
- The sampling distribution is symmetric, unimodal, without outliers, and the sample size is 15 or less.
- The sampling distribution is moderately skewed, unimodal, without outliers, and the sample size is between 16 and 40.

- The sample size is greater than 40, without outliers.

These recommendations are based on extensive computer work and documented in these articles:

- Harry O. Posten, "The robustness of the two-sample t-test over the Pearson system", *Journal of Statistical Computation and Simulation*, Volume 6, Issue 3 & 4, 1978 , pages 295 – 311. From the abstract: "The results indicate that the equal-sample size two-sample t-test is quite robust with respect to departures from normality, perhaps even more so than most people realize."
- Harry O. Posten, "The robustness of the one-sample t-test over the Pearson system", *Journal of Statistical Computation and Simulation*, 9, (1979), pp 133-149.
- E. S. Pearson and N. W. Please, "Relation between the shape of population distribution and the robustness of four simple test statistics", *Biometrica*, 62 (1975), pp 223-241.]

If conditions for the t-test are not met, that usually means either:

1. The distribution is not sufficiently Normal. Try using a transformation, such as taking the logarithm of the data, to make the distribution closer to Normal.
2. There are outliers. Try using a transformation, such as Winsorizing, to trim outliers.

If transformations do not correct the problems, consider using a non-parametric test, such as chi-square or Kolmogorov-Smirnov.

How to Use T-test

The data used in the 60% / 50% example appears to be uniformly distributed, there are no outliers, and there are many data points. We will use the t-test to compare gain per trade between the 60% and 50% accuracy groups to determine if they are different. Refer to figure 11.5, above.

The period of 60% winning trades runs from the left edge to the vertical line at trade 112. Then accuracy falls to 50%. Given full hindsight, the two sub-series can be compared using a t-test. It is not necessary that the number of data points in the two series be the same. It is also not necessary that the variance in the two series be the same, although the test is more conclusive if the variances are equal.

The default null hypothesis for the Excel calculation is:

H_0: The difference between means is 0.

If H_0 is rejected, the means are probably different. If the mean of the later data is higher, that is in our favor, we will not penalize the system. If the mean is lower, the system is probably broken.

Figure 11.16 shows the results of the t-test as provided by Excel's Data Analysis tools. Two runs were made – one using the option assuming equal variances, the other unequal.

Excel's statistical package has the difference between the two means as a parameter (we used 0.0), then gives both the one-tail and two-tail results.

t-Test: Two-Sample Assuming Equal Variances		
	60% Winners	*50% Winners*
Mean	0.0759	-0.0085
Variance	0.0983	0.0904
Observations	111	194
Pooled Variance	0.0933	
Hypothesized Mean Difference	0	
df	303	
t Stat	2.3231	
P(T<=t) one-tail	0.0104	
t Critical one-tail	1.6499	
P(T<=t) two-tail	0.0208	
t Critical two-tail	1.9678	

t-Test: Two-Sample Assuming Unequal Variances		
	60% Winners	*50% Winners*
Mean	0.0759	-0.0085
Variance	0.0983	0.0904
Observations	111	194
Hypothesized Mean Difference	0	
df	221	
t Stat	2.2969	
P(T<=t) one-tail	0.0113	
t Critical one-tail	1.6518	
P(T<=t) two-tail	0.0226	
t Critical two-tail	1.9708	

FIGURE 11.16

We can see from the chart that the mean of the more recent data is lower. The Excel report confirms that, 0.0759 vs -0.0085. The t-statistic ("t Stat" in the reported results) for the two tests is 2.32 and 2.30, respectively. Both show that they are significant at about the 1% level ("P(T<=t) one-tail" in the reported results), or equivalently give about 99% confidence. The variance is essentially the same in the two groups, so the test that assumes equal variances can be used. The t-test indicates that the two series come from distributions that have different means with confidence at about the 1% level.

We conclude that the more recent data has a significantly lower mean and the system is probably broken.

Hindsight is great. The t-test does tell us that the means of the two samples are different. It would be more useful to compute a test statistic after every trade to see whether the latest trades seem to have come from a different – poorer – distribution. To focus on the point at which the accuracy changes and make the chart easier to follow, we redefine the two samples. The first sample is the first 90 trades from the group that has been 60% accurate. The second sample is a sliding window of the 30 most recent data points. After each trade is closed, compute the t-statistic comparing the most recent 30 trades with the benchmark of 90 trades. The Excel Data Analysis t-test Routine could be used. Or the calculation could be computed in the cells. Figure 11.17 shows the spreadsheet and the calculations.

	L	M	N	O	P	Q	R	S	T	U
94			0.561222							
95			-0.33947							
96			-0.03631						N11:N103 Trade return known to be acceptable	
97			0.356939						Benchmark data	
98			-0.3384				moving		O100:	=AVERAGE(N11:N100)
99			0.32471				window		P100:	=STDEV(N11:N100)
100			-0.12333	0.080002	0.310448		size			
101			0.371171	mean	stdev		30		Moving window data	
102		above here	0.518043						R101:	30 -- moving window size
103		known good	0.569456	0.115376	0.326387		-0.52033		O103:	=AVERAGE(OFFSET(N103,-R$101+1,0,R$101,1))
104		at 60%	-0.17215	0.122668	0.316995		-0.64173		P103:	=STDEV(OFFSET(N103,-R$101+1,0,R$101,1))
105		accuracy	-0.29335	0.11824	0.321976		-0.56835		R103:	=(O$100-O103)/SQRT(P$100*P$100/90 + P103*P103/30)
106			-0.24572	0.093462	0.320371		-0.20082			
107			-0.24062	0.07431	0.322665		0.084462			
108			-0.23203	0.054894	0.323002		0.372276			
109			-0.214	0.033466	0.318631		0.697206			
110			0.530548	0.059943	0.325998		0.295324			
111			-0.38976	0.058098	0.328455		0.320636			
112			0.477976	0.072606	0.337247		0.106073			
113			0.399714	0.089561	0.340575		-0.13604			
114			-0.24464	0.077194	0.345888		0.039481			
115			0.060074	0.083324	0.343826		-0.04692			
116			0.077049	0.095351	0.33678		-0.22036			
117			0.030109	0.086157	0.334591		-0.08881			
118			0.029617	0.090455	0.33295		-0.15141			
119			-0.01185	0.071688	0.321766		0.123635			
120			-0.2967	0.06742	0.325887		0.185293			
121			0.501389	0.069474	0.328499		0.154096			
122		begin 50%	-0.00805	0.054944	0.321671		0.37271			
123			0.015765	0.05458	0.32171		0.378092			
124			0.220781	0.043232	0.308975		0.563819			
125			0.13141	0.058928	0.300713		0.329713			
126			0.314963	0.070637	0.303701		0.145448			
127			-0.12807	0.05447	0.30083		0.399348			
128			0.184572	0.071903	0.292311		0.129376			
129			-0.49164	0.044691	0.305658		0.545827			
130			-0.22466	0.041313	0.308129		0.594461			
131			-0.09187	0.025879	0.302583		0.842928			
132			-0.37419	-0.00386	0.296324		1.326378			
133			-0.27004	-0.03185	0.279476		1.845151	Broken		
134			-0.41202	-0.03984	0.28696		1.940106			
135			-0.33461	-0.04122	0.288313		1.955736			

FIGURE 11.17

The critical level for a one-tail test at the 5% level of significance is 1.66; and 2.36 at the 1% level. (There is very little change in the critical values beyond about 30 degrees of freedom.)

Figure 11.18 shows the chart of the t-statistic as it is computed after each trade. The accuracy is known to have dropped from 60% to 50% beginning with trade 20 of the data plotted. After trade 31, the t-statistic rises through the 1.66 level, indicating there is probably a significant change in the system.

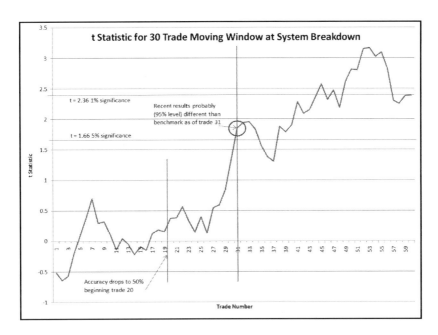

FIGURE 11.18

Figure 11.19 shows the returns for each trade for the same period. The system is known to be broken beginning with trade 20. After trade 31, the moving window t-test shows that the system is probably broken.

As is typical with statistical tests, there is a trade-off between the certainty of a test and the amount of data used to compute the test statistic. Increasing the number of data points gives the test better ability to detect a difference, but, since this is a time series, also increases the lag. Shortening the length of the moving window reduces the lag, but also makes the t-test less sensitive.

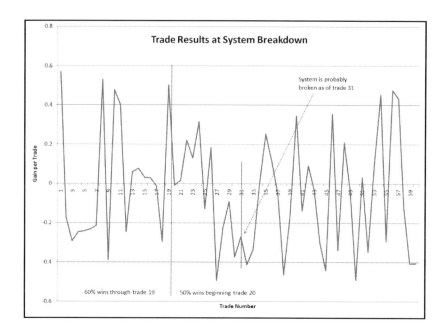

FIGURE 11.19

It is appropriate and useful to use the t-test to compare the means of two groups of trading results.

WILCOXON

Wilcoxon is often suggested as a non-parametric alternative to the t-test.

The Wilcoxon test requires paired data points and is generally not useful in evaluating trading system performance.

CONTROL CHARTS

Development of quality control techniques, including statistical quality control, control charts, and acceptance sampling, dates from the 1920's with work done by W. A. Shewhart and his colleagues at the Bell Telephone Laboratories.

Control charts were developed to help monitor ongoing quality of a process over time. They are especially useful for manufacturing processes. In this section, we examine whether applying control chart techniques to trading system results can help identify deterioration in trading results. Two major differences between manufacturing and trading are:

- **Manufacturing**. The target metric of a manufactured item, such as a ball bearing and its diameter, is predetermined by the specifications of the product, and is constant (or at least predictable) throughout monitoring.
  Trading. The target metric of a trading system is estimated from real trades or the out-of-sample results from test runs and varies considerably over time.

- **Manufacturing**. The variation in the metric of manufactured items is very small. A milling operation might require a 20 mm deep cut in a piece of metal. The accuracy of the machine and the operator are such that the standard deviation of the depth is 0.1 mm. Resulting in a coefficient of variation of 0.5%. For the entire period the machine is being monitored, the depth required remains 20 mm.
  Trading. The variation of trades is very high. The most consistent systems hold for a short period of time and often exit through profit targets. Even then, it is very rare to have the standard deviation less than two times the mean, and not unusual for it to be three or four times the mean. If the average gain per trade is 0.2% and the standard deviation is 0.6%, the coefficient of variation is 300%.

The same data that was used with the t-test is used again with the control chart.

One of the points made by Shewhart, and reinforced by practitioners who followed, including W. Edwards Deming, is that control charts are intended to be heuristic rather than theoretical. Consequently, there are many different ways to establish the control charts, and many ways to interpret them. Statisticians would want to test the data to see if it followed the Normal distribution, compute standard deviations, and draw control lines at 1, 2, and 3 standard deviations above and below the mean. Figure 11.20 does exactly that for a 90 day period while the accuracy was 60 percent through the period.

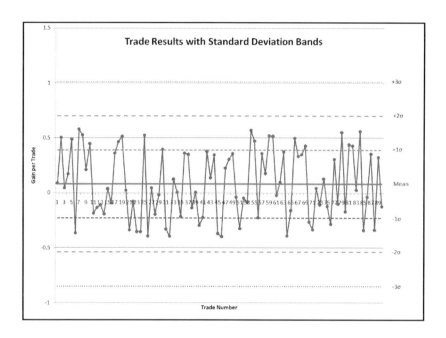

FIGURE 11.20

In a carefully controlled manufacturing process, small samples of data (1 to 15 individual machined parts) are collected at regular intervals. The product specification (or the mean of the data) is used as the center line, and the standard error (the standard deviation of the means on the samples) is used to establish the upper control limit (UCL) and lower control limit (LCL) at + / - 3 standard errors, respectively. Additional lines are drawn between the mean and the control lines to establish zones. The mean of each successive sample is plotted, and the position of the mean relative to the zones and control lines is used to monitor the health of the system. In a manufacturing process, the control target is established by the product specifications and is not expected to change as the manufacturing runs are made.

To take the control chart approach with a trading system, decide what the control target will be. A logical choice is previous performance. Then establish the center line and the limits based on historical results for actual trades or for out-of-sample test results. The number of points in the samples used will be the number of trades to accumulate into a sample. In this example, we used five. Any number can be used, but there is the usual trade-off between sensitivity in the ability to detect an anomaly and lag before it can be detected.

The average of 12 samples, each consisting of 5 trades, all recorded when the system was trading at 60% accuracy, is used to establish the controls. Figure 11.21 shows the control chart.

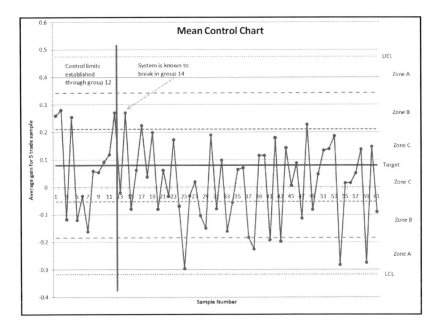

FIGURE 11.21

As each additional sample is collected and plotted, a set of heuristic rules is consulted to determine whether the system is in control or out of control.

One set of rules suggests the system is out of control when any of the following are true:

- 1 data point falling outside the control limits, which are UCL at 4.8 or LCL at -3.2. There are none of these in figure 11.21.

- 6 or more points in a row steadily increasing or decreasing. There are none of these.

- 8 or more points in a row on one side of the centerline. There are none of these.

- 14 or more points alternating up and down. There are none of these.

Another set of rules:
- 9 data points in a row on one side of the centerline. There are none of these.
- 6 or more points in a row steadily increasing or decreasing. There are none of these.
- 14 or more points alternating up and down. There are none of these.
- 2 out of 3 points in a row in Zone A or beyond. There are none of these.
- 4 out of 5 points in a row in Zone B or beyond. There are several of these, including one in the period the system was known to have been working – trades 1 through 5. Another set is trades 28 through 31.
- 15 points in a row in Zone C. This test suggests the results are too good. There are none of these.
- 8 points in a row in Zones A or B, but none in Zone C. This test suggests the results are bimodal. There are none of these.

Developers of trading systems might want to adjust the rules to reflect trading:
- Do not penalize points above the mean.

One expert, the American Society for Quality Control, advises that if the system is thought to be out of control when the process of setting up the control charts is begun, use a 20 sample window to establish provisional limits. When the system is in control for a period of 20 samples, reestablish control limits.

In this example, use of control charts was unable to detect the change in accuracy of the system.

Applying the intraocular impact test to figure 11.21, the system appears to be broken at about sample 25. But none of the heuristic rules listed alerted us to that.

It is appropriate to construct control charts and use them to monitor ongoing performance, but the high coefficient of variation hinders their effectiveness.

GOODNESS OF FIT

Goodness of fit tests will give insight into whether a sample came from a specific distribution or whether two samples came from the same distribution.

The goodness of fit most important when monitoring the performance of trading systems is the fit between the current trading results and the benchmark results. Benchmark data comes from historical live trades, historical paper trades, or out-of-sample tests. Be aware that in-sample results are always better than out-of-sample or live results. In lieu of benchmark comparable trading results, comparisons can be made against random results, or buy and hold. Whatever the benchmark is, it must be expressed as a CDF with the same periodicity as the trading results.

It may be of theoretical interest to know whether or not the day to day changes in the price of a stock follow the Normal distribution or some other known distribution. And that may be of practical interest if you are working with a model that assumes a particular distribution. If that is important, do one of these things:

- Consult more advanced references and learn about tests that are applicable to specific distributions, then use those tests.
- Make data transformations so that the data does follow the distribution of interest, and then use those tests.
- Using simulations or research, determine the effect of using tests designed for one distribution with data from another distribution. Some tests are quite forgiving, so they can be used even when the sample data is not from the desired distribution.

KOLMOGOROV-SMIRNOV

The K-S test is a goodness-of-fit test used to compare two cumulative distribution functions. The test is non-parametric and distribution-free, but the data must be continuous. If the reference CDF is that of the Normal distribution, then the K-S statistic can be used to reject the hypothesis that the observed distribution is Normal. K-S is very robust, and transformations can be made to improve the spread of the data on the graph. K-S does not require that the two samples have the same number of data points.

To prepare the data for the test, each of the 30 trade samples was used to create a CDF. Figure 11.22 shows the CDF for the final 30 trades when the system was known to be 60% accurate – the lower line – and the first 30 trades when the system was known to be 50% accurate – the upper line.

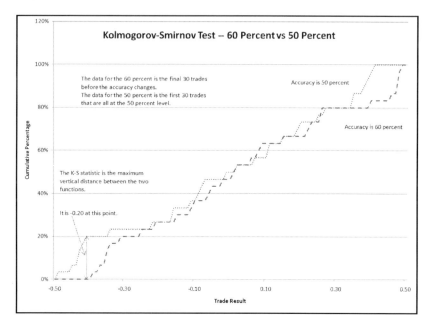

Kolmogorov-Smirnov Test -- 60 Percent vs 50 Percent

The data for the 60 percent is the final 30 trades before the accuracy changes.
The data for the 50 percent is the first 30 trades that are all at the 50 percent level.

Accuracy is 50 percent

Accuracy is 60 percent

The K-S statistic is the maximum vertical distance between the two functions.

It is -0.20 at this point.

Cumulative Percentage

Trade Result

FIGURE 11.22

The K-S statistic, D, is defined to be the largest vertical difference between the two CDFs. Figure 11.23 shows the difference.

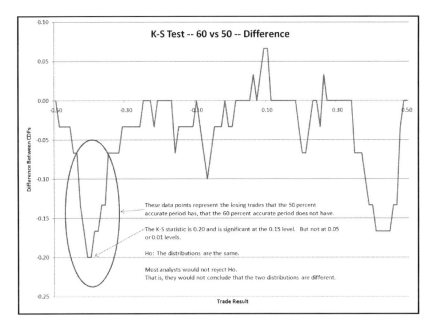

FIGURE 11.23

The maximum difference occurs at the left end, where the 50% line has losses that the 60% line does not have. The maximum value is 0.20, which is not significant at the 0.05 level, so most analysts would not reject H_0. That is, they would not conclude that the system was broken and needed to be taken off line.

The Kolmogorov-Smirnov test is appropriate, but is not very sensitive. Several transformations are needed to prepare the data for the test, which further reduces its attractiveness.

ANDERSON-DARLING

The Anderson-Darling test is a parametric goodness-of-fit statistical test of whether a sample comes from a specified distribution. It is commonly used to compare a sample with the Normal distribution, and is one of the best tests for that purpose. Anderson-Darling is often compared with Kolmogorov-Smirnov and, when conditions for its use are met, preferred because it is much more sensitive to outliers and differences in the tails of the distribution being tested.

The Anderson-Darling statistic, A^2, must be compared with a table specific to the specified distribution. Tables are available for Normal, exponential, and Weibull distributions, and a few others, but not for empirical data of unknown distribution.

The Anderson-Darling test could be used to determine whether data fit the Normal distribution well enough to proceed with other tests that are depend on that. But the rules of thumb given on pages 232 and 233 are adequate for our purposes.

The Anderson-Darling test is not appropriate for testing whether two samples came from the same unknown distribution, so is of little value in detecting whether a trading system is broken.

CHI-SQUARE TEST

The chi-square is a goodness-of-fit test that works with nominal data. It is non-parametric and distribution-free. It is used to test whether two samples came from the same population. The test is made either between two observed samples, or between an observed sample and a known distribution.

The test uses binned data, so it depends on how the data is binned. Bin interval can be either equal probability or equal width; with equal probability usually preferable, but equal width most commonly used. Each bin should contain a minimum of 5 data points. If necessary, adjacent bins are combined to give the necessary count. Once binned, the only thing that matters is the number of data points in each bin.

One recommendation for the number of bins, k, for N data elements is:

$$k = 1 + \log_2 N$$

Another method for selecting bin size is to set it to 0.3 times the standard deviation of the sample data.

The chi-square statistic, χ^2, is computed as:

$$\chi^2 = \sum_{i=1}^{k} \frac{(O_i - E_i)^2}{E_i}$$

Where O_i is the observed frequency for bin i, E_i is the expected frequency for bin i.

> H_0: The data come from the same distribution and all bin proportions agree.
>
> H_1: At least one of the specified proportions is unusually large or small.

Reject H_0 if the test statistic is greater than the chosen significance level, α, as listed in the chi-square table using k-1 degrees of freedom.

The same data that was used for the moving window of the t-test was used for a moving window test using chi-square as the test statistic.

The first 90 trades from period when accuracy was known to be 60% are used to define the expected data. Knowing in advance that the observed data would be a 30 trade window and that chi-square works best when bins have at least 5 data points, 6 bins were defined using equal probability boundaries based on the 60% data. Each bin of the 60% data has 15 elements. Those boundaries are then used to define bins for the 30 observed data points in the moving window, anticipating that each bin will have 5 data points.

Eight windows were tested. The first was the final 30 trades just before the accuracy dropped from 60% to 50%, so all 30 trades were 60% and none were 50%. The next test used the window that had 25 60% trades and 5 50% trades. The number of 50% trades was increased by 5 each for tests 3 through 7. Test 7 had all 30 trades from the 50% accuracy, and an 8th test was 5 trades further, also all 50%. Figure 11.24 shows the calculations in the spreadsheet.

Population data										
bins boundaries	60% trades			Observed data						
-1	0	Expected	0 50%	5 50%	10 50%	15 50%	20 50%	25 50%	30 50%	30 50%
-0.29	15	5	5	4	4	6	6	7	8	10
-0.11	15	5	7	7	8	7	5	5	5	5
0.04	15	5	5	5	6	7	8	9	7	6
0.33	15	5	3	6	6	6	8	7	8	6
0.44	15	5	4	3	1	1	1	1	2	2
1	15	5	6	5	5	3	2	1	0	1
	90	30	30	30	30	30	30	30	30	30
			0.00	0.20	0.20	0.20	0.20	0.80	1.80	5.00
			0.80	0.80	1.80	0.80	0.00	0.00	0.00	0.00
			0.00	0.00	0.20	0.80	1.80	3.20	0.80	0.20
			0.80	0.20	0.20	0.20	1.80	0.80	1.80	0.20
			0.20	0.80	3.20	3.20	3.20	3.20	1.80	1.80
			0.20	0.00	0.00	0.80	1.80	3.20	5.00	3.20
		chi-square	2.00	2.00	5.60	6.00	8.80	11.20	11.20	10.40
		run	0	5	10	15	20	25	30	30
		df = 5	critical							
		5%	11.07							
		10%	9.24							
		20%	7.29							

FIGURE 11.24

Figure 11.25 shows the plot of the chi-square statistic for each of the windows.

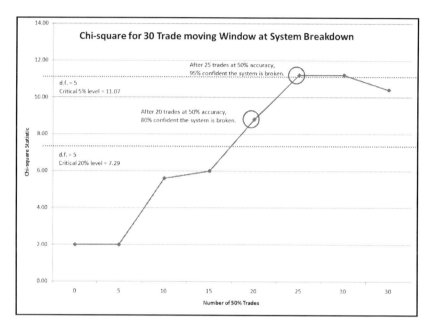

FIGURE 11.25

The chi-square statistic for the first two tests is 2.0. A low number indicates good agreement between the observed data and the expected data. As the number of 50% trades increases, the number of trades that fall into the bins changes, more into the lower bins and less into the upper bins, and the chi-square statistic increases. With 20 of the trades coming from the 50% accuracy data, the chi-square statistic is above the critical level for 0.20, suggesting at a level of about 80% that the system is broken. When there are 25 trades from the 50% data, the chi-square statistic is above the critical level for 0.05, suggesting at a level of about 95% that the system is broken.

The chi-square test does show system deterioration, but with a longer lag than the t-test. The t-test showed the system to be broken after about 12 trades, the chi-square test after about 25 trades.

Chi-square is an appropriate test, and may be helpful.

OTHER TECHNIQUES

PROBABILITY REFRESHER

Pr(A) means or represents the probability that event A will happen.

> For example, when drawing a single card from a shuffled full deck,
>
> Pr(Card is an Ace) = ?
>
> Pr(Ace) = 4/52.
>
> There are 4 Aces among the 52 cards.

Pr(A and B) means the probability that both A and B are True or will happen.

> Pr(A and B) = Pr(A) x Pr(B), provided A and B are independent.
>
> Pr(Ace and Spade) = ?
>
> Pr(Ace and Spade) = 4/52 x 13/52 = 1/52.
>
> There are 4 Aces and 13 Spades. 1 of the Spades is an Ace.

Pr(A or B) means the probability that either A is true or B is true.

> Pr(A or B) = Pr(A) + Pr(B) - Pr(A and B).
>
> Pr(Ace or King) = ?
>
>> There are 4 Aces among the 52 cards and 4 Kings, and there are no cards that are both Ace and King, so Pr(Ace and King) = 0.
>>
>> Pr(Ace or King) = 4/52 + 4/52 - 0/52 = 8/52 = 0.154 = 15.4%.
>
> Pr(Ace or Spade) = ?
>
>> There are 4 Aces and 13 Spades. 1 card is both an Ace and a Spade.
>>
>> Pr(Ace or Spade) = 4/52 + 13/52 - 1/52 = 16/52 = 0.308.

Pr(A|B) means the probability that A will happen given that B happens. This is called conditional probability.

> Pr(A|B) = Pr(A and B) / Pr(B).
>
> Pr(Spade|Ace) asks "What is the probability a card is a Spade, given that it is an Ace?"
>
> Pr(Spade|Ace) = Pr(Spade and Ace) / Pr(Ace)
>
> Pr(Spade|Ace) = 1/52 / 4/52 = 1/4 = 0.25

For example, a survey showed that 48% of all teenagers own a skateboard, and 39% of all teenagers own both a skateboard and roller blades. What is the probability that a teenager owns rollerblades given that that teenager owns a skateboard?

Pr(SK) = 0.48

Pr(RB and SK) = 0.39

Pr(Rollerblades|Skateboard) = ?
    Pr(RB|SK) = Pr(RB and SK) / Pr(SK)
    Pr(RB|SK) = 0.39 / 0.48 = 0.812 = 81.2%

BAYES

Thomas Bayes was a mathematician and theologian who lived in England from 1702 to 1761. He held a subjectivist view, maintaining that belief is governed by the laws of probability and depend heavily on conditional probabilities. When he died, he left some unpublished papers that were discovered by a colleague and sent to the Royal Society, where they were largely ignored. Pierre-Simon Laplace independently discovered Bayes' Theorem, published a more understandable version of it in 1774, and applied it to problems in mechanics and medicine.

Sir Ronald Fisher, 1890 to 1962, is often regarded as the founder of modern experimental design. He was one of the most influential statisticians of the 20th century and a dedicated frequentist, and he argued strongly against the more subjective Bayesian approach.

The frequentist vs Bayesian argument is sometimes described as deductive logic (observing causes and their effects) versus inductive logic (inferring possible causes based on observations of effects).

The deductive logic begins with a fair coin and asks how many times four heads can be expected when it is tossed ten times. The inductive logic begins with a observation that there were seven heads observed in ten tosses and asks whether the coin is fair.

Bayesian statistics draws on Bayes' theorem, which is a statement about the probability of events.

Using a series of transformations and following laws of probability, this relationship, Bayes' Theorem, can be derived:
    $\Pr(B|A) = \Pr(A|B) \times \Pr(B) / \Pr(A)$.

An example from medical testing will help.

- 1% of women at age forty who participate in routine screening have breast cancer.
- 80% of women with breast cancer will get positive mammographies.
- 9.6% of women without breast cancer will also get positive mammographies.

A woman in this age group had a positive mammography in a routine screening. What is the probability that she actually has breast cancer?

The correct answer is 7.8%, obtained as follows:

- Out of 10,000 women, 100 have breast cancer; 80 of those 100 have positive mammographies.
- From the same 10,000 women, 9,900 will not have breast cancer and of those 9,900 women, 950 will also get positive mammographies.
- This makes the total number of women with positive mammographies 950+80 or 1,030.
- Of those 1,030 women with positive mammographies, 80 will have cancer.
- Expressed as a proportion, this is 80/1,030 or 0.07767 or 7.8%.

DURBIN-WATSON TEST

The Durbin-Watson test is designed to analyze the residuals from a regression analysis to test for first order autocorrelation. The Durbin-Watson test uses numeric data where each data point is the difference between the observed data and the value predicted by the regression equation.

The Durbin-Watson statistic is:

$$DW = \frac{\sum_2^n (x_i - x_{i-1})^2}{\sum_1^n (x_i)^2}$$

DW is approximately 2*(1-r), where r is the autocorrelation of the data. DW values range from 0.0 to 4.0. A DW value of 2.0 suggests there is no autocorrelation. Very low values indicate significant positive autocorrelation.

While it may be appropriate to use the Durbin-Watson test on the residuals from a regression, it is probably inappropriate to use the Durbin-Watson test on raw trading results or account equity data. If you want to use the Durbin-Watson test, first run a regression model – for example, regress the raw data against its own value lagged by one bar. Consult statistics references for more details.

EQUITY CURVE

One method of using the equity curve compares the account balance with a moving average of account balance. When the equity drops below its average, take the system offline, but continue to track "shadow" equity that would have resulted from trades made while the system was offline. When the shadow equity rises above the average equity, put the system back into operation. The data being filtered can be either trades or daily account equity. Fast moving averages usually work best. Slow moving averages keep the system offline for long periods of time.

If you are using an equity curve filter on daily equity, decide how you will handle an intra-trade signal. Either wait for the normal exit, then keep the system offline until the filter permits new trades; or exit immediately. If you are using the equity curve filter on the equity after the close of each trade, it becomes a simple filter to allow or block the next trade.

Run some tests on your own system, using results from trading only a single unit, to see if an equity curve filter works.

An equity curve filter can help make a good system better, but it seldom helps make a mediocre system good. If the equity curve filter helps, that usually indicates that there is a serial dependence among trades. If possible, identify that dependence and modify the logic to incorporate it into the trading system. The system will probably benefit more by having the logic improved than by using an equity curve filter.

Depending on the characteristics of the system – particularly if the percentage of trades that are winners is high – it might be possible to use the running average of accuracy as a surrogate for an equity curve. This would be a visual technique equivalent to the runs test.

Another method computes percentage drawdown from equity peak, and takes the system offline when the drawdown exceeds a predetermined limit. As with the equity curve average, continue to track shadow trades and put the system back in operation when enough equity has been earned to recover from the drawdown.

The data used for the equity curve filter must be results from trading a single unit. It is not possible to use the equity curve or drawdown to tell whether the system is broken if the data includes compounding or any level of leverage.

SUMMARY AND RECOMMENDATION

Several points are key in my thinking:

1. There is no certainty; the best we can hope for is a high degree of confidence.
2. Statistical tests will not result in a certain conclusion. Become comfortable thinking in terms of probabilities.
3. There is definitely judgment involved in deciding when to take a system offline.
4. Trading a broken system results in losing money, while just watching a working, but offline, system results in losing opportunity.
5. There is a lag between the time when the system falls out of sync and the time the statistics confirm that it is broken.
6. Not all tests work equally well on all trade result sequences.

In summary, I recommend:

- Use tests that are easy to understand, easy to apply, easy to compute, and easy to evaluate.
- The t-test is one of the most straightforward tests available. It is easily understood and easily computed. Unless the data is wildly different than Normal, treat it as if it is Normal and use the t-test.
- Lower the confidence level required to assume the system is broken and take it offline.
- Be quick to take a system offline, or at least cut back the amount of leverage, particularly when using aggressive position sizing.
- Instead of risking money by trading a broken system, risk losing opportunity. Make up for the lost opportunity by developing other systems.

QUOTE TO REMEMBER

Statistics means never having to say you are certain.

Chapter 12

Summary

Short List of Recommendations

- Treat trading as a business. Have a business plan. Have a metric by which you measure your success. Know the monthly expenses, the capital requirement, the profit potential, and the risk. Design your own trading system and position sizing to maximize profit while holding losses to an acceptable level. Recognize that there is no certainty. Of every twenty traders who have a plan that will work 95% of the time, one will fail; and there may be no evidence that the plan was flawed.

- Your system absolutely must have a positive expectancy. Be very conservative when evaluating test results and be certain the expectancy is positive when measured on truly out-of-sample results.

- Systems alternately work and break. When they break, they begin with the logic losing synchronization with the data. Perhaps the system will resync itself, perhaps it will require adjustment of parameters, or perhaps it will never work again. Be quick to take systems off line. Do not listen to advice that says that the deeper the drawdown the better the time to begin, or resume, trading a system.

- Do not expect to be successful at trading without being skilled in both programming and statistics. You must be able to write your own trading system code and your own simulation code. You must be able to perform your own statistical analysis and interpret the results.

- Learn to set up and run simulations. Practice is important. Use data typical of your own trading system, or of the trading system of your dreams. Study the effect that changes in trading frequency, accuracy, size of losses, and other variables will have. Look at the distribution of results, rather than a single number.

- Collect data and monitor system health daily.

- Keep your per-trade risk to an acceptable level. Keep losses on losing trades small. Given systems with the same expectancy, the one with the smaller standard deviation is better. The one with the smaller semi-deviation is best.

- Systems that have a few large winners must take every signal. Missing a 10x trade makes a big difference. When the system goes out of sync, it is hard to tell because the expected string of losers is always high.

- Trade frequently. 30 to 50 trades per year per system at a minimum. If you are trading frequently, it is natural and easy to change positions as conditions change. Increasing the number of trades increases the number of compoundings of your equity.

- Trading based on a single result from a single backtest using generic position sizing under the assumption that the future will be similar is a recipe for bankruptcy.

- Focus on a few tradables and develop systems for these. Do not build a portfolio thinking there is safety in diversification. With the exception of truly inverse holdings, diversification fails at precisely the time it is needed. In a panic, when you need portfolio components to have low correlations, that is precisely the time correlations all rise toward 1.0 together and all prices drop together. All diversification does is dilute your attention, increase trading cost, and blur results toward the mean.

- Focus on developing trading systems for major indexes. Using an index gives the advantage of diversification across its sector without the effort and distraction of portfolio construction or the exposure to bad stock choices. Indexes are ideal for modeling in trading systems because of the smoothing effect of combining the index components; and the structure of the index allows use of diffusion techniques.

- Trade only highly liquid issues. You must be able to exit any position on any day – preferably any minute of any day.

- Trade highly liquid issues related to the index. Many major indexes have ETFs whose price changes are closely correlated, but offer both positive and negative beta, increased leverage, and can be purchased and held in almost any type of account.

- Use ETFs rather than traditional mutual funds. Expenses are lower, there are no trading or minimum holding period restrictions, and trading is not limited to a single time and price each day.

- The data used to develop and trade should be daily OHLC or perhaps intra-day. Daily close-only is too restrictive because it removes the opportunity to design in profit targets. Weekly or anything longer is too coarse.

- Every trade is a trend following trade while you are in it. But traditional trend following system based on daily, or longer, data are not practical. They get in too late, get out too late, have deep drawdowns, and trade too infrequently. Statistical, pattern, and mean reversion systems are much more responsive and lend themselves to the monitor and control process much better.

System = Model + Data

Recall that a system is defined as a model – an algorithm or set of logic – and a series of price and volume data – a tradable issue or portfolio. The purpose of the model is to identify some characteristic of the data that indicates that a profitable trading opportunity is about to occur. The data consists of a signal portion and a noise portion. During the system development process, the model was designed and adjusted so that it recognizes the signal portion of the data. Everything that is not specifically recognized by the model as signal is noise, even if it contains other valuable information that could be profitably traded using some other model. The system – model plus data – remains profitable as long as the model remains synchronized to the data. Systems break and lose profitability when that synchronization is lost. As a trader watching your system, you have no way of knowing whether the loss of synchronization is temporary or permanent – every permanent system failure begins as a temporary system failure

Optimistic Bias

Review the straw broom charts and distributions of final equity in earlier chapters. There are many, say ten, individual equity curves on the straw broom chart. Each represents a possible equity curve from a single trading system. Without knowledge of the future, all ten are equally likely. There are many, say 1000, points on the distribution curve of final wealth of that system. Each point corresponds to one of the ten equity curves. The entire line represents the distribution of 1000 equity curves, all equally likely. Similarly for the drawdown curves.

The process of designing, testing, and validating a trading system produces equity (and drawdown) curves—lots of them. Eventually, one or more will look good. It is one of a possible many – it is one line on a straw broom chart – it is one dot on one line of a distribution chart – it is one dot on one of many possible distributions.

The question is – which dot on which distribution?

In the process of developing trading systems, we keep adjusting the parameters and logic until the result looks good. There is no avoiding that process, but in doing that, we introduce a bias. When we decide to stop developing and start trading, the equity curves we use to make that decision are more likely to be at the right-hand side of the distribution. We are overly optimistic about the results the system will produce. That is one reason so many people lose money trading. They believe the results are typical – at the 50% level. In reality, the results are optimistic – at the 90% level. Real trades with real money come from throughout the distribution and are less profitable.

Eventually, the randomness will be resolved and you will know which dot on which distribution. But only after the fact.

What is a system developer to do to deal with the optimistic bias produced during the trading system development process?

1. Recognize the bias. In-sample backtest results are so biased that they are worse than useless – they are dangerous. Out-of-sample test results are still biased because of the many iterations of the adjust and test cycle. Walk forward test results are less biased. But, there will always be a bias.

2. Design the trading system knowing that you will need to manage it using statistical analysis and process control techniques.

REQUIREMENTS FOR SUCCESS

Achieving high equity growth requires three components:

- A profitable trading system.
- A healthy trading system.
- A sound position sizing technique.

Profitable. The better the trading system is, the easier it is to determine its health and the more effective the position sizing will be. The quality of the trading system is determined in the design, test, and validation process.

Be aware of the entire range of possible outcomes, rather than just focusing on a single point. The flatter the distribution is, the more consistent, predictable, and reliable the results will be.

Look for the combination of trading frequency, win to loss ratio, holding period, and other characteristics of the trading system that fit your trading requirements. Given a choice, prefer frequent trading, high winning percentage, short holding period, and careful control over losses.

Healthy.   The healthier the trading system is, the better the synchronization between the logic and the data, and the more confidence that the system is performing as expected.

Pay attention to the health of the system. However good the backtest and walk forward results were, equity growth requires that the system be profitable now, with real money. Determining whether a system is working or broken means making a comparison between current performance and some benchmark. Statistical analysis provides the techniques to make the comparison. There is a considerable amount of subjectivity in applying and interpreting the statistics. Be quick to take a system whose health is questionable offline.

Position Sizing.   The sounder the position sizing technique, the higher the leverage can be raised while keeping drawdown within limits.

Position sizing acts as an amplifier, similar to a music system. Increasing the volume when the song is bad or the recording is damaged simply makes the lack of talent of the artist or the flaws in the recording more apparent. Position sizing is not a magic elixir that can be used to improve any system under any conditions. It is one of three important components.

WHAT CAN GO WRONG?
- Trading a system that is unprofitable.
- Failing to monitor system health.
- Trade too aggressively.
- Future is not like the past.
- Model falls out of sync with the data.
- Get unlucky and hit the 5%.

TRADING AND GAMBLING

There is a subtle difference between a roulette player increasing bet size with winnings and a blackjack player or trading system using aggressive position sizing with profits. The odds on the next turn of the roulette wheel are the same as every previous one, and they all have a negative expectancy. The roulette player's winnings give the illusion of control and success, but it confuses luck with skill. Certainly there is a substantial component of luck in the success of a blackjack player or trading system. But there is also a recognition that the expectancy has changed, and it now favors the player. Profits or winnings provide a measure of validation. If there is any time to use aggressive position sizing, it is when the system has recently been profitable. Equally, if there is a time to be cautious, it is when the system has experienced losses. All serious losses are preceded by moderate losses; and all moderate losses are preceded by small losses. Use losing trades as an early warning that the system may be losing its edge – not as an indication that the luck is certain to change soon and an indication to increase exposure. Because of the similarities in the rewards of winning and punishment of losing, traders are subject to the same social and psychological risks, including compulsive behavior, as gamblers.

Remember the prayer, attributed to both gamblers and traders. "Please, just let me get back to even and I promise I will never do this again."

Trading is not like roulette or slot machines. They have a negative expectancy that never changes. Each play is independent and recent plays have no effect on the next play.

Trading is not like poker. A poker player is in a contest with a limited number of competitors. While there is luck and skill involved, there is a great deal of game theory, gamesmanship, and psychology.

Trading is a lot like blackjack. The expectancy changes as cards are exposed. Skillful card counters can compute the advantage or disadvantage they have and adjust the size of their bet accordingly.

TRADING AND STATISTICS

In Scott Patterson's book, *The Quants*, Nick Patterson, former Renaissance analyst, is quoted.

> "It's a statistical game. You discern phenomena in the market. Are they real? That's the key question. You must make sure it's not model error or just noise. If the phenomenon is for real, capitalizing on it can be an even tougher challenge. How much leverage should be used? How much cash can be tossed at the

strategy before it vanishes into thin air? The deep thinkers at Renaissance consider all of these issues and more. Our edge was quite small, but it's like being the house player at a casino, You have a small edge on every bet, and you have to know how to handle that."

SUMMARY

There are an infinite number of possible trading systems. Each is a combination of some logic and some price series. Imagine each one fully described and engraved onto a grain of sand. The system development process is sorting through these choices looking for one that fits your needs and that will work in the future.

During system development, the only data available is the static, historical price and volume data. But our decision must be made based on our best estimates of the future profitability. We would certainly not trade a random system, a system that was never tested, or a system that lost money when backtested. But showing a profit in backtesting is not sufficient.

Once trading begins, the most important task is monitoring the health of the system. This is the stage where we find out whether past results translate into future performance. Start cautiously, monitor carefully, be quick to stop trading.

Know your own utility function. How deep a drawdown can you tolerate? How much gain do you need before you can quit? Run simulations to estimate the distribution of results.

Consider increasing leverage only after the system has generated real profits. As long as the system is healthy, be aggressive.

Of the three—trading system development, system health, position sizing—we spend most of our time searching for something that worked in the past. Developing a trading system is a searching process. Pass enough candidates through the filters and some will look promising. We focus too closely on single values, such as averages, and we ignore the bias we have built into our selection process. When we find a promising system, we ignore the bias, apply position sizing, and imagine the wealth it will generate when we trade it.

In my opinion, the most important of the three is monitoring the system health during live trading. We should be continually asking and answering the question "Is the system working? Or is it broken?" Unfortunately, that phase is the most difficult, least understood, and most subjective.

Being able to perform triage on a live trading system is the key. Should a system be retired completely, traded cautiously, or traded aggressively?

I know, when you took statistics, you hated it. Complicated procedures, conflicting sets of rules about what test could be applied under what circumstances, and subjective decisions. But try again, it might be the critical factor in your trading business.

Thanks for listening,

Howard

DOWNLOAD AND INSTALL BUILDTABLE

Familiarity with computers, the Windows operating system, and Microsoft Excel is assumed. If necessary, refer to other books or websites for tutorials.

Go to this book's website and download the Excel add-in that builds the distribution tables.

http://www.modelingtradingsystemperformance.com/book.html

Click the link for Simulation Add-in. You will be downloading a 45 KB file named MTSPSimulation.xla.

Copy that file to the library subfolder of your Microsoft Office folder. I am using Excel 2007. The path for the library folder on my computer is:

    C:\Program Files\Microsoft Office\Office 12\Library

Under the 64 bit version of Windows 7 it will be in Program Files (x86)

That folder probably already exists and may contain other Excel add-ins, such as Analysis and Solver.

Start Excel, open Excel Options (using the "Office Button"), Click Add-Ins. From the Manage drop-down list at the bottom of the page, select Excel Add-ins, Click Go. Check the box for MTSP Simulation Tools, Click OK.

MTSP BuildTable will be available from the Excel Add-Ins menu.

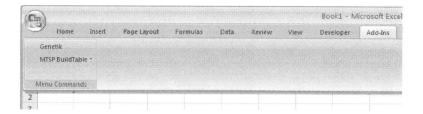

Use of BuildTable

The purpose of BuildTable is to run many individual simulations and record the result of each run into a table. The format of the table makes it easy to display, plot, and analyze the distribution of the results.

A dice tossing example will illustrate.

Step 1—Enter the Excel code necessary to toss each of two dice one time and compute their sum. Unless otherwise noted, text in cells is simply typed in as text. Numbers in cells may be numeric values or formulas. Read the "FORMULAS" area of the spreadsheet for instructions.

	A	B	C	D	E	F	G	H
1	Toy problem to illustrate use of BuildTable							
2	Toss two dice, and generate the cumulative distribution of the sum.							
3								
4								
5	Die 1	Die 2	Sum					
6	3	6	9					
7								
8	FORMULAS							
9	A6 =RANDBETWEEN(1,6)							
10	B6 =RANDBETWEEN(1,6)							
11	C6 =SUM(A6:B6)							
12								
13								

Step 2—Copy the data you want to have appear in the CDF to the top of an area where the CDF will be created. Leave at least one blank column to the left of those cells, and have no data in the rows below. In this example, the table will be created from cell E6 down and to the right.

	A	B	C	D	E	F	G	H
1	Toy problem to illustrate use of BuildTable							
2	Toss two dice, and generate the cumulative distribution of the sum.							
3								
4								
5	Die 1	Die 2	Sum			Sum		
6	6	2	8			8		
7								
8	FORMULAS							
9	A6 =RANDBETWEEN(1,6)							
10	B6 =RANDBETWEEN(1,6)							
11	C6 =SUM(A6:B6)							
12	F6 =C6							
13								
14								

Step 3—Generate the table. Select the range E6 through F17. Pay close attention to the location of the upper left cell of this range. It should be one cell to the left of the first results cell. The column it is in should be empty below. The table will have one header row and 11 (in this example) data rows.

	A	B	C	D	E	F	G
1	Toy problem to illustrate use of BuildTable						
2	Toss two dice, and generate the cumulative distribution of the sum.						
3							
4							
5	Die 1	Die 2	Sum			Sum	
6	6	2	8			8	
7							
8	FORMULAS						
9	A6 =RANDBETWEEN(1,6)						
10	B6 =RANDBETWEEN(1,6)						
11	C6 =SUM(A6:B6)						
12	F6 =C6						
13							
14							
15							
16							
17							
18							

Step 4—From Excel's Add-Ins menu, select MTSP BuildTable, Click BuildTable.

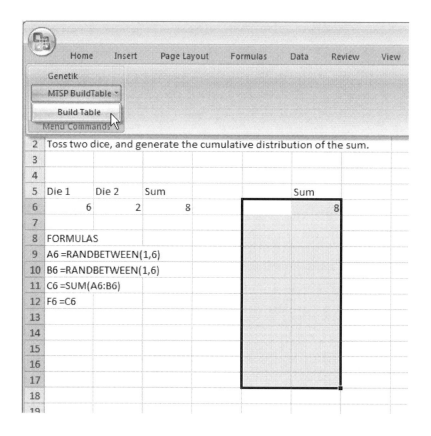

Step 5—The simulation runs will be made. There are 11 runs, each run a toss of two dice. The sum of each run is stored in a cell in column F. Any number of runs can be made, but BuildTable uses the length of the area selected to establish both the bins for the distribution and the number of runs, so picking the right number of bins / runs makes the display of the results neater. One row will be a header. The remainder will hold the simulation runs, one row for each run. Use 12 rows to test that you have everything set up correctly. Use 102 for a small run. Use 1002 for a reasonable-sized run.

	A	B	C	D	E	F	G	H
1	Toy problem to illustrate use of BuildTable							
2	Toss two dice, and generate the cumulative distribution of the sum.							
3								
4								
5	Die 1	Die 2	Sum			Sum		
6	3	1	4		BuildTable	4		
7					.0000	8		
8	FORMULAS				.1000	5		
9	A6 =RANDBETWEEN(1,6)				.2000	3		
10	B6 =RANDBETWEEN(1,6)				.3000	6		
11	C6 =SUM(A6:B6)				.4000	7		
12	F6 =C6				.5000	8		
13					.6000	9		
14					.7000	4		
15					.8000	6		
16					.9000	12		
17					1.0000	2		
18								

Step 6—The test worked as planned. Select the range E6 through F107 and run BuildTable again. The result will be 101 tosses. The previous contents of the table are overwritten.

Step 7—Analyze the results. Begin by sorting the column of sums, column F, into ascending order. Sort only column F. Column E has the cumulative probability values and is already in the correct order.

After sorting, the values for the sum will be in the proper order in Column F and the cumulative probability will be in Column E. Together they define the CDF.

If you will be making several simulation studies, copy the results and paste them in another area or another sheet.

Step 8—Plot the resulting CDF.

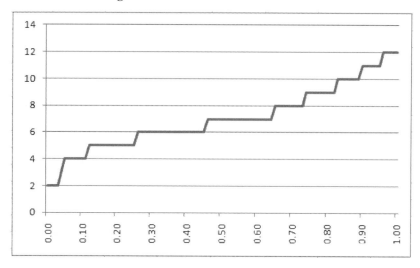

Continue on with whatever other analysis you want to do.

How to analyze your own data

This section is a series of step-by-step instructions and examples showing how to prepare your own data for your own analysis of trading systems.

Decide which simulation platform to use

Using Excel to run Monte Carlo simulations to generate distributions of terminal wealth and drawdown has five phases:

1. Set up the input data.
2. Select individual trades.
3. Create a single trade sequence.
4. Call BuildTable to create a distribution of many sequences.
5. Analyze the distributions.

The first four phases will be in successive columns, or groups of columns, left to right across the spreadsheet. Each phase has an initial configuration and a final configuration. The final configuration of one phase being the initial configuration of the next phase. Each phase will be described in turn. The fifth phase is anywhere you want it to be—perhaps in a separate spreadsheet.

Using Equity Monaco (EM) or Market System Analyzer (MSA) simulations to generate distributions has two phases:

1. Set up the input data (as above) as a list of closed trades.
2. Run EM or MSA to create a distribution.

For EM or MSA, the input data must be a list of closed trades, or periodic equity changes, in dollars per trade. The appropriate section is noted below.

PHASE 1   SET UP THE INPUT DATA

The data will be referred to as a list of closed trades. That description is meant to include any of: a list of actual closed trades; a list of hypothetical trades; a list of trades that follow a distribution; a list of daily or weekly equity changes. Each trade should represent the amount gained or lost from trading a single unit without compounding.

When you use the position sizing methods, you will be trading multiples of whatever has been defined as the single unit.

If the trades represent the amount gained or lost when trading a percentage of the account on each trade, the dollar amounts include a compounding factor. Remove the compounding effect by determining the percentage gained on each trade. Your trading system platform can probably report this for you. If not, divide the dollar gain on each trade by the dollars invested in each trade giving a percentage gain per trade.

If the data is in terms of percentages, decide on the dollar size of a single unit, then multiply the unit size by the percentage to obtain the single-unit dollar amount of the gain. Examples of single units are:

- $10,000 or some other fixed dollar amount that is a fraction of your notional trading account.
- Some dollar amount related to the size of a single futures contract.

If you are using EM or MSA, the final configuration of the input data will be a list of closed trades. If you are using Excel, the final configuration of the input data will be either a list of closed trades or a table representing an Inverse Cumulative Distribution Function (InvCDF).

The results of the simulation depend in large part on the quality of the data used as input.

One component of data quality is that it is a realistic representation of what is anticipated for the future.

It is legitimate to make runs with a variety of hypothetical data to evaluate possible alternative future scenarios. But recall my caution against using data from in-sample backtest or optimization runs to estimate future performance of a trading system. Using in-sample backtest data will seriously over-estimate probability of success and seriously under-estimate probability of failure.

Another component of data quality is the resolution of the data.

In order to get good resolution for the results, you need good resolution for the input data. The examples used in this book represent simulations of four years – however many trades it takes to cover that time period. The number of data elements in the input should be the same order of magnitude as the number of trades in the period being simulated, but need not be exactly the same number. To simulate four years of daily trades, use several hundred to one thousand individual daily closed trades – or an InvCDF with several hundred steps. To simulate four years of weekly trades, use several dozen to several hundred closed trades – or an InvCDF table with about 100 steps. For proof-of-concept runs, data with coarser resolution can be used.

Initial configuration

The data you begin to work with may be in any of these formats:

- List of trades. A list of closed trades in dollar amount, closed trades in percentage amounts, periodic equity changes in dollar amounts, or periodic equity changes in percentage amounts. The output from test runs of trading systems is typically a list of trades. If you have a list of trades and you want to make changes, such as adding or removing trades, or changing the values of individual trades, you can work with the list directly or create a pdf from the list, modify the pdf, and transform the pdf to either another list or an InvCDF.

- Inverse CDF. A table representing an inverse cumulative distribution function. If you already have an InvCDF and do not need to see the pdf or the individual trades, you can use the InvCDF directly.

- pdf. A probability density function or histogram. The pdf format is one of the best for seeing the distribution. It is easy to modify a pdf to change the proportion of trades at various levels of profit or loss, including transformations such as Winsorizing.

- Hypothetical distribution.   Such as the standard Normal distribution. Trade data seldom follows hypothetical distributions. But it might be interesting to begin with a hypothetical distribution and study the effect of changes to it.
- Journal listing.   A description of trade results, such as 30% of trades gain 5%, 40% of trades are flat, 30% of trades lose 2%. Journal listings are usually too coarse to be good sources of input data. It is easy to transform a journal listing into either a pdf or an InvCDF.

Final Configuration

- List of trades. Required by EM and MSA. Acceptable to Excel.
- Inverse CDF. Acceptable to Excel.

The matrix shows the processing module to use for a given combination of initial configuration of the data and desired final configuration. Each processing module has a page of its own in this Appendix.

		Phase 1. Input Data	
		Final Configuration	
		List of Trades	InvCDF
	List of Trades	No processing needed	List_to_InvCDF
Initial			
Configuration			
	InvCDF	InvCDF_to_List	No processing needed
	pdf	pdf_to_List	pdf_to_InvCDF

Intermediate Processing

When necessary or desired, perform some transformation on the data, then return it to one of the final configurations.

- Modify trade distribution.   Increase or decrease trades in some categories, including Winsorizing. Use a sequence such as:
  List_to_pdf
  Modify_pdf
  pdf_to_List or pdf_to_InvCDF
- Journal Listing.
  Use Text_to_InvCDF
- Hypothetical.
  Use StdNormal_to_pdf

Next Step

If you will be using EM or MSA to perform the simulations, the final configuration must be a list of trades. Copy that list from the Excel column it is in, paste it into a new Excel spreadsheet or text editor (not Word), and save it as a text file. Then go on to run Equity Monaco or Market System Analyzer.

If you will be using Excel to perform the simulations, proceed with Phases 2, 3, 4, and 5.

PHASE 2   SELECT INDIVIDUAL TRADES

The initial configuration to Phase 2 will be either a list of trades or an inverse CDF. The final configuration will be a single column, one row for each day (or whatever period is being simulated), with a gain for that day. The gain can be either dollar amount or a percentage amount, at your choice, with your logic to handle it correctly.

Use either List_to_Trades or InvCDF_to_Trades, depending on your preference.

PHASE 3   CREATE A SINGLE TRADE SEQUENCE

The initial configuration to Phase 3 will be a column, one row for each day, with the gain for a single unit for that day. The Excel code will depend on the method of position sizing used. The control area above the sets of columns can be used for values for key variables such as:

- fraction to use with fixed fraction
- delta to use with fixed ratio
- maximum contracts

- retire goal
- ruin barrier

The final configuration will be a series of columns that have data for variables associated with the trading results, such as:

- number of units traded
- running equity in dollars
- maximum equity in dollars
- running drawdown in dollars
- maximum drawdown in dollars
- running relative equity
- maximum relative equity
- running drawdown as percent
- maximum drawdown as percent
- barrier reached flags

Key values, such as the terminal wealth at the final day of the simulated period, are copied to specific locations for use in phase 4.

Use Trades_to_Equity.

PHASE 4   CALL BUILDTABLE

The initial configuration to Phase 4 is a set of key values, each copied from the trade sequence results. A table of some user-defined length, say 1000 entries, is established. The final configuration has 1000 sets of key values, one for each simulated run.

Use Equity_to_BuildTable.

PHASE 5   ANALYZE THE DISTRIBUTIONS

The table created by BuildTable has results for each of the trade sequences in one of its rows. Copy those and paste them in a separate area of the spreadsheet for analysis.

Use Analyze_Distributions.

TEXT _ TO _ INVCDF

This section demonstrates how to transform a journal listing of trades to an inverted cumulative distribution function (InvCDF).

Books, articles, blogs, and advertisements describe the results of a trading system by listing the results in a loose format, such as:

- 1% lose $500
- 6% lose $300
- 11% lose $200
- 10% lose $100
- 57% win $100
- 15% win $200

By transforming that information into an InvCDF you can use that data to simulate the results of trading that system.

The spreadsheet shows the data entered just as it was described. Each entry is a pair of numbers. Column A has the number of times a result occurred and Column B has the dollar gain or lost. The data makes better sense if it is in order from worst loss to best gain, as this is. After all of the pairs have been entered, a formula is entered into the cell after the last entry in Column A to total the number of results.

	A	B
2		
3		
10		
11	Journal Data	
12	Percent	Result
13	1	-500
14	6	-300
15	11	-200
16	10	-100
17	57	100
18	15	200
19	100	
20		
21		
22		
23	A19 =SUM(A13:A18)	
24		

The inverse CDF is computed into cells D13 through E19. The formulas needed are shown in the lower left section of the spreadsheet.

	A	B	C	D	E	F
2						
3						
10						
11	Journal Data			Inverse CDF		
12	Percent	Result		Cum Prob	Trade Result	
13	1	-500		0.00	-500	
14	6	-300		0.01	-300	
15	11	-200		0.07	-200	
16	10	-100		0.18	-100	
17	57	100		0.28	100	
18	15	200		0.85	200	
19	100			1.00	0	
20						
21						
22						
23	A19 =SUM(A13:A18)					
24						
25	D13 =0					
26	D14 =A13/A$19 + D13					
27	D15:D19 Copy down					
28	E13 =B13					
29	E14:E19 copy down					
20						

The Excel LOOKUP function will be used to select random trades. A uniform random number is generated using the =RAND() function. The random value will always be between 0.000000 and 0.999999; it can never be 1.0. Given a random number, r, begin at cell D13 and look down until you come to a value larger than r. The trade result for that is the value in Column E, one row higher.

For example, if the random number is 0.063, cell D15 is the first cell in Column D that has a higher value, so the trade result is -300, found in cell E14.

To both give a check that the table was setup correctly, and to illustrate how to use it, Column H has 100 values, from 0.00 to 0.99, and Column I has the values drawn from the table for each. The code to set up columns H and I is listed in the lower left section of the spreadsheet.

	A	B	C	D	E	F	G	H	I
2									
3									
10									
11	Journal Data			Inverse CDF				Verification	
12	Percent	Result		Cum Prob	Trade Result			random	random tr
13	1	-500		0.00	-500			0	-500
14	6	-300		0.01	-300			0.01	-300
15	11	-200		0.07	-200			0.02	-300
16	10	-100		0.18	-100			0.03	-300
17	57	100		0.28	100			0.04	-300
18	15	200		0.85	200			0.05	-300
19	100			1.00	0			0.06	-300
20								0.07	-200
21								0.08	-200
22								0.09	-200
23	A19 =SUM(A13:A18)							0.1	-200
24								0.11	-200
25	D13 =0							0.12	-200
26	D14 =A13/A$19 + D13							0.13	-200
27	D15:D19 Copy down							0.14	-200
28	E13 =B13							0.15	-200
29	E14:E19 copy down							0.16	-200
30								0.17	-200
31								0.18	-100
32	H13 =0.0							0.19	-100
33	H14 =H13 + 0.01							0.2	-100
34	H15:H112 copy down							0.21	-100
35	I13 =LOOKUP(H13,D$13:E$19)							0.22	-100
36	I14:I112 copy down							0.23	-100
37								0.24	-100

By setting up some bins and using the Data Analysis Histogram function, we can verify that the distribution of the trades selected by using the inverse cumulative distribution function matches the distribution read from the journal.

	H	I	J	K	L	M
2						
3						
10						
11	Verification					
12	random	random tr	bin	bin	Frequency	umulative %
13	0	-500	-550	-550	0	0.00%
14	0.01	-300	-450	-450	1	1.00%
15	0.02	-300	-350	-350	0	1.00%
16	0.03	-300	-250	-250	6	7.00%
17	0.04	-300	-150	-150	11	18.00%
18	0.05	-300	-50	-50	10	28.00%
19	0.06	-300	50	50	0	28.00%
20	0.07	-200	150	150	57	85.00%
21	0.08	-200	250	250	15	100.00%
22	0.09	-200		More	0	100.00%
23	0.1	-200				
24	0.11	-200				
25	0.12	-200				
26	0.13	-200		J13 =-550		
27	0.14	-200		J14 =J13+100		
28	0.15	-200		J15:J21 copy down		
29	0.16	-200				
30	0.17	-200				
31	0.18	-100				

List _ to _ InvCDF

This section demonstrates how to transform a list of closed trades to an inverted cumulative distribution function (InvCDF).

You might want to do this to:

- Summarize a large number of trades into a more easily described format.
- Prepare an InvCDF so that it can be modified to study the effects of different trade distributions.

Transforming from a list of individual trades to an inverted cumulative distribution function is a process of assigning each individual trade one of a limited number of values. A set of bins is created, each bin having a lower boundary and upper boundary, and each trade being assigned to the bin into which it falls.

You need to make a decision on the number and spacing of the bins to use for the InvCDF. The more bins and the finer the spacing between them, the smoother the CDF curve will be.

If the InvCDF will be used to generate trades for a simulation, the value associated with each bin will probably be the midpoint of the bin's lower and upper boundaries.

This transformation makes sense only when there are more individual trades than bins—usually several times more trades than bins.

Information will be lost in this transformation. Assuming that the trades are in dollars and to the nearest dollar, any bin size greater than one dollar will result in some trades, probably most trades, being put into bins where the value of the trade is different than the value of the bin.

Begin with the list of trades in Column A. The label for the data in each column is in row 11. Rows 1 through 10 are reserved for comments and control variables.

	A
1	
2	
3	
10	
11	Trades
12	101
13	90
14	209
15	16
16	-2
17	27
18	-4
19	245
20	107
21	84
22	65
23	152
24	-44
25	134
26	191
27	-24
28	-82
29	179
30	90
31	28
32	146

Plot the data as a line chart.

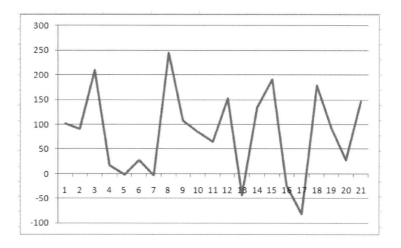

Determine what the lowest and highest data values are.

Decide how many bins you want to use. It is common to have them equally spaced. Create a list of the bins in Column B. The first bin should have a value less than the smallest data value. The final bin should have a value greater than the largest data value.

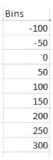

Bins
-100
-50
0
50
100
150
200
250
300

Use Excel's Data Analysis Histogram to create a table.

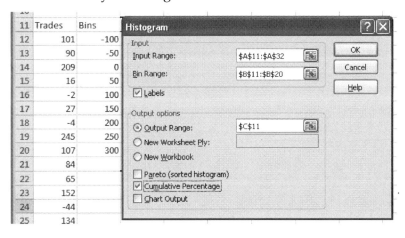

With this result.

Bins	Frequency	Cumulative %
-100	0	0.00%
-50	1	4.76%
0	4	23.81%
50	3	38.10%
100	4	57.14%
150	4	76.19%
200	3	90.48%
250	2	100.00%
300	0	100.00%
More	0	100.00%

Create the InvCDF from the output of the Histogram. The distribution of the data drawn from the InvCDF will be most closely correlated to the original data if the data drawn is assigned the value of the midpoint of the bin.

Bins	Frequency	umulative %		Cumulativ	Trade
-100	0	0.00%		0.00%	-75
-50	1	4.76%		4.76%	-25
0	4	23.81%		23.81%	25
50	3	38.10%		38.10%	75
100	4	57.14%		57.14%	125
150	4	76.19%		76.19%	175
200	3	90.48%		90.48%	225
250	2	100.00%		100.00%	275
300	0	100.00%			
More	0	100.00%			

PDF _ TO _ INvCDF

This section demonstrates how to transform a probability density function (pdf), or histogram, to an inverse cumulative distribution function (InvCDF).

It easiest to recognize the distribution of trades when they are displayed in histogram format.

pdf table		
Bins	Frequency	Relative %
-100	0	0.0000
-50	1	0.0476
0	4	0.1905
50	3	0.1429
100	4	0.1905
150	4	0.1905
200	3	0.1429
250	2	0.0952
300	0	0.0000
	21	

The pdf and histogram charts are the same. Only the scale changes.

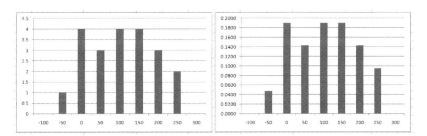

The probability density function and cumulative distribution function are very closely related. When both are continuous functions, the CDF is the integral of the pdf. Since we are working with discrete data, the CDF is the summation of the pdf, which is the discrete equivalent to being an integral.

pdf table			
Bins	Frequency	Relative %	Cumulative %
-100	0	0.0000	0.0000
-50	1	0.0476	0.0476
0	4	0.1905	0.2381
50	3	0.1429	0.3810
100	4	0.1905	0.5714
150	4	0.1905	0.7619
200	3	0.1429	0.9048
250	2	0.0952	1.0000
300	0	0.0000	1.0000
	21		

If your pdf came from using the Excel Data Analysis Histogram function, the values in the Bins column are the lower boundary of the bin. You might want to calculate and use the value of the midpoint of the bin. It is simply the average of the bin boundaries.

Whether you use the bin value as listed or the midpoint, the InvCDF is two columns. The left column is the cumulative percent; the right column is the value for that bin.

InvCDF Table	
Cumulative %	Trade
0.0000	-75
0.0476	-25
0.2381	25
0.3810	75
0.5714	125
0.7619	175
0.9048	225
1.0000	275

List _ to _ pdf

This section demonstrates how to transform a list of trades to a probability density function (pdf). That is, how to create a histogram from a list of trades.

You might want to do this to:

- Summarize a large number of trades into a more easily described format.
- Prepare a pdf so that it can be modified to study the effect of different trade distributions.

Transforming from a list of individual trades to a pdf is a process of assigning each individual trade one of a limited number of values. A set of bins is created, each bin having a lower boundary and upper boundary, and each trade being assigned to the bin into which it falls.

You need to make a decision on the number and spacing of the bins to use for the pdf. The more bins and the finer the spacing between them, the more precise the pdf will be.

Use the Excel Data Analysis Histogram function and the same technique used in List_to_InvCDF.

Begin with a list of trades in Column A. The label for the data in each column is in row 11. Rows 1 through 10 are reserved for comments and control variables.

Plot the data as a line chart.

Determine what the lowest and highest data values are.

Decide how many bins you want to use. It is common to have them equally spaced. Create a list of the bins in Column B. The first bin should have a value less than the smallest data value. The final bin should have a value greater than the largest data value.

	A	B
1		
2		
3		
10		
11	Trades	Bins
12	101	-100
13	90	-50
14	209	0
15	16	50
16	-2	100
17	27	150
18	-4	200
19	245	250
20	107	300
21	84	
22	65	
23	152	
24	-44	
25	134	
26	191	
27	-24	
28	-82	
29	179	
30	90	
31	28	
32	146	

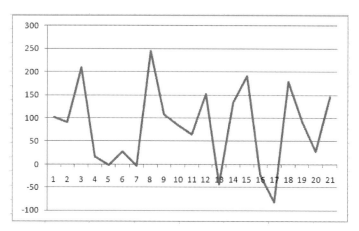

Use Excel's Data Analysis Histogram (see List_to_InvCDF for screen capture) to create a table, with this result.

Bins	Frequency	Cumulative %
-100	0	0.00%
-50	1	4.76%
0	4	23.81%
50	3	38.10%
100	4	57.14%
150	4	76.19%
200	3	90.48%
250	2	100.00%
300	0	100.00%
More	0	100.00%

The histogram is the plot of Frequency and Bins.

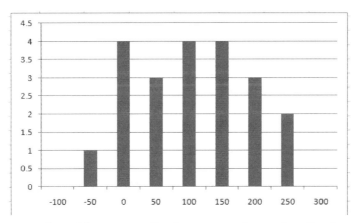

If you want the pdf, convert the frequency from the absolute number of trades in each bin to the relative number of trades in each bin. Do this by dividing the number in each bin by the sum of all the numbers in all the bins. Or, compute the differences between the cumulative percentage for each of the bins. Either way, you will get a table like the one shown in the next figure.

pdf table		
Bins	Frequency	Relative %
-100	0	0.0000
-50	1	0.0476
0	4	0.1905
50	3	0.1429
100	4	0.1905
150	4	0.1905
200	3	0.1429
250	2	0.0952
300	0	0.0000
	21	

The pdf chart is a plot of Relative percentage and Bins.

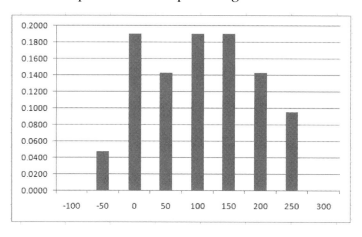

MODIFY _ PDF

This section demonstrates how to modify a pdf or histogram.

You might want to do this to study the effect of adding or removing trades, particularly at the extremes.

Assume that the trade data has been transformed into a histogram using the Excel Data Analysis Histogram function, and a table produced.

Bins	Frequency	Cumulative %
-100	0	0.00%
-50	1	4.76%
0	4	23.81%
50	3	38.10%
100	4	57.14%
150	4	76.19%
200	3	90.48%
250	2	100.00%
300	0	100.00%
More	0	100.00%

You might want to calculate the midpoint of the bin to use as the trade values.

Trade	Frequency
-75	0
-25	1
25	4
75	3
125	4
175	4
225	3
275	2
300	0
More	0

Remove one of the biggest winners and add one to the biggest losers.

Trade	Frequency	New Frequency
-75	0	0
-25	1	2
25	4	4
75	3	3
125	4	4
175	4	4
225	3	3
275	2	1
300	0	0
More	0	0

Compute new relative and cumulative percentages.

Trade	Frequency	New Frequency	Relative %	Cumulative %
-75	0	0	0.0000	0.0000
-25	1	2	0.0952	0.0952
25	4	4	0.1905	0.2857
75	3	3	0.1429	0.4286
125	4	4	0.1905	0.6190
175	4	4	0.1905	0.8095
225	3	3	0.1429	0.9524
275	2	1	0.0476	1.0000
300	0	0	0.0000	1.0000
More	0	21		

If desired, create an InvCDF to use for a simulation.

Cumulative %	Trade
0.0000	-75
0.0952	-25
0.2857	25
0.4286	75
0.6190	125
0.8095	175
0.9524	225
1.0000	275

PDF _ TO _ LIST

This section demonstrates how to transform a probability density function (pdf), or histogram, to a list of closed trades.

An easy way to get a list of trades given a pdf is to use two of the other procedures in two steps:

1. Use the pdf_to_InvCDF procedure.
2. Followed by the InvCDF_to_List procedure.

INVCDF _ TO _ LIST

This section demonstrates how to transform an inverted cumulative distribution function (InvCDF) to a list of trades.

The InvCDF will have two columns and a number of rows. Each row represents a bin containing trades. The cumulative probability is in the left column and the value associated with the bin is in the right column.

Cumulative %	Trade
0.00%	-75
4.76%	-25
23.81%	25
38.10%	75
57.14%	125
76.19%	175
90.48%	225
100.00%	275

To generate a random trade from the distribution represented by the InvCDF:

1. Generate a uniform random number between 0.00 and 0.99. Call it r.
2. Look down the left column to find the first value of the cumulative probability greater than r. Return the value of the bin one row above.

Assuming this will be used in a trading simulation, you will want as many trades as it takes to complete the time period being simulated. If the system trades once per week, on average, and you are simulating a four year period, you need 208 trades. Use two columns with 208 rows. The left column holds a random number, the right column the random trade.

rand	Trade
0	-75
0.590751	125
0.434035	75
0.825013	175
0.283717	25
0.267939	25
0.333007	25
0.053369	-25
0.04578	-75
0.538291	75
0.881442	175
0.560611	75

StdNormal _ to _ List

This section demonstrates how to use a standard statistical distribution to create a trade list. The example will use the standard Normal distribution and the Excel functions associated with it.

Row 8 has values for the mean and standard deviation you want to use. Column A has the list of values for the range of z-scores you want to use.

	A	B	C	D	E
1	You know the mean and standard deviation				
2	and you want to build either a				
3	probability denstity function (pdf)				
4	Cumulative Distribution Function (CDF)				
5					
6					
7	Mean	Stdev			
8	0.05	0.20			
9					
10	Number				
11	Std Dev	X	pdf	CDF	
12	-3.00	-0.55	0.0222	0.0013	
13	-2.90	-0.53	0.0298	0.0019	
14	-2.80	-0.51	0.0396	0.0026	
15	-2.70	-0.49	0.0521	0.0035	
16	-2.60	-0.47	0.0679	0.0047	
66	2.40	0.53	0.1120	0.9918	
67	2.50	0.55	0.0876	0.9938	
68	2.60	0.57	0.0679	0.9953	
69	2.70	0.59	0.0521	0.9965	
70	2.80	0.61	0.0396	0.9974	
71	2.90	0.63	0.0298	0.9981	
72	3.00	0.65	0.0222	0.9987	
73					
74	Column A has the list of z-scores you want to use.				
75	Assume you want 61 bins, -3.0 to +3.0 std dev				
76	A8 The mean of the distribution				
77	B8 The standard deviation of the distribution				
78	B12 =A$8 + A12*B$8				
79	B13:72 Copy down				
80	C12 =NORMDIST(B12,A$8,B$8,FALSE)				
81	C13:C72 Copy down				
82	D12 =NORMDIST(B12,A$8,B$8,TRUE)				
83	D13:D72 Copy down				

Plot the pdf.

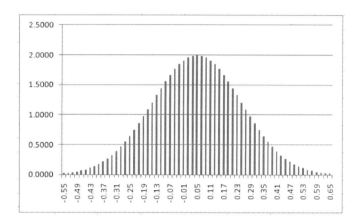

This example represents trades with a mean of 0.05 and standard deviation of 0.20, which could be percentages gained or lost on individual trades. Convert them into dollar amounts by multiplying by the dollar value of the basic unit, say $1000. The mean is then $50.00 and the standard deviation $200.00.

You might want to modify the pdf as desired, particularly increase the frequency of trades at the tails, convert it to an InvCDF, and use it to simulate four years of trades.

Or you might want to study the effect of limiting losing trades by successively removing losing trades.

LIST _ TO _ TRADES

This section demonstrates how to convert a list of closed trades that define the distribution of trades to a series of individual randomly selected trades that will be used to create the four year series.

The list of trades is one of two choices for the final configuration of phase 1. The other choice is an inverse cumulative distribution function, InvCDF, which is explained in a separate example. There can be any number of trades. Once the phase 1 processing is complete, the list of trades remains unchanged for the entire series of simulation runs.

The randomly selected trades created in phase 2 will change with each simulation run. There will be enough trades to cover the period being simulated. Each will be chosen at random from the list of trades prepared in phase 1.

For this example, Column A contains a list of 21 closed trades. The first data point is in cell A12 and the final in A32.

Assume that the period being simulated is 10 trades. In general, this is not enough, but I want to show the entire equity series. If the system being simulated trades once per week, on average, and the period being simulated is four years, 208 trades are needed rather than 10.

Column C contains uniform random numbers chosen to be between 1 and 21—the number of trades in Column A. There is one random number for each simulated trade—10 in this case.

For a four year simulation of trading once per week, entries in Column C would extend down through cell C219. But the parameters for RANDBETWEEN would still be 1 to 21.

Column D contains the trade that is in the position in the list of closed trades given by the random number to its left. The Excel OFFSET function is used to return the value of that cell.

The example uses numeric values to make the example clearer. You can substitute references to the cells containing the values if you wish.

Your spreadsheet should be set so that calculation is automatic. If necessary, use Excel Options, Formulas, Calculation Options to set that. Every time any cell is changed, or the <F9> key is pressed, or the RANDOMIZE function is called, a new set of random number will be generated and a new set of trades chosen. The method being used is "sampling with replacement," which means that duplicates can occur.

	A	B	C	D	E
1	Phase 1		Phase 2		
2					
3					
4					
5	First entry		Number		
6	12		trades		
7	Last entry		needed		
8	32		10		
9					
10			Uniform	Chosen	
11	Trades		Random	Trade	
12	101		10	84	
13	90		18	179	
14	209		10	84	
15	16		4	16	
16	-2		1	101	
17	27		19	90	
18	-4		12	152	
19	245		12	152	
20	107		11	65	
21	84		2	90	
22	65				
23	152		C12 =RANDBETWEEN(1,21)		
24	-44		C13:C21 Copy down		
25	134		D12 =OFFSET(A$11,C12,0,1,1)		
26	191		CD13:D21 Copy down		
27	-24				
28	-82				
29	179				
30	90				
31	28				
32	146				

If the list of closed trades in Column A is percentage gain or loss, there is one additional step which multiplies the percentage chosen by the dollar amount of the basic trading unit to arrive on a dollar amount for each randomly selected trade.

The trades in Column D will be used in phase 3.

INVCDF _ TO _ TRADES

This section demonstrates how to convert an inverse cumulative distribution function, InvCDF, that defines the distribution of trades to a series of individual randomly selected trades that will be used to create the four year series.

The InvCDF is one of two choices for the final configuration of phase 1. The other choice is a list of trades, which is explained in a separate example. There can be any number of trades. Once the phase 1 processing is complete, the InvCDF remains unchanged for the entire series of simulation runs.

The randomly selected trades created in phase 2 will change with each simulation run. There will be enough trades to cover the period being simulated. Each will be chosen at random from the InvCDF prepared in phase 1.

For this example, Columns A and B contain the InvCDF. It is the InvCDF formed from the same trades used in other examples, including List_to_Trades. Notice how transforming the individual closed trades into a CDF have reduced the number of choices from 21 to 7.

Assume that the period being simulated is 10 trades. In general, this is not enough, but I want to show the entire equity series. If the system being simulated trades once per week, on average, and the period being simulated is four years, 208 trades are needed rather than 10.

Column D contains uniform random numbers chosen to be between 0.0000 and 0.9999. There is one random number for each simulated trade—10 in this case.

For a four year simulation of trading once per week, entries in Column D would extend down through cell D219.

Column E contains the trade that is chosen by using the Excel LOOKUP function with the InvCDF.

The example uses numeric values to make the example clearer. You can substitute references to the cells containing the values if you wish.

Your spreadsheet should be set so that calculation is automatic. If necessary, use Excel Options, Formulas, Calculation Options to set that.

Every time any cell is changed, or the <F9> key is pressed, or the RAN-DOMIZE function is called, a new set of random number will be generated and a new set of trades chosen. The method being used is "sampling with replacement," which means that duplicates can occur.

	A	B	C	D	E	F
1	Phase 1			Phase 2		
2						
3						
4						
5				Number		
6				trades		
7				needed		
8				10		
9						
10				Uniform	Chosen	
11	Cumulative %	Trade		Random	Trade	
12	0.0000	-75		0.8876	175	
13	0.0476	-25		0.8836	175	
14	0.2381	25		0.3263	25	
15	0.3810	75		0.1176	-25	
16	0.5714	125		0.2625	25	
17	0.7619	175		0.3901	75	
18	0.9048	225		0.2933	25	
19	1.0000	275		0.3310	25	
20				0.2483	25	
21				0.5968	125	
22						
23				C12 =RAND()		
24				C13:C21 Copy down		
25				D12 =LOOKUP(D12,A$12:B$19)		
26				CD13:D21 Copy down		
27						

If the trades in Column B are percentage gain or loss, there is one additional step which multiplies the percentage chosen by the dollar amount of the basic trading unit to arrive on a dollar amount for each randomly selected trade.

The trades in Column E will be used in phase 3.

TRADES _ TO _ EQUITY

This section demonstrates the phase 3 activity including how to convert a sequence of simulated trades to an equity series for the entire simulated period, and how to expose the key results to the simulation table.

There are many options available to the modeler. This example will illustrate just a very basic set of them. Every reader will have his or her own model and metrics to be computed and analyzed, so the remainder are left as exercises. Phase 3 may be a little complex, depending on the model, but it is straight forward and should present little difficulty.

The sequence of 10 trades produced by phase 2 are in Column D. Cell F3 holds the fraction to use for each trade. F6 holds the size of the basic unit. I3 holds the initial equity.

Column F holds the amount exposed for the next trade. It is computed as the fraction, F3, times the previous equity, Column I.

Column G holds the trade size. In this example, fractional units are allowed. If the trades are taken in a futures contract, round this number down to the next integer.

Column H is the gain or loss. It is the product of the trade size for this trade, Column G, and the gain or loss for a single unit, Column D.

Column I holds the running equity. It begins at the initial equity. After each trade, the gain or loss, Column H, is added to the previous value of the running equity.

Column J keeps track of the maximum equity achieved so far.

Column K computes the drawdown as the difference between maximum equity, Column J and running equity, Column I.

Column L keeps track of the maximum drawdown so far.

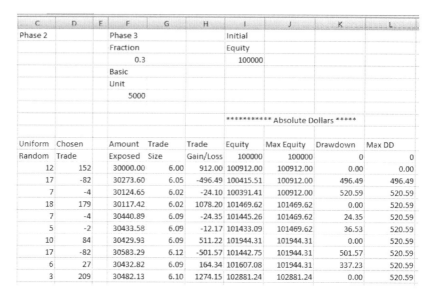

C	D	E	F	F	G	H	I	J	K	L
Phase 2			Phase 3				Initial			
			Fraction				Equity			
				0.3				100000		
			Basic							
			Unit							
				5000						
								*********** Absolute Dollars *****		
Uniform	Chosen		Amount	Trade		Trade	Equity	Max Equity	Drawdown	Max DD
Random	Trade		Exposed	Size		Gain/Loss	100000	100000	0	0
12	152		30000.00	6.00		912.00	100912.00	100912.00	0.00	0.00
17	-82		30273.60	6.05		-496.49	100415.51	100912.00	496.49	496.49
7	-4		30124.65	6.02		-24.10	100391.41	100912.00	520.59	520.59
18	179		30117.42	6.02		1078.20	101469.62	101469.62	0.00	520.59
7	-4		30440.89	6.09		-24.35	101445.26	101469.62	24.35	520.59
5	-2		30433.58	6.09		-12.17	101433.09	101469.62	36.53	520.59
10	84		30429.93	6.09		511.22	101944.31	101944.31	0.00	520.59
17	-82		30583.29	6.12		-501.57	101442.75	101944.31	501.57	520.59
6	27		30432.82	6.09		164.34	101607.08	101944.31	337.23	520.59
3	209		30482.13	6.10		1274.15	102881.24	102881.24	0.00	520.59

Columns N through Q keep track of the same series, but using relative values. Equity is relative to initial equity.

N	O	P	Q
********** Relative *******			
Rel Equity	Rel Max Equity	Rel Drawdown	Rel Max DD
1.0000	1.0000	0.0000	0.0000
1.0091	1.0091	0.0000	0.0000
1.0042	1.0091	0.0049	0.0049
1.0039	1.0091	0.0052	0.0052
1.0147	1.0147	0.0000	0.0052
1.0145	1.0147	0.0002	0.0052
1.0143	1.0147	0.0004	0.0052
1.0194	1.0194	0.0000	0.0052
1.0144	1.0194	0.0049	0.0052
1.0161	1.0194	0.0033	0.0052
1.0288	1.0288	0.0000	0.0052

The equity curves are in agreement.

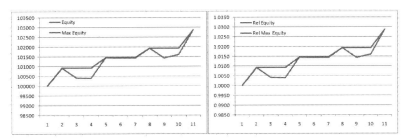

For this example, the final figures, including equity, drawdown, and anything else each reader wants to record, are in row 21. If this had been a simulated four year period, the results would be further down —row 219 for four years of weekly trading, row 1019 for four years of daily trading.

These final results are captured by copying the row 21 results into easily found locations in row 6.

N	O	P	Q
Final Equity		MaxDD	
1.0288			0.0052
********** Relative ******			
Rel Equity	Rel Max Equity	Rel Drawdown	Rel Max DD
1.0000	1.0000	0.0000	0.0000
1.0091	1.0091	0.0000	0.0000
1.0042	1.0091	0.0049	0.0049
1.0039	1.0091	0.0052	0.0052
1.0147	1.0147	0.0000	0.0052
1.0145	1.0147	0.0002	0.0052
1.0143	1.0147	0.0004	0.0052
1.0194	1.0194	0.0000	0.0052
1.0144	1.0194	0.0049	0.0052
1.0161	1.0194	0.0033	0.0052
1.0288	1.0288	0.0000	0.0052

The metrics that can be collected from the simulation are limited only by the reader's imagination. Whatever is important and is to be included in the distributions should be copied to row 6 as well.

EQUITY _ TO _ BUILDTABLE

This section demonstrates the phase 4 activities of capturing the results of many individual simulation runs and forming distributions.

Continuing on from the Trades_to_Equity example, the results we want to capture and analyze as distributions are in Row 6. Using Excel formulas, copy them to Row 10 in Columns T and U.

	N	O	P	Q	R	S	T	U
1						Phase 4		
2						Build the distribution table		
3								
4								
5	Final Equity			MaxDD				
6	1.0288			0.0052				
7								
8	********** Relative *******							
9							Final Equity	MaxDD
10	Rel Equity	Rel Max Equity	Rel Drawdown	Rel Max DD			1.0288	0.0052
11	1.0000	1.0000	0.0000	0.0000				
12	1.0091	1.0091	0.0000	0.0000				
13	1.0042	1.0091	0.0049	0.0049			T6 =N6	
14	1.0039	1.0091	0.0052	0.0052			U6 =Q6	
15	1.0147	1.0147	0.0000	0.0052				
16	1.0145	1.0147	0.0002	0.0052				
17	1.0143	1.0147	0.0004	0.0052				
18	1.0194	1.0194	0.0000	0.0052				
19	1.0144	1.0194	0.0049	0.0052				
20	1.0161	1.0194	0.0033	0.0052				
21	1.0288	1.0288	0.0000	0.0052				
22								

Be sure there is nothing below Row 10 in Columns S, T, and U. These cells will be overwritten by the macro that builds the distribution table.

Click Cell S10, one cell to the left of the copied values. Select the area that includes all of the rows that have copied values, and a total of 12 columns.

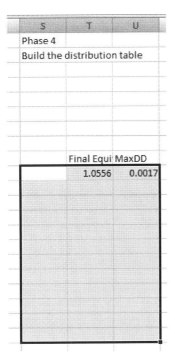

	Final Equi	MaxDD
	1.0556	0.0017

From the Add-Ins menu, select MTSP BuildTable, then Click BuildTable.

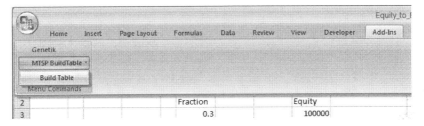

			Fraction		Equity	
2						
3			0.3		100000	

The table will fill in.

	Final Equi	MaxDD
BuildTable	1.0643	0.0014
.0000	1.081876	0.00276
.1000	1.06934	0.004076
.2000	1.034496	0.002879
.3000	1.040692	0.00144
.4000	1.081266	0.005039
.5000	1.076548	0.00144
.6000	1.019123	0.00276
.7000	1.048954	0
.8000	1.060207	0
.9000	1.017583	0.00144
1.0000	1.044269	0.00144

You can use as many rows as you wish. The top row must contain the cells that receive the values of the individual simulation run after each run is complete. The next rows, no matter how many you select, store the values copied from the top row. The leftmost column, S in this example, has the probability values that will be used for the horizontal axis when the table is transformed into a distribution. Choosing 12, 52, 102, 1002, or some equally well chosen number of rows, the probability values come out as neatly formatted numbers. But you can choose any number.

Each row in the table is the result of a single simulation run. It is the equivalent of pressing the <F9> key which randomizes the trades, copying the final values of equity and drawdown, and pasting them as values into the table.

ANALYZE _ DISTRIBUTIONS

This section demonstrates the phase 5 activities of analysis of the distribution.

Continuing on from the Equity_to_BuildTable example, the results we want to work with are in the table that was just created. Select the entire table, copy it, and paste it somewhere convenient.

9		Final Equi	MaxDD
10	BuildTable	#REF!	#REF!
11	.0000	1.081876	0.00276
12	.1000	1.06934	0.004076
13	.2000	1.034496	0.002879
14	.3000	1.040692	0.00144
15	.4000	1.081266	0.005039
16	.5000	1.076548	0.00144
17	.6000	1.019123	0.00276
18	.7000	1.048954	0
19	.8000	1.060207	0
20	.9000	1.017583	0.00144
21	1.0000	1.044269	0.00144

As you can see, all but the topmost row that had been selected when the table was built has values rather than formulas. You can clear or ignore Row 10. You will not be using it.

Select the second column.

9		Final Equi	MaxDD
10			
11	.0000	1.081876	0.00276
12	.1000	1.06934	0.004076
13	.2000	1.034496	0.002879
14	.3000	1.040692	0.00144
15	.4000	1.081266	0.005039
16	.5000	1.076548	0.00144
17	.6000	1.019123	0.00276
18	.7000	1.048954	0
19	.8000	1.060207	0
20	.9000	1.017583	0.00144
21	1.0000	1.044269	0.00144

Using Excel's Data Menu, Sort that column. Do not expand the selection, because the column to the left is already sorted and you will be using that column.

9		Final Equi	MaxDD
10			
11	.0000	1.017583	0.00276
12	.1000	1.019123	0.004076
13	.2000	1.034496	0.002879
14	.3000	1.040692	0.00144
15	.4000	1.044269	0.005039
16	.5000	1.048954	0.00144
17	.6000	1.060207	0.00276
18	.7000	1.06934	0
19	.8000	1.076548	0
20	.9000	1.081266	0.00144
21	1.0000	1.081876	0.00144

Create a chart using the selected column as the line and the leftmost column as the horizontal axis.

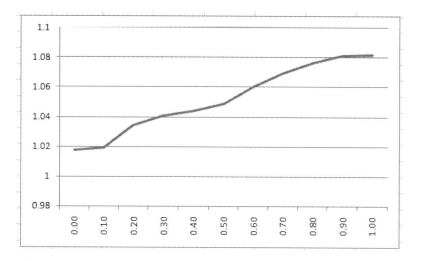

The sorted column contains the distribution of whatever metric was copied into that column. In this example, it is terminal wealth. The chart shows the distribution.

Sort the remaining columns and plot them.

Evaluate the performance of the system as it relates to your goals.

MARKET SYSTEM ANALYZER

Market System Analyzer is published by Adaptrade Software. It has a free 30 day trial period, after which a license is required. Download the trial from their website: http://www.adaptrade.com.

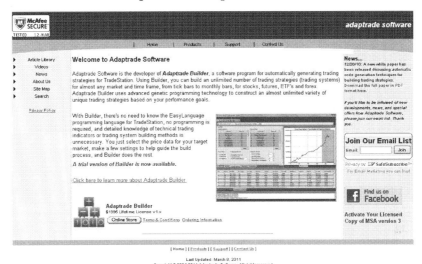

From the Products menu, click on the large icon of the Market System Analyzer (MSA) chart. Read about the product, then click Try MSA for Free.

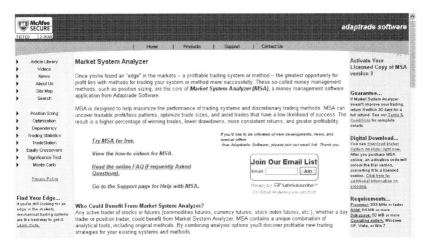

Scroll down until you come to the description of the latest version of MSA. At the time of this writing, it is MSA Version 3.2.1. Use the download link to download a copy of the program (a 6.6 MB exe file) and User's Guide (a 1.8 MB pdf file).

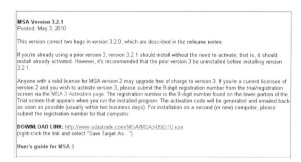

Install MSA, accepting the defaults.

Read the User's Guide and follow the tutorials.

MSA accepts data as a trade list, either as profit in dollars or as profit in percent. The data can be as simple as a list of single values, or it can include entry date and time, entry price, exit date and time, exit price, stop price, trade direction, trade risk, and position size. The more information MSA has, the more analysis options are available to you.

MSA allow the use to specify basic settings, such as initial equity, limits to the number of contracts, slippage, commissions, periodic withdrawals.

Many position sizing options are available, including fixed size, constant value, percent volatility, profit risk, fixed fractional, fixed ratio, generalized ratio, margin target, leverage target, maximum drawdown, maximum possible.

Several varieties of equity curve analysis are available.

When position sizing calculations are made during the simulations, they refer to the account balance and its history to determine the position size for the next trade. After you have completed the position sizing analysis, determined that your system is in fact working, and are ready to place your next trade, you need to know what that position size should be. MSA has a real time position sizing module that calculates that for you.

Equity curves and analysis summaries are produced for individual runs or for simulations. The next figure show the result of a single run trading one corn contract. Pressing the Control-R key generates additional randomized runs.

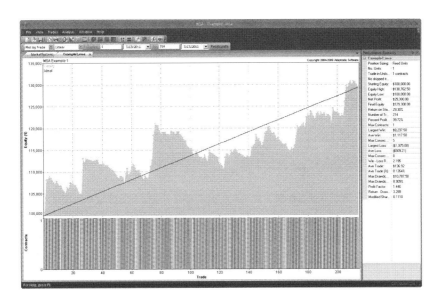

Note that the final equity is $130,762 and the maximum drawdown is $10,787, both in agreement with the analysis done in Chapter 1, and with Equity Monaco.

A summary created from 500 Monte Carlo runs shows the mean terminal wealth to be $129,300, and maximum drawdown at the 95% level to be 12.9%.

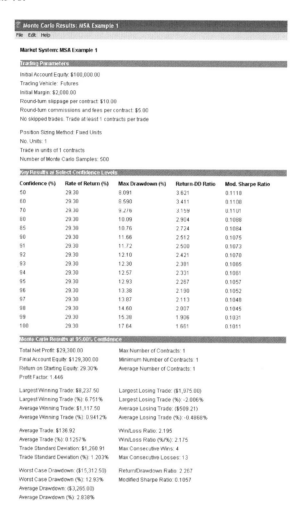

If you prefer a fully featured commercial tool, Market System Analyzer is an excellent choice that I highly recommend.

STATOR

Stator is investment management software published Anfield Capital. The trial version is available for free download from their website: http://www.stator-afm.com/.

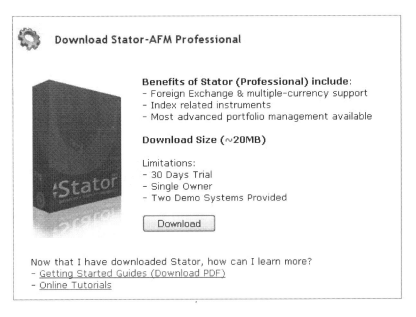

It comes in three versions:

- Lite
- Standard
- Professional

When you download the 30 day demo from their website, you are getting access to all of the features of all three versions of the program. When the program is activated, after an online purchase, no additional download is required.

Download the User Guides.

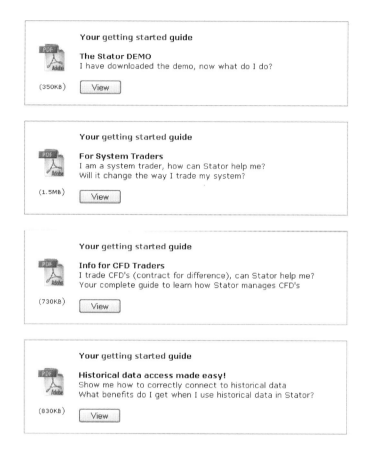

And the Sample Data Pack.

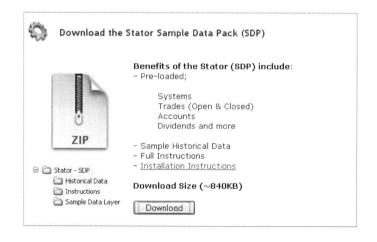

Load the sample data. Look at the positions table.

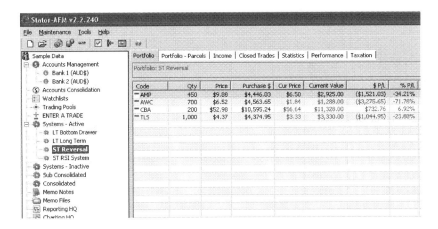

Look at the statistical analysis of trades.

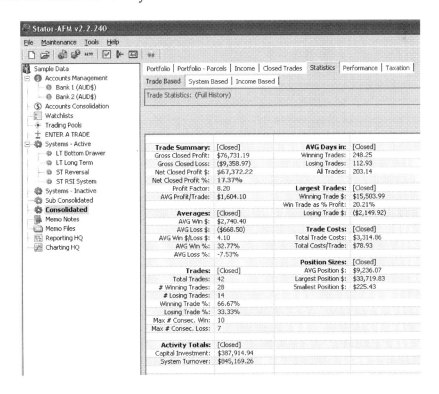

The website has several tutorials.

FIND TRADE SURROGATE

AmiBroker code to find tradable issues that are highly correlated with another issue.

This program tests the profitability of trading one issue based on signal from another.

Typical use is to develop a trading system using some index or ETF, then check to see if trades should be taken in some other tradable issues.

```
//  FindTradeSurrogate.afl
//
//  Using whatever index, ETF, or stock
//  you want to find trading surrogates for.
//  Enter the ticker for that in the "SetForeign"
//  statement.
//
//  Using the AA Settings:
//  On the General tab, set periodicity to daily.
//  On the General tab, set Long and Short.
//  On the Report tab, set Summary.
//  Use whatever watchlist you want to search --
//  probably ETFs, stocks.
//  Set the date range to whatever period you want
//  to test.
//  Pulldown the menu next to Backtest and
//  click Individual Backtest.
//
//  You will get a line for each potential surrogate.
//
//  This program looks ahead to see whether the
//  week ahead will be up or down, then takes the
//  correct position at the close of Friday's trading.
//

SetOption( "InitialEquity", 100000 );
SetOption( "AllowPositionShrinking", True );

SetTradeDelays( 0, 0, 0, 0 );
BuyPrice = SellPrice = C;
ShortPrice = CoverPrice = C;

SetForeign( "XLF" );     //  Financial sector ETF

ForeignClose = C;

TimeFrameSet( inWeekly );

AheadUp = Ref( C, 1 ) > C;
```

```
TimeFrameRestore();

AUp = TimeFrameExpand( AheadUp, inWeekly );
dow = DayOfWeek();
BuyDay = Ref( dow, 1 ) < dow;
Plot( ForeignClose, "C", colorBlack, styleLine );
Plot( AUp, "AheadIsUp", colorGreen, styleLine | styleOwnScale );
Plot( BuyDay, "BD", colorRed, styleLine | styleOwnScale );

Normal =  1; // Set to 1 to buy when the
//  week ahead is higher.
//  Set to 0 to invert signal

if ( Normal )
{
//Buying Up
    Cover = Buy = BuyDay && AUp;
    Short = Sell = BuyDay && !AUp;
}
else
{
//Buying Down
    Short = Sell = BuyDay && AUp;
    Cover = Buy = BuyDay && !AUp;
}

e = Equity();
Plot ( e, "e", colorGreen, styleLine | styleOwnScale );
```

FIND CORRELATION

AmiBroker code to find issues that are highly correlated with another issue.

This program tests only the correlation between one issue and a list of others, not the profitability.

```
//   FindCorrelation.afl
//
//   Using whatever index, ETF, or stock
//   you want to find correlated issues for.
//   Enter the ticker for that in the "SetForeign"
//   statement.
//
//   Using the AA Settings:
//   On the General tab, set periodicity to whatever
//   you want each incremental change to be.
//   Probably daily or weekly.
//   Use whatever watchlist you want to search --
//   probably ETFs, stocks.
//   Set the date range to whatever period you want
//   to test.
//   Setting "n last days" to 1 is a good start.
//   Click Explore.
//
//   You will get a line for each entry in the watchlist
//   for each date.
//
//

CorrelationLength = 21;

SetForeign( "SPY" );

ForeignClose = C;

RestorePriceArrays();

Corr = Correlation( ForeignClose, C, CorrelationLength );

Filter = 1;

AddColumn( Corr, "Correlation", 10.4 );
```

WRITE DATA TO FILE

AmiBroker code to write the price and volume of the data being displayed to a disk file. The resulting file can be opened directly by Excel.

```
//  WriteDataToFile.afl
//  This program exports the data for
//  the current stock in comma separated
//  separated file format.
//
//  Open this file using Formula Editor.
//  Click the Verify Syntax icon.
//  The data will be written to a file in the AmiBroker directory.
//
//  Whatever periodicity is displayed will be used for the output.
//  If it is set to Daily, Hour and Minute will each be 0
//
//  The first few lines of the file are:
//  Ticker,Date,Hr:Min,Open,High,Low,Close,Volume
//  IWM,2008-01-02,07:05,76.5000, 76.5000, 76.5000, 76.5000, 100
//  IWM,2008-01-02,07:10,76.4500, 76.4500, 76.3700, 76.3700, 3400
//  IWM,2008-01-02,07:15,76.3900, 76.3900, 76.3900, 76.3900, 200
//  IWM,2008-01-02,07:20,76.4200, 76.4200, 76.4200, 76.4200, 200
//  IWM,2008-01-02,07:55,76.2900, 76.2900, 76.2900, 76.2900, 25000
//
//  Excel will open it without further modification.
//  AmiBroker will re-import it using the Import ASCII Wizard.
//

fh = fopen( "quotes.csv", "w" );

if ( fh )
{
    fputs( "Ticker,Date,Hr:Min,Open,High,Low,Close,Volume\n", fh );

    nm = Name();

    y = Year();
    m = Month();
    d = Day();

    Hr = Hour();
    Mn = Minute();
```

```
for ( i = 0; i < BarCount; i++ )
{
    ns = nm + ",";
    fputs( ns, fh );
    ds = StrFormat( "%02.0f-%02.0f-%02.0f,",
                        y[ i ], m[ i ], d[ i ] );
    fputs( ds, fh );

    ts = StrFormat( "%02.0f:%02.0f,",
                        hr[ i ], mn[ i ] );
    fputs( ts, fh );

    qs = StrFormat( "%.4f, %.4f, %.4f, %.4f, %.0f\n",
                        O[ i ], H[ i ], L[ i ], C[ i ], V[ i ] );
    fputs( qs, fh );
}

fclose( fh );
}
```

INSTALL AND USE MERSENNE TWISTER FOR EXCEL

DOWNLOAD AND INSTALL NTRAND

1. Download the free Mersenne Twister add-in for Excel from
    Numerical Technologies.

    In your browser, enter this url:

    http://www.ntrand.com/

2. Click the GET NOW icon.

The download page appears.

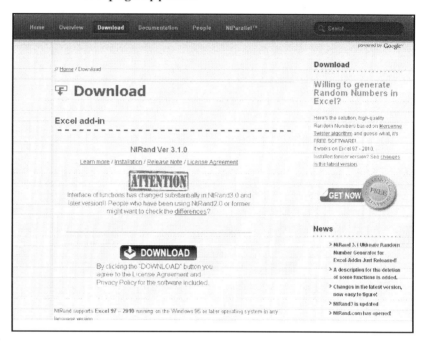

3. Click the DOWNLOAD icon.

    A dialog box will ask what to do with the file. Save it.

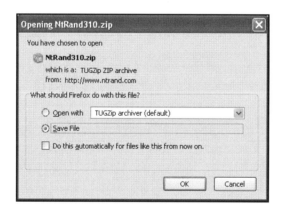

4. Using Windows Explorer, nagivate to the file you just
    downloaded, copy it to a separate directory if necessary, then
    unzip it. (TugZIP is free and works fine.
    http://www.tugzip.com)

5. Copy NtRand3.xll to a location where Excel can always find it. I'll make a directory for it on the C drive, C:\NTRand3, and copy it there.

6. Start Excel (I am using Excel 2007).

   Left-click the Office button.

   Click Excel Options.

   Click Add-Ins.

   In the Manage box, select Excel Add-Ins, click Go.

   An Add-Ins dialog box will open. Click Browse.

   Navigate to the directory you created, select NtRand3.xll, click OK.

7. A security box will appear telling you there is no digital signature. Click Enable this add-in for this session only.

   NtRand Addin will appear in the Add-ins box. Be sure there is a check mark next to it. Click OK.

   A dialog box will appear telling you that NtRand has been installed. Click OK.

8. There are some sample .xls files on the download page:

   http://www.ntrand.com/download/

   Download those for examples of the functions available.

   There is documentation on the release notes page:

   http://www.ntrand.com/release-note/

   There is good information on the FAQ page:

   http://www.ntrand.com/documentation/faq/

And also on the function reference page:

http://www.ntrand.com/function-reference/

Numerical Technologies site's glossary is also excellent:

http://www.ntrand.com/glossary

Use NTRAND

NTRAND is an array formula. The syntax is:

```
Syntax

    NTRAND (
            Size,
            Algorithm,
            Random seed1,
            Random seed2
    )



Parameters

        Size is # of random numbers (Positive integer).
        Algorithm is a integer value that determines a method to generate uniform random number.

            0: Mersenne Twister(2002)
            1: Mersenne Twister(1998)
            2: Numerical Recipes ran2 ()

        Random seed1 is 1st. random seed.
        Random seed2 is 2nd. random seed.
```

To generate 10 uniform random numbers:

1.   Select 10 cells.

     In the formula bar, enter =NTRAND(10,0,1,3)

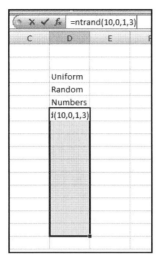

2. To enter an array formula, rather than just pressing the <enter> key, hold <shift> and <control>, then press <enter>.

The random numbers will be generated and the braces around the formula show that it is an array formula.

That works fine to generate a single set of random numbers. The trading system simulations use from a few to several hundred uniform random numbers that are randomized for every pass of the BuildTable run. Pressing <F9> (or executing the Randomize statement) tells Excel to recalculate, which automatically generates a new set of random numbers if you are using the Excel function RAND() or RANDBETWEEN(). But that does not work for NTRAND.

To have new Mersenne Twister random numbers whenever the spreadsheet is recalculated, enter this formula instead (as an array formula):

=NTRAND(10,0,RAND()*2147483647,RAND()*2147483647)

The FAQ page explains in more detail.

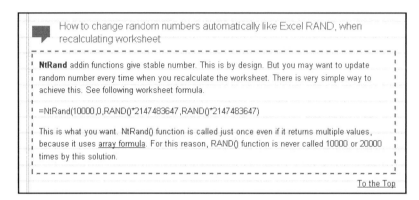

It is not necessary to make changes to the table created by Sim-Table, because all it does is copy the most recent result of the four year simulation and paste it as a value in the BuildTable area.

STATISTICS BEYOND EXCEL

Eventually you will want to, or need to, perform some statistical analysis that is beyond the capabilities of Excel. There are three alternatives: stand-alone packages, add-ins for Excel, and interfaces that give access to stand-alone packages from Excel. The lists are by no means complete, but focus on high quality and low cost.

STAND-ALONE PACKAGES

R   There is no doubt that the new standard in statistical analysis packages, rivaling SAS, SPSS, and Statistica, is R. R is a free, open source package available for many operating systems, including Windows. This book's Reference Appendix lists several books, articles, and websites that explain how to download, install, and operate R, as well as documentation of the statistical methods available in R and and tutorials for their use.

R Commander   As it is installed, R is operated from the command line. R Commander is a free, open source graphical interface for R.

Weka Weka is a free, open source package for data mining and machine learning.

ADD-INS FOR EXCEL

There are many add-in statistical packages for Excel. They come in a wide range of capabilities and prices. Most have trial versions or trial periods. Some that are reasonably priced that I have tried and feel are worthy of further investigation are:

Analyse-it   A statistical analysis and charting add-in for Excel. Several versions are available with prices starting at about $200.

StatistiXL   A statistical analysis add-in for Excel. The price of a one-year license is $40, and a permanent license is $75.

INTERFACES TO STAND-ALONE PACKAGES FROM EXCEL

R Excel   RExcel is a free, open source add-in for Excel that provides an interface to R functions. Data is prepared in Excel and passed to R for analysis.

AREA UNDER STANDARD NORMAL CURVE

The values in the table represent the area under the standard normal curve between 0.0 and the relative z-score selected. Select the desired z-score by adding the value of a row header plus a column header. The value in the cell, at the intersection of that row and column gives the desired area.

For examples:
- To find the area between the mean and 1.52 standard deviations, use row 1.50 and column 0.02. The area is 0.4357.
- To find the area to the right of a z-score of 1.52, subtract the value from 0.50, giving 0.0643.
- To find the area from the left infinite tail to 1.52, add 0.50 to the value, giving 0.9357.
- To find the area to left of -1.52, subtract the value from 0.50, giving 0.0643.

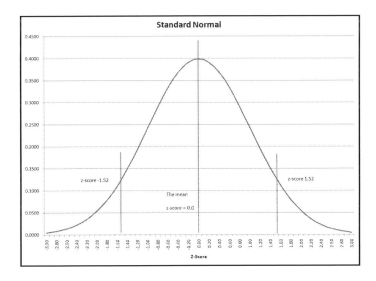

	0.00	0.01	0.02	0.03	0.04
0.00	0.0000	0.0040	0.0080	0.0120	0.0160
0.10	0.0398	0.0438	0.0478	0.0517	0.0557
0.20	0.0793	0.0832	0.0871	0.0910	0.0948
0.30	0.1179	0.1217	0.1255	0.1293	0.1331
0.40	0.1554	0.1591	0.1628	0.1664	0.1700
0.50	0.1915	0.1950	0.1985	0.2019	0.2054
0.60	0.2257	0.2291	0.2324	0.2357	0.2389
0.70	0.2580	0.2611	0.2642	0.2673	0.2704
0.80	0.2881	0.2910	0.2939	0.2967	0.2995
0.90	0.3159	0.3186	0.3212	0.3238	0.3264
1.00	0.3413	0.3438	0.3461	0.3485	0.3508
1.10	0.3643	0.3665	0.3686	0.3708	0.3729
1.20	0.3849	0.3869	0.3888	0.3907	0.3925
1.30	0.4032	0.4049	0.4066	0.4082	0.4099
1.40	0.4192	0.4207	0.4222	0.4236	0.4251
1.50	0.4332	0.4345	0.4357	0.4370	0.4382
1.60	0.4452	0.4463	0.4474	0.4484	0.4495
1.70	0.4554	0.4564	0.4573	0.4582	0.4591
1.80	0.4641	0.4649	0.4656	0.4664	0.4671
1.90	0.4713	0.4719	0.4726	0.4732	0.4738
2.00	0.4772	0.4778	0.4783	0.4788	0.4793
2.10	0.4821	0.4826	0.4830	0.4834	0.4838
2.20	0.4861	0.4864	0.4868	0.4871	0.4875
2.30	0.4893	0.4896	0.4898	0.4901	0.4904
2.40	0.4918	0.4920	0.4922	0.4925	0.4927
2.50	0.4938	0.4940	0.4941	0.4943	0.4945
2.60	0.4953	0.4955	0.4956	0.4957	0.4959
2.70	0.4965	0.4966	0.4967	0.4968	0.4969
2.80	0.4974	0.4975	0.4976	0.4977	0.4977
2.90	0.4981	0.4982	0.4982	0.4983	0.4984
3.00	0.4987	0.4987	0.4987	0.4988	0.4988

0.05	0.06	0.07	0.08	0.09
0.0199	0.0239	0.0279	0.0319	0.0359
0.0596	0.0636	0.0675	0.0714	0.0753
0.0987	0.1026	0.1064	0.1103	0.1141
0.1368	0.1406	0.1443	0.1480	0.1517
0.1736	0.1772	0.1808	0.1844	0.1879
0.2088	0.2123	0.2157	0.2190	0.2224
0.2422	0.2454	0.2486	0.2517	0.2549
0.2734	0.2764	0.2794	0.2823	0.2852
0.3023	0.3051	0.3078	0.3106	0.3133
0.3289	0.3315	0.3340	0.3365	0.3389
0.3531	0.3554	0.3577	0.3599	0.3621
0.3749	0.3770	0.3790	0.3810	0.3830
0.3944	0.3962	0.3980	0.3997	0.4015
0.4115	0.4131	0.4147	0.4162	0.4177
0.4265	0.4279	0.4292	0.4306	0.4319
0.4394	0.4406	0.4418	0.4429	0.4441
0.4505	0.4515	0.4525	0.4535	0.4545
0.4599	0.4608	0.4616	0.4625	0.4633
0.4678	0.4686	0.4693	0.4699	0.4706
0.4744	0.4750	0.4756	0.4761	0.4767
0.4798	0.4803	0.4808	0.4812	0.4817
0.4842	0.4846	0.4850	0.4854	0.4857
0.4878	0.4881	0.4884	0.4887	0.4890
0.4906	0.4909	0.4911	0.4913	0.4916
0.4929	0.4931	0.4932	0.4934	0.4936
0.4946	0.4948	0.4949	0.4951	0.4952
0.4960	0.4961	0.4962	0.4963	0.4964
0.4970	0.4971	0.4972	0.4973	0.4974
0.4978	0.4979	0.4979	0.4980	0.4981
0.4984	0.4985	0.4985	0.4986	0.4986
0.4989	0.4989	0.4989	0.4990	0.4990

CRITICAL VALUES OF T

Most of the time, traders are interested in whether the recent performance is worse than the benchmark, so a one-tail test is used.

A two-tail test would be used to test whether recent performance is different, not just worse, but most would not worry about being different if the difference was better performance.

If the mean of the recent performance is greater than the mean of the benchmark, no further analysis is needed.

Compute the t-statistic comparing the two means and take its absolute value. The larger the t statistic, the more confident you can be that the two means are different.

Look in the column for the level of confidence you want to use and the row for the degrees of freedom, which is the number of data points minus 1. Interpolate between rows or columns if necessary. If the t-statistic is larger than the entry in the table, the recent performance is worse than the benchmark.

EXAMPLE

Recent mean, m_r = 0.005, stdev = 0.015, n = 26.

Benchmark mean, m_b = 0.010, stdev = 0.015.

Null hypothesis, H_0, is the difference between the means is 0.

t-statistic = -1.70

The t-statistic is negative because m_r is less than m_b. Is it enough less to be significant at 0.05 level, or 95% confidence? There are 25 degrees of freedom. The entry in the row for 25, column for 95%, is 1.71. With 95% confidence, the system is underperforming the benchmark.

Critical values of t

Level of significance for one-tail test

		0.250	0.200	0.150	0.100	0.050	0.025	0.010	0.005	0.001
Confidence		75.0%	80.0%	85.0%	90.0%	95.0%	97.5%	99.0%	99.5%	99.9%
Degrees of Freedom	1	1.00	1.38	1.96	3.08	6.31	12.71	31.82	63.66	318.31
	2	0.82	1.06	1.39	1.89	2.92	4.30	6.96	9.92	22.33
	3	0.76	0.98	1.25	1.64	2.35	3.18	4.54	5.84	10.21
	4	0.74	0.94	1.19	1.53	2.13	2.78	3.75	4.60	7.17
	5	0.73	0.92	1.16	1.48	2.02	2.57	3.36	4.03	5.89
	6	0.72	0.91	1.13	1.44	1.94	2.45	3.14	3.71	5.21
	7	0.71	0.90	1.12	1.41	1.89	2.36	3.00	3.50	4.79
	8	0.71	0.89	1.11	1.40	1.86	2.31	2.90	3.36	4.50
	9	0.70	0.88	1.10	1.38	1.83	2.26	2.82	3.25	4.30
	10	0.70	0.88	1.09	1.37	1.81	2.23	2.76	3.17	4.14
	11	0.70	0.88	1.09	1.36	1.80	2.20	2.72	3.11	4.02
	12	0.70	0.87	1.08	1.36	1.78	2.18	2.68	3.05	3.93
	13	0.69	0.87	1.08	1.35	1.77	2.16	2.65	3.01	3.85
	14	0.69	0.87	1.08	1.35	1.76	2.14	2.62	2.98	3.79
	15	0.69	0.87	1.07	1.34	1.75	2.13	2.60	2.95	3.73
	20	0.69	0.86	1.06	1.33	1.72	2.09	2.53	2.85	3.55
	25	0.68	0.86	1.06	1.32	1.71	2.06	2.49	2.79	3.45
	30	0.68	0.85	1.05	1.31	1.70	2.04	2.46	2.75	3.39
	35	0.68	0.85	1.05	1.31	1.69	2.03	2.44	2.72	3.34
	40	0.68	0.85	1.05	1.30	1.68	2.02	2.42	2.70	3.31
	50	0.68	0.85	1.05	1.30	1.68	2.01	2.40	2.68	3.26
	60	0.68	0.85	1.05	1.30	1.67	2.00	2.39	2.66	3.23
	70	0.68	0.85	1.04	1.29	1.67	1.99	2.38	2.65	3.21
	80	0.68	0.85	1.04	1.29	1.66	1.99	2.37	2.64	3.20
	90	0.68	0.85	1.04	1.29	1.66	1.99	2.37	2.63	3.18
	100	0.68	0.85	1.04	1.29	1.66	1.98	2.36	2.63	3.17
	Infinite	0.67	0.84	1.04	1.28	1.65	1.96	2.33	2.58	3.09

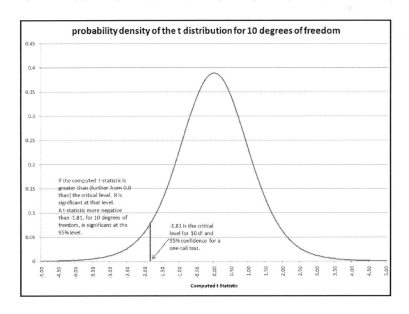

probability density of the t distribution for 10 degrees of freedom

If the computed t-statistic is greater than (further from 0.0 than) the critical level, it is significant at that level. A t-statistic more negative than -1.81, for 10 degrees of freedom, is significant at the 95% level.

-1.81 is the critical level for 10 df and 95% confidence for a one-tail test.

Computed t Statistic

CRITICAL VALUES OF CHI-SQUARE

There are two tables. One for the critical areas at the left of the distribution that is used to determine whether the agreement is unusually good.

	area	0.995	0.990	0.975	0.950	0.900	0.750	0.500
		Left tail areas for the Chi-square distribution						
		Chi-square is very small Distributions match very closely						
	1	0.0000	0.0002	0.0010	0.0039	0.0158	0.102	0.455
	2	0.0100	0.0201	0.0506	0.103	0.211	0.575	1.386
	3	0.0717	0.115	0.216	0.352	0.584	1.213	2.366
	4	0.207	0.297	0.484	0.711	1.064	1.923	3.357
	5	0.412	0.554	0.831	1.145	1.610	2.675	4.351
	6	0.676	0.872	1.237	1.635	2.204	3.455	5.348
	7	0.989	1.239	1.690	2.167	2.833	4.255	6.346
	8	1.344	1.647	2.180	2.733	3.490	5.071	7.344
	9	1.735	2.088	2.700	3.325	4.168	5.899	8.343
	10	2.156	2.558	3.247	3.940	4.865	6.737	9.342
	11	2.603	3.053	3.816	4.575	5.578	7.584	10.34
Degrees of Freedom	12	3.074	3.571	4.404	5.226	6.304	8.438	11.34
	13	3.565	4.107	5.009	5.892	7.042	9.299	12.34
	14	4.075	4.660	5.629	6.571	7.790	10.17	13.34
	15	4.601	5.229	6.262	7.261	8.547	11.04	14.34
	16	5.142	5.812	6.908	7.962	9.312	11.91	15.34
	17	5.697	6.408	7.564	8.672	10.09	12.79	16.34
	18	6.265	7.015	8.231	9.390	10.86	13.68	17.34
	19	6.844	7.633	8.907	10.12	11.65	14.56	18.34
	20	7.434	8.260	9.591	10.85	12.44	15.45	19.34
	21	8.034	8.897	10.28	11.59	13.24	16.34	20.34
	22	8.643	9.542	10.98	12.34	14.04	17.24	21.34
	23	9.260	10.20	11.69	13.09	14.85	18.14	22.34
	24	9.886	10.86	12.40	13.85	15.66	19.04	23.34
	25	10.52	11.52	13.12	14.61	16.47	19.94	24.34
	26	11.16	12.20	13.84	15.38	17.29	20.84	25.34
	27	11.81	12.88	14.57	16.15	18.11	21.75	26.34
	28	12.46	13.56	15.31	16.93	18.94	22.66	27.34
	29	13.12	14.26	16.05	17.71	19.77	23.57	28.34
	30	13.79	14.95	16.79	18.49	20.60	24.48	29.34
	35	17.19	18.51	20.57	22.47	24.80	29.05	34.34
	40	20.71	22.16	24.43	26.51	29.05	33.66	39.34
	45	24.31	25.90	28.37	30.61	33.35	38.29	44.34
	50	27.99	29.71	32.36	34.76	37.69	42.94	49.33

And one for the critical area at the right of the distribution that is used to determine whether the agreement is unusually poor.

	area	0.500	0.250	0.100	0.050	0.025	0.010	0.005
		Right tail areas for the Chi-square distribution						
					Chi-square is very large			
					Distributions are not the same			
Degrees of Freedom	1	0.455	1.323	2.706	3.841	5.024	6.635	7.879
	2	1.386	2.773	4.605	5.991	7.378	9.210	10.60
	3	2.366	4.108	6.251	7.815	9.348	11.34	12.84
	4	3.357	5.385	7.779	9.488	11.14	13.28	14.86
	5	4.351	6.626	9.236	11.07	12.83	15.09	16.75
	6	5.348	7.841	10.64	12.59	14.45	16.81	18.55
	7	6.346	9.037	12.02	14.07	16.01	18.48	20.28
	8	7.344	10.22	13.36	15.51	17.53	20.09	21.95
	9	8.343	11.39	14.68	16.92	19.02	21.67	23.59
	10	9.342	12.55	15.99	18.31	20.48	23.21	25.19
	11	10.34	13.70	17.28	19.68	21.92	24.72	26.76
	12	11.34	14.85	18.55	21.03	23.34	26.22	28.30
	13	12.34	15.98	19.81	22.36	24.74	27.69	29.82
	14	13.34	17.12	21.06	23.68	26.12	29.14	31.32
	15	14.34	18.25	22.31	25.00	27.49	30.58	32.80
	16	15.34	19.37	23.54	26.30	28.85	32.00	34.27
	17	16.34	20.49	24.77	27.59	30.19	33.41	35.72
	18	17.34	21.60	25.99	28.87	31.53	34.81	37.16
	19	18.34	22.72	27.20	30.14	32.85	36.19	38.58
	20	19.34	23.83	28.41	31.41	34.17	37.57	40.00
	21	20.34	24.93	29.62	32.67	35.48	38.93	41.40
	22	21.34	26.04	30.81	33.92	36.78	40.29	42.80
	23	22.34	27.14	32.01	35.17	38.08	41.64	44.18
	24	23.34	28.24	33.20	36.42	39.36	42.98	45.56
	25	24.34	29.34	34.38	37.65	40.65	44.31	46.93
	26	25.34	30.43	35.56	38.89	41.92	45.64	48.29
	27	26.34	31.53	36.74	40.11	43.19	46.96	49.64
	28	27.34	32.62	37.92	41.34	44.46	48.28	50.99
	29	28.34	33.71	39.09	42.56	45.72	49.59	52.34
	30	29.34	34.80	40.26	43.77	46.98	50.89	53.67
	35	34.34	40.22	46.06	49.80	53.20	57.34	60.27
	40	39.34	45.62	51.81	55.76	59.34	63.69	66.77
	45	44.34	50.98	57.51	61.66	65.41	69.96	73.17
	50	49.33	56.33	63.17	67.50	71.42	76.15	79.49

Glossary

The diagrams and definitions that follow will refresh your memories on the basic terms and concepts.

Absorbing barrier   An absorbing barrier in reference to a sequential process such as a game or trading system is a level at which the process stops. Trading systems have an absorbing barrier at the point of bankruptcy, and they may have an absorbing barrier at the point of sufficient success. When the equity in the trading account reaches either level, trading stops.

Anderson-Darling   The Anderson-Darling test is a statistical test to determine whether two samples or distributions, each represented by its *cumulative distribution function*, came from the same distribution. It is a very powerful test for determining whether a sample came from the *Normal distribution*. One of its advantages is that it is relatively unaffected by *outliers*.

Autocorrelation   Autocorrelation is correlation between values of the same variable at different times – that is, the correlation between pairs of values of the same variable separated by a fixed number of points.

Average absolute deviation   The average absolute deviation is a measure of variability of a sample of data. It is relatively unaffected by extremes, even extremes in the tails of the distribution. Average absolute deviation, AAD, is computed as

$$AAD = \frac{\sum_{i=1}^{n}(|x_i - \overline{x}|)}{n}$$

where x_i are individual data points, $\overline{x}$ is the mean, and n is the number of data points.

Average True Range (ATR)   Average true range is a measure of bar to bar volatility. The normal range of a bar is high - low. The true range of a bar is maximum (high, previous close) - minimum (low, previous close). Average true range is the average of true range over some lookback period.

Bernoulli experiment   See *binomial distribution*.

Bimodal   A bimodal sample or distribution has two modes.

Binomial distribution   A binomial distribution is a discrete distribution that represents the number of successes from a sequence of binary experiments. Such an experiment is also called a Bernoulli experiment.

Central limit theorem   The central limit theorem is the second fundamental theorem of probability, and states that the mean of a large number of independent random variables, each with finite mean and variance, will be approximately normally distributed. The important, and largely not intuitive, point is that the independent random variables can be drawn from any distribution, even one that is itself non-Normal. The number of random variables required for their mean to approximate a normal distribution depends on how different their distribution is from normal. Under most circumstances, about 30 samples are sufficient.

Central tendency   Central tendency refers to the way quantitative data tends to cluster around some value. Common measures of central tendency include: *mean* or arithmetic average, *median, mode, geometric mean.*

Chi-square   The chi-square test is a non-parametric statistical test used to test the *goodness of fit* between a sample of observed data and either another set of data or a theoretical distribution. Data is prepared by establishing a set of bins for each distribution, counting the number data points in each bin from each distribution, computing χ_i^2, the chi-square statistic, and comparing with a table.

Coefficient of determination   The coefficient of determination, r^2, is the square of the *correlation coefficient*. It measures the proportion of the variability in a data set that is explained by the statistical model.

Coefficient of variation   Coefficient of variation is defined as the ratio of the standard deviation to the mean. In a manufacturing process, say ball bearings, the mean may be 10.00 mm and the standard deviation 0.02 mm. The coefficient of variation is 0.02 / 10 = 0.002 – expressed as a percent, it is 0.2%.

Compound Annual Rate of Return (CAR)   CAR is the annualized rate of return for a given series of trades. It indicates the increase per year, without regard for the percentage of time the system holds a position. A system that returns 10% per year while being exposed only 40% of the time has a CAR value of 10%. See Risk Adjusted Rate of Return (RAR) for comparison.

Continuous distribution   A continuous probability distribution is a statistical distribution whose variables may take on a continuous range of values. A continuous distribution is characterized by a probability density function.

Correlation   Correlation measures the degree to which two or more variables change with respect to each other. There are several methods of computing the correlation coefficient, r, all of which result in a number between -1 and +1. The most common is the Pearson product-moment method which works well when used with numeric data and linear relationships. Other methods, such as Spearman's rank correlation or Kendall's rank correlation, are available for use with discrete numeric and ordinal data. Perfect correlation, r = 1, indicates that changes in one variable is matched by a corresponding change in the other. When r = -1, a change in one variable is matched by an opposite change in the other. The correlation coefficient measures only the degree to which the variables change, and cannot suggest whether one change causes the other change. *See also coefficient of determination.*

Cumulative Distribution Function (CDF)   The cumulative distribution function is the integral of the probability density function. Graphically, it is represented by a curve whose vertical axis ranges from 0 to 1, and whose horizontal axis covers the range of values present in the sample or distribution. For a given point on the curve, (f,x), the vertical value f is the probability that a randomly chosen sample will be less than the horizontal value x. A cumulative distribution function completely defines a distribution. *Goodness of fit* tests that determine how closely two distributions agree accept two CDFs and return a goodness metric.

Discrete distribution   A discrete probability distribution is a statistical distribution whose variables can take on only discrete values – that is, values from a finite or countable set. Discrete distributions are characterized by probability mass functions, the equivalent of continuous distribution's probability density functions.

Expectancy   See mathematical expectation.

Expectation   See mathematical expectation.

Gaussian distribution   See Normal distribution.

Geometric mean   The geometric mean is a measure of the central tendency of a set of n numbers. It is that value which, when raised to the power n, equals the product of the numbers in the set. The geometric mean is computed by multiplying all of the numbers together, then taking their nth root.

$$GM = (x_1 + x_2 + x_3 + ... + x_n)^{1/n}$$

Another method of computing the geometric mean of a series of numbers is:

1. Take the logarithm of each number.
2. Compute the average of the logarithms.
3. Take the anti-logarithm of the average.

Goodness of fit   The goodness of fit of a statistical model measures the discrepancy between two distributions. The distributions can be theoretical or observed. Depending on the characteristics of the two distributions, such as whether the data is continuous or discrete, one of several tests is applied. Tests commonly used when analyzing trading data include *chi-square*, *Kolmogorov-Smirnov*, and *Anderson-Darling*. Each test returns a metric that is evaluated according to the methods of that test and a table that indicates the statistical significance of the test.

Holding Period Return (HPR)   Holding period return is the rate of return achieved by holding an asset for a period of time.

It is sometimes defined (including Vince) as:

HPR = (final value - initial value) / initial value

and sometimes as

HPR = ((final value - initial value) / initial value) - 1

Interquartile range   Interquartile range is a measure of the variability of a sample of data. It is the value of the 75th percentile minus the 25th percentile.

Kolmogorov-Smirnov   The Kolmogorov-Smirnov test is a powerful non-parametric statistical test to determine whether two samples or distributions, each represented by its *cumulative distribution function*, came from the same distribution.

Kurtosis   Kurtosis is a measure of the peak and tails of the distribution – the extreme values. Kurtosis is the fourth central moment of a distribution. Increasing kurtosis is associated with the movement of probability mass from the shoulders of a distribution into its center and tails. Distributions with sharp peaks and "fat" tails have high kurtosis and are termed *leptokurtic*. The kurtosis, *K*, is computed as:

$$K = \frac{\frac{1}{n}\sum_{i}^{n}(x_i - \overline{x})^4}{\sigma^4}$$

where *n* is the number of data points, σ is the standard deviation.

A Normal distribution has kurtosis value of 3. (Excel, and some other statistical analysis packages, compute kurtosis using the formula given here, then subtract 3, report the result and call it *excess kurtosis*. Thus, if you use Excel's Data Analysis package to compute the descriptive statistics of data that fits a Normal distribution, the reported value for kurtosis will be 0.)

Law of large numbers   The law of large numbers is the first fundamental theorem of probability, and states that as the number of repeated trials of a random process increases, the percentage difference between the average of the trials and the true mean of the population from which they are drawn approaches zero. The more times you do something, the closer the average of your trials will be to the true mean.

Leptokurtic   A leptokurtic distribution has a high *kurtosis* value – greater than 3.

Mathematical expectation   Also known as expectation or expectancy. The average amount won or lost for a group of trades.

Expectation = (proportion of trades won * amount won per winning trade) - (proportion of trades lost * amount lost per losing trade)

Expectation can be expressed as a percentage, as in 0.5% per trade, or as a dollar amount, as in $550 per contract per trade.

No trading system can be profitable over an extended period of trades unless the expectation is positive.

Maximum Adverse Excursion (MAE)   Maximum adverse excursion is a measure of the worst intra-trade drawdown. Imagine a bar created by using the entry to a long position as the open of the bar, the exit of the trade as the close of the bar, and the lowest price reached during the trade as the low of the bar. MAE is the open of that bar minus the low.

Maximum Favorable Excursion (MFE)   Maximum favorable excursion is a measure of the best intra-trade gain. Imagine a bar created by using the entry to a long position as the open of the bar, the exit of the trade as the close of the bar, and the highest price reached during the trade as the high of the bar. MFE is the high of that bar minus the open.

Mean   The mean is a measure of *central tendency* of a sample of data, commonly called the arithmetic average. The mean is the first central moment of a distribution. It is computed by adding the values of all of the data points in the sample, and dividing by the number of data points, n. The symbol for the mean of a sample is $\bar{x}$, pronounced x-bar. The mean of a finite sample is computed as:

$$\bar{x} = \frac{\sum_{i=1}^{n} x_i}{n}$$

Median   The median is a measure of *central tendency* of a sample of data. It is the middle value in the sorted list of data values. Median is less affected by extreme values than mean. Median is used to describe ordinal, interval, or numeric data.

Median absolute deviation (MAD)   The median absolute deviation is a measure of variability of a sample of data. It is relatively unaffected by extremes, even extremes in the tails of the distribution. Median absolute deviation, MAD, is defined as

$$MAD = median(|x_i - \overline{x}|)$$

where x_i are individual data points, and $\overline{x}$ is the mean.

Mesokurtic   A mesokurtic distribution has a low *kurtosis* value – less than 3.

Mode   The mode is a measure of *central tendency* of a sample of data. It is the most frequently occurring value. If that value is unique, the sample is called unimodal; a distribution with more than one mode is said to be *bimodal*, trimodal, or in general, multimodal. Mode is used when describing nominal data to identify the most frequently occurring value. If the data is continuous, the mode is not defined. Nevertheless, mode is used to describe the general appearance of numeric data, as in unimodal or bimodal.

Moment   Moments of a distribution are mathematical descriptions of the shape of the distribution. So far as they are discussed in this book, there are four central moments, all computed relative to the mean. They are mean, variance, skew, and kurtosis. In that order, the exponent used to compute each increases from one to four. The higher the moment, the more sensitive the value is to extremes in the tails of the distribution.

Normal distribution   The Normal distribution is one of the most basic probability distributions. Its probability density function is the familiar bell-shaped curve. It is of importance because of its role in the *central limit theorem*, and consequently, because of its common occurrence in practice.

Outlier   An outlier is an observation that lies an abnormal distance from other values in a random sample. Determination of exactly what an abnormal distance is requires the judgment of the analyst. As a rule of thumb, if the value of a computed statistic changes significantly depending whether a specific value is included in the calculation or not, that value is an outlier.

Parametric tests   Parametric tests assume knowledge of, or the ability to calculate, values for parameters that describe distributions. The Normal distribution, for example, is characterized by two parameters – mean and standard deviation. Tests for goodness of fit to a Normal distribution must have values for these two parameters – either know what they are or estimate them from the sample. Non-parametric tests make no assumptions.

Parametric tests usually require numeric data, often assume the data follows the Normal distribution, test relationships between means, and can draw more conclusions. Non-parametric tests can operate on nominal or ordinal data, test medians, are simpler, are less affected by outliers.

Percentile   If a given set of numeric data is sorted into ascending order, the 0th percentile data point has the lowest value, the 100th percentile data point has the highest value, and p percent of the data is less than or equal to the pth percentile. For example, 70 percent of the data should be less than the value of the 70th percentile. The 50th percentile is called the *median*.

Platykurtic   A platykurtic distribution has a low *kurtosis* value – less than 3.

Population   A population is the group of all items of data being processed. Descriptive measures of a population are called its parameters. Within a population, a parameter is a fixed value that does not vary. The parameters of the population are usually unknown and must be estimated. Much of statistics is concerned with estimating numerical properties of an entire population based on a random sample of items from the population. Parameters are often assigned Greek symbols. For example, σ is used to represent the true standard deviation of the population.

Probability density function (pdf)   A probability density function is a function that describes the relative likelihood of a random variable occurring at a given point. The probability density function is nonnegative everywhere, and integrates to a value of 1. The familiar bell-shaped curve of the Normal distribution is an example of a probability density function. The probability a variable has a particular value within a range is given by the integral of the pdf over that range – it is the area under the pdf curve over that range.

Probability mass function (pmf)   A probability mass function is a function that describes the probability of a discrete random variable having a specific value. When displayed graphically, probability mass functions are histograms, with the height of each bar representing the probability. Historically, the term probability density function has been used to describe both the pdf associated with a continuous distribution and the pmf associated with the discrete distribution.

Profit factor   The profit factor is the ratio of total dollars won to total dollars lost.

Profit ratio   The profit ratio is the ratio of amount won on winning trades to amount lost on losing trades.

Prospect theory   Prospect theory is an economic theory of behavior that attempts to explain people's decisions when risk is involved. Prospect theory shows that risk tolerance is not linear, as suggested by *utility theory*.

Range   Range is a measure of the variability of a set of data. Unless the range is qualified in some way, it is measured from the extreme minimum to the extreme maximum. Range is sometimes qualified to be the distance between deciles or quartiles. For example, the interquartile range is the difference between the third quartile and the first quartile, $Q_3 - Q_1$.

Risk Adjusted Annual Rate of Return (RAR)   RAR is the annualized rate of return for a given series of trades, adjusted for the percentage of time the system holds a position. A system that returns 10% per year while being exposed only 40% of the time has a RAR value of 25%. This metric makes the assumption that equally attractive use of funds is available during the periods the system is out of the market. See Compound Annual Rate of Return (CAR) for comparison.

Sample   A sample is a subset of a population that is meant to be representative of the population and is used to estimate parameters of the population. For any population, there are many possible samples. A sample statistic gives information about a corresponding population parameter. For example, the mean of a sample gives an estimate of the mean of the population. Sample statistics are often assigned Roman symbols. For example, s is used to represent the sample statistic that estimates the standard deviation. In other literature, the term estimator is sometimes used to describe an unknown parameter of a population. The symbol used for an estimator is the same Greek symbol used for the parameter, but given a "hat". For example, $\hat{\sigma}$, sigma hat, is used to represent an estimator of the standard deviation.

Sampling distribution   The sampling distribution describes probabilities associated with a statistic when a random sample is drawn from a population. The sampling distribution is the probability distribution or *probability density function* of the statistic.

Semi-Deviation Semi-deviation is a measure of the variability of the data. It is computed the same as standard deviation, except that all positive data values are replaced with zero. The semi-deviation is the standard deviation of the negative values in a data set.

Skew   Skew, or skewness, is the degree to which the distribution is lopsided. Skew is the third central moment of a distribution. The skew, *S*, is computed as:

$$S = \frac{\frac{1}{n-1}\sum_{i=1}^{n}(x_i - \overline{x})^2}{\sigma^2}$$

where n is the number of data points, σ is the standard deviation.

Distributions that have longer tails to the left than the right are left skewed and the skew value of those distributions is negative. Distributions that have longer tails to the right are right skewed and the skew value is positive. There is not a consistent relationship between the skew, the mean, and the median. The skew value of a Normal distribution is 0.

Standard deviation   The standard deviation is a measure of the variability of the data. The standard deviation is the second central moment of a distribution. A low standard deviation indicates that the data points are close to the mean, while a high standard deviation indicates that the data is widely spread. The symbol used for the standard deviation of a sample is usually s. The standard deviation is the square root of the *variance* of a set of data.

Statistic   A statistic is a quantity that is calculated from a sample of data and used to give information about the unknown values in the corresponding population. It is possible to draw more than one sample from the same population, and the value of a statistic will in general vary from sample to sample. For example, the average value in a sample is a statistic. The average values in more than one sample, drawn from the same population, will not necessarily be equal.

Terminal Wealth Relative (TWR)   Terminal wealth relative is the number resulting from dividing final equity by initial equity. If you begin with $100,000 and end with $250,000, your TWR is 2.50.

TWR for a series of plays or trades is determined by two numbers – the geometric mean of the trades, G, and the number of trades, n.

$TWR = (G)^n$

Underlying   Derivatives, such as options and warrants, have their value based on the value of an underlying security.

Utility theory   Utility theory suggests that choices are made by outcomes of actions by their probabilities, then choosing the alternative with the maximum utility. Prospect theory suggests that other factors are important.

Variance   The variance is a measure of the variability of the data. The variance is the second central moment. The variance is the square of the standard deviation. The variance, s^2, of a finite sample is computed as:

$$s^2 = \frac{\sum_{i=1}^{n}(x_i - \bar{x})^2}{n-1}$$

where $\bar{x}$ is the mean of the sample.

Winsorize   Winsorization is a data transformation that replaces outliers by values a specified percentile of the data. For example, a 90% winzorization sets all data values greater than the 95th percentile to the 95th percentile, and all data values less than the 5th percentile to the 5th percentile.

z-score   Z-score is a measurement of the position of a data point within the sample. It is the number of standard deviations the data point is away from the mean.

$$z = \frac{x - \bar{x}}{s}$$

where $\bar{x}$ is the mean of the sample and s is the standard deviation of the sample.

Books and Articles

Abner, David, *The ETF Handbook: How to Value and Trade Exchange Traded Funds*, Wiley, 2010.

Albright, S. Christian, *VBA for Modelers: Developing Decision Support Systems with Microsoft Excel*, Second Edition, Thomson, 2007.

Alexander, Carol, *Market Models: A Guide to Financial Data Analysis*, Wiley, 2001.

Bacon, Carl, *Practical Portfolio Performance Measurement and Attribution*, Wiley, 2004.

Bandy, Howard, *Introduction to AmiBroker: Advanced Technical Analysis Software for Charting and Trading System Development*, Second Edition, Blue Owl Press, 2012. http://www.introductiontoamibroker.com/

—, *Mean Reversion Trading Systems: Practical Methods for Swing Trading*, Blue Owl Press, 2013.

—, *Quantitative Technical Analysis: An Integrated Approach to Trading System Development and Trading Management*, Blue Owl Press, 2015.

—, *Quantitative Trading Systems: Practical Methods for Design, Testing, and Validation*, Second Edition, Blue Owl Press, 2011.

Barreto, Humberto and Frank Howland, *Introductory Economics Using Monte Carlo Simulation with Microsoft Excel*, Cambridge, 2006.

Benninga, Simon, *Financial Modeling*, 3rd Edition, MIT Press, 2008.

Berk, Kenneth, and Patrick Carey, *Data Analysis with Microsoft Excel*, Duxbury, 2000.

Bernstein, Peter, *Against the Gods: The Remarkable Story of Risk*, Wiley, 1998.

Bolstad, William, *Introduction to Bayesian Statistics*, Second Edition, Wiley, 2007.

Box, George, *Improving Almost Anything*, Wiley, 2006.

Box, George, William Hunter, and J. Stuart Hunter, *Statistics for Experimenters: An Introduction to Design, Data Analysis, and Model Building*, Wiley, 1978.

Box, George, and Alberto Luceno, *Statistical Control by Monitoring and Feedback Adjustment*, Wiley, 1997.

Brown, Aaron, *The Poker Face of Wall Street*, Wiley, 2006.

Carpenter, Michael, *The Risk Wise Investor*, Wiley, 2009.

Chin, William, and Marc Ingenoso, *Risk Formulas for Proportional Betting*, pdf file, 2004.
http://www.bjmath.com/bjmath/proport/riskpaper1.pdf

Christoffersen, Peter, et al, *Is the Potential for International Diversification Disappearing?*, McGill University, 2010.
http://papers.ssrn.com/sol3/papers.cfm?abstract_id=1573345

Clemen, Robert, and Terence Reilly, *Making Hard Decision Decisions with DecisionTools*, South-Western, 2001.

Conrad, Bud, *Profiting from the World's Economic Crisis*, Wiley, 2010.

Dale Besterfield, *Quality Control*, Pearson, 2009.

Dalgaard, Peter, *Introductory Statistics with R*, Spring, 2002.

Davis, Morton, *Game Theory, A Nontechnical Introduction*, Dover, 1970.

DeFusco, Richard, et al, *Quantitative Methods for Investment Analysis*, AIMR, 2001.

Dixit, Avinash, and Barry Nalebuff, *Thinking Strategically: The Competitive Edge in Business, Politics, and Everyday Life*, Norton, 1993.

Drobny, Steven, *Inside the House of Money*, Wiley, 2006.

Dutta, Prajit, *Strategies and Games*, MIT Press, 2000.

Epstein, Richard, *The Theory of Gambling and Statistical Logic*, Revised Edition, Academic Press, 1977.

Ferri, *The ETF Book: All You Need to Know About Exchange-Traded Funds*, Wiley, 2009.

Fisher, Len, *Rock, Paper, Scissors: Game Theory in Everyday Life*, Basic Books, 2008.

Fox, John, The R Commander: A Basic-Statistics Graphical User Interface to R, *Journal of Statistical Software*, V14, 2005. http://www.jstatsoft.org/v14/i09/paper

Fox, Justin, *The Myth of the Rational Market*, Harper, 2009.

Frey, Bruce, *Statistics Hacks*, O'Reilly, 2006.

Gelman, Andrew and Deborah Nolan, *Teaching Statistics, a Bag of Tricks*, Oxford, 2002.

Gottfried, Byron, *Spreadsheet Tools for Engineers Using Excel*, McGraw Hill, 2003.

Griffin, Peter, *Extra Stuff: Gambling Ramblings*, Huntington Press, 1991.

—, *The Theory of Blackjack*, Sixth Edition, Huntington Press, 1999.

Grinstead, Charles, and Laurie Snell, *Introduction to Probability*, 1997. http://www.dartmouth.edu/~chance/teaching_aids/books_articles/probability_book/amsbook.mac.pdf

Haigh, John, *Taking Chances: Winning with Probability*, Oxford, 2003.

Hammersley, J. M. and D. C. Handscomb, *Monte Carlo Methods*, Chapman and Hall, 1964. http://www.cs.fsu.edu/~mascagni/Hammersley-Handscomb.pdf

Heiberger, Richard, and Erich Neuwirth, *R Through Excel*, Springer, 2009.

Hubbard, Douglas, *How to Measure Anything*, Wiley, 2007.

—, *The Failure of Risk Management: Why It's Broken and How to Fix It*, Wiley, 2009.

Jaisingh, Lloyd, *Statistics for the Utterly Confused*, Second Edition, McGraw-Hill, 2005.

Jelen, Bill, and Tracy Syrstad, *VBA and Macros for Microsoft Office Excel 2007*, Que, 2008.

Jones, Ryan, *The Trading Game*, Wiley, 1999.

Kahneman, Daniel, *Thinking, Fast and Slow*, Farrar, Straus, and Giroux, 2011.

Kahneman, Daniel and Amos Tversky, "Prospect Theory: An Analysis of Decision Making under Risk." *Econometrica*, Vol 47, No. 2 (Mar 1979), pp 263-292.
http://www.jstor.org/pss/1914185
http://www.hss.caltech.edu/~camerer/Ec101/ProspectTheory.pdf

Karp, Natasha, *R Commander, An Introduction*, 2010.
http://cran.r-project.org/doc/contrib/Karp-Rcommander-intro.pdf

Kelly, J. L., Jr., "A New Interpretation of Information Rate." *Bell System Technical Journal*, 35 (1956): 917-26.
http://www.racing.saratoga.ny.us/kelly.pdf

Keller, Gerald, *Applied Statistics with Microsoft Excel*, Duxbury, 2001.

Knight, Gerald, *Analyzing Business Data with Excel*, O'Reilly, 2006.

Lane, Randall, *The Zeros*, Portfolio, 2010.

Leach, Patrick, *Why Can't You Just Give Me the Number?*, Probabilistic Publishing, 2006.

Levitt, Steven, and Stephen Dubner, *Freakonomics: A Rogue Economist Explores the Hidden Side of Everything*, Harper, 2009.

Loffler, Gunter, and Peter Posch, *Credit Risk Modeling using Excel and VBA*, Wiley, 2007.

Lowenstein, Roger, *When Genius Failed: The Rise and Fall of Long-Term Capital Management*, Random House, 2000.

Mallaby, Sebastian, *More Money than God*, Penguin Press, 2010.

Malmuth, Mason, *Gambling Theory*, Two Plus Two Publishing, 1987.

March, James, *A Primer on Decision Making: How Decisions Happen*, Free Press, 2009.

Marrison, Chris, *The Fundamentals of Risk Measurement*, McGraw-Hill, 2002.

Mazur, Joseph, *What's Luck Got to Do with It?*, Princeton, 2010.

McCullough, Keith, *Diary of a Hedge Fund Manager*, Wiley, 2010.

Meredith, Jack, et al, *Quantitative Business Modeling*, South-Western, 2002.

Metropolis, Nicholas, The Beginning of the Monte Carlo Process, *Los Alamos Science*, Special Issue, 1987. http://library.lanl.gov/cgi-bin/getfile?00326866.pdf

Metropolis, Nicholas, and S. Ulam, "The Monte Carlo Method," *Journal of the American Statistical Association*, Number 247, Volume 44, September 1949.

Mlodinow, Leonard, *The Drunkard's Walk*, Pantheon, 2008.

Montgomery, Douglas, *Introduction to Quality Control*, Sixth Edition, Wiley, 2008.

Montier, James, *Behavioural Investing: A Practitioners Guide to Applying Behavioural Finance*, Wiley, 2007.

Morgan, M. Granger, and Max Henrion, *Uncertainty: A Guide to Dealing with Uncertainty in Quantitative Risk and Policy Analysis*, Cambridge University Press, 1992.

Moore, David and George McCabe, *Introduction to the Practice of Statistics*, Freeman, 2005.

Murphy, Joseph, *Stock Market Probability: Using Statistics to Predict and Optimize Investment Outcomes*, Irwin, 1994.

Myerson, Roger, *Probability Models for Economic Decisions*, Thomson, 2005.

Nahin, Paul, *Digital Dice: Computational Solutions to Practical Probability Problems*, Princeton, 2008.

Norstad, John, *An Introduction to Utility Theory*, 2010. http://homepage.mac.com/j.norstad/finance/util.pdf

Patterson, Scott, *The Quants*, Crown, 2010.

Pfaffenberger, Roger, and James Patterson, *Statistical Methods for Business and Economics*, Irwin, 1987.

Plous, Scott, *The Psychology of Judgment and Decision Making*, McGraw-Hill, 1993.

Pompian, Michael, *Behavioral Finance and Wealth Managment*, Wiley, 2006.

Poundstone, William, *Prisoner's Dilemma*, Anchor, 1992.

—, *Fortune's Formula, The Untold Story of the Scientific Betting System that Beat the Casinos and Wall Street*, Hill and Wang, 2005.

—, *Priceless: The Myth of Fair Value*, Hill and Wang, 2010.

Press, W. H., et al, *Numerical Recipes: The Art of Scientific Computing*, 3rd Edition, Cambridge, 2007. http://www.nr.com/

Robert, Christian, and George Casella, *Introducing Monte Carlo Methods with R*, Springer Verlag, 2009.

Rosenberg, Kenneth, *The Excel Statistics Companion*, Thomson, 2007.

Ross, Sheldon, *Simulation*, 3rd Edition, Academic Press, 2002.

Rubinstein, Reuven, *Simulation and the Monte Carlo Method*, Wiley, 1981.

Salsburg, David, *The Lady Tasting Tea, How Statistics Revolutionized Science in the Twentieth Century*, Holt, 2001.

Savage, Sam, *Decision Making with Insight*, Thomson, 2003.

—, *The Flaw of Averages*, Wiley, 2009.

Sivia, D. S., *Data Analysis, A Bayesian Tutorial*, Second Edition, Oxford, 2006

Snyder, Arnold, *Blackbelt in Blackjack*, RGE Publishing, 1998.

Taleb, Nassim Nicholas, *Fooled by Randomness*, Random House, 2005.

—, *The Black Swan*, Random House, 2007.

Thaler, Richard, *The Winner's Curse: Paradoxes and Anomalies of Economic Life*, Princeton, 1992.

Tharp, Van, *Trade Your Way to Financial Freedom*, Second Edition, McGraw-Hill, 2007.

—, *Definitive Guide to Position Sizing*, IITM, 2008.

Thorp, Edward, *Beat the Dealer*, Vintage, 1966.

—, *Beat the Market*, 1967.
http://www.edwardothorp.com/sitebuildercontent/sitebuilder-
files/beatthemarket.pdf

—, *The Mathematics of Gambling*, 1984.
http://www.edwardothorp.com/sitebuildercontent/sitebuilder-
files/tog1.pdf

—, *The Kelly Criterion in Blackjack, Sports Betting, and the Stock Market*,
10th International Conference on Gambling and Risk Taking,
Montreal, 1997.
http://www.bjmath.com/bjmath/thorp/paper.htm

Verzani, John, *simpleR - Using R for Introductory Statistics*, CUNY, 2002.
http://cran.r-project.org/doc/contrib/Verzani-SimpleR.pdf

Vickers, Andrew, *What is a p-value anyway?*, Addison-Wesley, 2010.

Vince, Ralph, *Portfolio Management Formulas*, Wiley, 1990.

—, *The Mathematics of Money Management*, Wiley, 1992.

—, *The New Money Management*, Wiley, 1995.

—, *The Handbook of Portfolio Mathematics*, Wiley, 2007.

—, *The Leverage Space Trading Model*, Wiley, 2009.

von Neumann, John, and Oskar Morgenstern, *Theory of Games and
Economic Behavior*, Commemorative Edition, Princeton, 2007.

Vose, David, *Risk Analysis: A Quantitative Guide*, Third Edition, Wiley,
2008.

Watson, Joel, *Strategy: An Introduction to Game Theory*, Second Edition,
Norton, 2008.

Wild, Russell, *Exchange-Traded Funds for Dummies*, Wild Dummies,
2006.

Wilson, Allan, *The Casino Gambler's Guide*, Harper and Row, 1970.

Winston, Wayne, *Excel 2007: Data Analysis and Business Modeling*,
Microsoft Press, 2007.

Yudkowsky, Eliezer, *An Intuitive Explanation of Bayes' Theorem*, Singu-
larity Institute for Artifical Intelligence, 2010.
http://yudkowsky.net/rational/bayes

SOFTWARE

AmiBroker

> AmiBroker is a high quality, inexpensive trading system development platform with capability to develop, test, and validate systems such as those described in this book.
> http://www.amibroker.com/

Analyse-it

> Statistical analysis add-in for Excel
> http://www.analyse-it.com/

Equity Monaco

> Equity Monaco is a free trading system simulator
> http://www.tickquest.com/?page_id=70

Market System Analyzer

> MSA is a fully-featured simulator with many position sizing techniques.
> Excellent articles by Dr. Michael Bryant.
> http://www.adaptrade.com/

R

> R is a free, open source programming language and software environment for statistical computing and graphics. The R language has become a de facto standard among statisticians for the development of statistical software and is widely used for statistical software development and data analysis. R is an implementation of the S programming language.
> http://www.r-project.org/

RExcel

> RExcel is an addin for Microsoft Excel. It allows access to the statistics package R from within Excel. RExcel's web site has a master installer RandFriendsSetup which installs R, many R packages, RExcel, and the infrastructure needed to run RExcel
> http://rcom.univie.ac.at/

StatistiXL

> StatistiXL is a statistical analysis add-in for Excel.
> http://www.statistixl.com/

Stator

> Stator is a commercial portfolio management and position
> sizing package.
> http://www.stator-afm.com/index.html

Weka

> Weka (Waikato Environment for Knowledge Analysis) is a
> popular suite of machine learning software written in Java,
> developed at the University of Waikato, New Zealand. Weka is
> free and open source.
> http://www.cs.waikato.ac.nz/ml/weka/

WEBSITES

Adaptive Trading Systems

> Developers of trading systems with characteristics similar to
> those recommended in this book.
> http://www.adaptivetradingsystems.com/

Bandy's views on the lack of value of fundamental data

> http://www.blueowlpress.com/Use%20of%20Fundamental%20
> Data%20in%20Active%20Investing.pdf

Blackjack Doc

> Blackjack information
> http://blackjackdoc.com

Blackjack Info

> Blackjack information and advice
> http://www.blackjackinfo.com/

Blackjack Mathematics

> http://www.bjmath.com/index.html

CodeForTraders

> Developers of trading systems with characteristics similar to
> those recommended in this book.
> http://www.codefortraders.com/

Comprehensive R Archive Network - CRAN
> http://cran.r-project.org/

Connors Research
> Developers of trading systems with characteristics similar to those recommended in this book.
> http://www.connorsresearch.com/

CSS Analytics
> Developers of trading systems with characteristics similar to those recommended in this book.
> http://cssanalytics.wordpress.com/

ETF - List of all
> http://www.masterdata.com/HelpFiles/ETF_List.htm

Excel for Statistical Data Analysis
> http://home.ubalt.edu/ntsbarsh/excel/excel.htm#rtwomeans

Flash trading - 60 Minutes TV
> http://www.tv.com/video/10493255/60-minutes-60-minutes-business--the-speed-traders

Gardener's Own - Using R for statistical analyses
> http://www.gardenersown.co.uk/Education/Lectures/R/index.htm

Garson's statistics notes
> http://faculty.chass.ncsu.edu/garson/PA765/statnote.htm

Hill / Statsoft Statistics Textbook
> http://www.statsoft.com/textbook/

Hubbard's web site
> http://www.hubbardresearch.com/index.html

Learn R
> http://www.fort.usgs.gov/brdscience/learnR.htm

Learn R by Example
> http://www.fort.usgs.gov/brdscience/LearnRE.htm

Mersenne twister code for Excel (this one is easier to use)
> http://www.ntrand.com/

Mersenne twister code for Excel
http://www.riskamp.com/mtrand.php

Montier's Societe General research report
https://www.sgresearch.com/publication/en/
585D2F913ECD24B3C125756700500200.pub

R Commander - John Fox's web site
http://socserv.mcmaster.ca/jfox/Misc/Rcmdr/

R Examples
http://www.math.mcmaster.ca/peter/s2ma3/s2ma3_0001/examplesinr.html

R for Excel
http://rcom.univie.ac.at/

R installation and administration
http://cran.r-project.org/doc/manuals/R-admin.html

R Project for statistical computing
http://www.r-project.org/

R Tutorial - Data import
http://www.r-tutor.com/r-introduction/data-frame/data-import

ReadyBetGo
General gambling information
http://www.readybetgo.com

Snyder's library of articles
http://www.blackjackforumonline.com/content/TOClibrary.html

Snyder's *The Snyder Profit Index*
http://plazcasino.com/2

SSC-Stat: A statistical add-in for Excel
http://www.reading.ac.uk/ssc/software/sscstat/sscstat.html

Statistical data on world exchanges
http://www.world-exchanges.org/

Statsoft - statistics glossary
http://www.statsoft.com/textbook/statistics-glossary/

Statsoft - quality control charts
        http://www.statsoft.com/textbook/quality-control-charts/

StatTrek - statistics tutorials
        http://stattrek.com/

Teaching resources - tutorials, books, forums
        http://probweb.berkeley.edu/teaching.html

Thorp's web site
        http://www.edwardothorp.com/

Tinn-R - Editor for use with R
        http://www.sciviews.org/Tinn-R/

TugZip, a free file compression and decompression program
        http://www.tugzip.com/Home.html

Tutorials for VBA
        http://www.anthony-vba.kefra.com/index.htm

Tutorial on Writing Excel Macros
        http://www.reading.ac.uk/ssc/software/excel/macros1.html

Using Excel for Statistical Analysis – Caveats
        http://www-unix.oit.umass.edu/~evagold/excel.html

Using Microsoft Excel for Statistics
        http://www.reading.ac.uk/ssc/software/excel/home.html

Wizard of Odds
        Cornucopia of information about history, strategy, odds of
        many gambling games.
        Hosted by Michael Shackleford, a professional actuary.
        http://wizardofodds.com/

Wong's blackjack site
        http://www.bj21.com

INDEX

27496782R00228

Printed in Great Britain
by Amazon